www.optumcoding.com

Coding and Payment Guide

Behavioral Health Services

An essential coding, billing, and reimbursement resource for psychiatrists, psychologists, and clinical social workers

2016

ICD-10

A full suite of resources including the latest code set, mapping products, and expert training to help you make a smooth transition. www.optumcoding.com/ICD10

Optum360 Notice

Coding and Payment Guide for Behavioral Health Services is designed to provide accurate and authoritative information in regard to the subject covered. Every reasonable effort has been made to ensure the accuracy and completeness of the information within these pages. However, Optum360 makes no guarantee, warranty, or representation that this publication is accurate, complete, or without errors. It is understood that Optum360 is not rendering any legal or other professional services or advice in this publication and that Optum360 bears no liability for any results or consequences that may arise from the use of this book. Please address all correspondence to:

Optum360
2525 Lake Park Blvd.
West Valley City, UT 84120

American Medical Association Notice

CPT © 2015 American Medical Association. All rights reserved.

Fee schedules, relative value units, conversion factors and/or related components are not assigned by the AMA, are not part of CPT, and the AMA is not recommending their use. The AMA does not directly or indirectly practice medicine or dispense medical services. The AMA assumes no liability for data contained or not contained herein.

CPT is a registered trademark of the American Medical Association.

The responsibility for the content of any "National Correct Coding Policy" included in this product is with the Centers for Medicare and Medicaid Services and no endorsement by the AMA is intended or should be implied. The AMA disclaims responsibility for any consequences or liability attributable to or related to any use, nonuse or interpretation of information contained in this product.

Our Commitment to Accuracy

Optum360 is committed to producing accurate and reliable materials.

To report corrections, please visit www.optumcoding.com/accuracy or email accuracy@optum.com. You can also reach customer service by calling 1.800.464.3649, option 1.

Acknowledgments

Kelly Armstrong, *Product Manager*
Karen Schmidt, BSN, *Technical Director*
Stacy Perry, *Manager, Desktop Publishing*
Lisa Singley, *Project Manager*
Deborah C. Hall, *Clinical/Technical Editor*
Karen H. Kachur, RN, CPC, *Clinical/Technical Editor*
Nannette Orme, CPC, CCS-P, CPMA, CEMC, *Clinical/Technical Editor*
Jacqueline Petersen, RHIT, CPC, *Clinical/Technical Editor*
Tracy Betzler, *Senior Desktop Publishing Specialist*
Hope M. Dunn, *Senior Desktop Publishing Specialist*
Katie Russell, *Desktop Publishing Specialist*
Regina Heppes, *Editor*

Technical Editors

Deborah C. Hall

Ms. Hall is a new product subject matter expert for Optum360. She has more than 35 years of experience in the health care field. Ms. Hall's experience includes 10 years as practice administrator for large multi-specialty medical practices. She has written several multi-specialty newsletters and coding and reimbursement manuals, and served as a health care consultant. She has taught seminars on CPT/HCPCS and ICD-9-CM coding and physician fee schedules.

Karen H. Kachur, RN, CPC

Ms. Kachur has expertise in CPT/HCPCS and ICD-9-CM coding, in addition to physician billing, compliance, and fraud and abuse. Prior to joining Optum360, she worked for many years as a staff RN in a variety of clinical settings, including medicine, surgery, intensive care, and psychiatry. In addition to her clinical background, Ms. Kachur served as assistant director of a hospital utilization management and quality assurance department and has extensive experience as a nurse reviewer for Blue Cross/Blue Shield. She is an active member of the American Academy of Professional Coders (AAPC).

Nannette Orme, CPC, CCS-P, CPMA, CEMC

Ms. Orme has more than 20 years of experience in the health care profession. She has extensive background in CPT/HCPCS and ICD-9-CM coding and has completed comprehensive ICD-10-CM and PCS training. Her prior experience includes physician clinics and health care consulting. Her areas of expertise include physician audits and education, compliance and HIPAA legislation, litigation support for Medicare self-disclosure cases, hospital chargemaster maintenance, workers' compensation, and emergency department coding. Ms. Orme has presented at national professional conferences and contributed articles for several professional publications. She is a member of the American Academy of Professional Coders (AAPC), American Health Information Management Association (AHIMA), and on the advisory board of a local college.

Jacqueline Petersen, RHIT, CPC

Ms. Petersen is a Clinical/Technical editor with Optum360. She recently served as Senior Clinical Product Research Analyst with Optum360 developing business requirements for edits to support correct coding for claims processing applications. Her experience includes development of data-driven and system rules for both professional and facility claims and in-depth analysis of claims data inclusive of ICD-9-CM, CPT, HCPCS, and modifiers. Ms. Petersen is a member of the American Academy of Professional Coders (AAPC), and the American Health Information Management Association (AHIMA).

December 2015

Dear Subscriber:

Thank you for purchasing the *Coding and Payment Guide.* Optum360 makes every effort to provide customers with accurate and the most up-to-date information possible.

The National Correct Coding Initiative (CCI) data is now in a separate section at the end of this book. This allows customers to see the CCI edits specific to a single code. The most current version of the CCI edits available at the time of publishing is 21.3. Optum360 maintains a website to accompany the *Coding and Payment Guide* series and posts updated CCI edits on this website so that current information is available before the next edition. The following URL and password provides access to download and view the complete list of CCI edits and the ICD-10-CM code index:

https://www.optumcoding.com/Product/Updates/specialty

2016 edition password: **SPEC16DLC**

Please note that you should log in each quarter to ensure you receive the most current updates. An email reminder will be sent to you to let you know when the updates are available.

The Medicare information is in an easier-to-read table. The Medically Unlikely Edits are still included and Optum360 has added the MUE Adjudication Indicator (MAI) information. This will display for each code with the MUE and the MAI in parentheses. In addition, HCPCS Level II equivalent codes have been added for instances in which Medicare and other payers may require the use of a HCPCS Level II code for a specific service.

If you have any questions regarding the *Coding and Payment Guide* series, please call Optum360 customer service at 1.800.464.3649, option 1. You may also visit Optum360's website at www.optumcoding.com for more information.

 **OPTUM**360°™

 REFRESH & RENEW

SAVE UP TO 25%*

when you renew your coding essentials.

>> Buy 1–2 items, save 15%
Buy 3–5 items, save 20%
Buy 6+ items, save 25%

ITEM #	TITLE INDICATE THE ITEMS YOU WISH TO PURCHASE	QUANTITY	PRICE PER PRODUCT	TOTAL
			Subtotal	
	(AK, DE, HI, MT, NH & OR are exempt)		Sales Tax	
	1 item $10.95 • 2–4 items $12.95 • 5+ CALL		Shipping & Handling	
			TOTAL AMOUNT ENCLOSED	

Save up to 25% when you renew.

 Visit **optumcoding.com** and enter the promo code below.

 Call **1-800-464-3649, option 1,** and mention the promo code below.

 Fax this order form with purchase order to **1-801-982-4033.** *Optum360 no longer accepts credit cards by fax.*

PROMO CODE
FOBA16WA

Mail this order form with payment and/or purchase order to:
Optum360, PO Box 88050, Chicago, IL 60680-9920.
Optum360 no longer accepts credit cards by mail.

Name _____

Address _____

_____

Customer Number _____ Contact Number _____

○ CHECK ENCLOSED (PAYABLE TO OPTUM360)

○ BILL ME ○ P.O.# _____

( ) _____
Telephone
( ) _____
Fax
_____ @ _____
E-mail

Optum360 respects your right to privacy. We will not sell or rent your email address or fax number to anyone outside Optum360 and its business partners. If you would like to remove your name from Optum360 promotions, please call 1-800-464-3649, option 1.

 OPTUM 360°™

P1ONEER
THE NEW FRONTIER OF CODING
WITH A TRUSTED, INDUSTRY LEADER BY YOUR SIDE.

Navigate the changing landscape of coding and move forward with confidence.

With Optum360 tools and resources at your fingertips, you can open a world of opportunities and help build the foundation for greater efficiencies, financial gains, and competitive advantages. For over 30 years, our print resources have remained trusted tools for coding professionals, and our 2016 editions offer the same quality and reliability you have come to expect from us.

Eliminate roadblocks with web-based coding solutions.
ICD-10 will have 668 percent more codes than ICD-9. Web-based coding solutions can help you experience a smooth, successful transition with fast access to ICD-10 codes, data and mapping tools, and can easily be used in conjunction with our ICD-10 books. Learn more about EncoderPro.com and RevenueCyclePro.com today by visiting **optumcoding.com/transitions.**

The new frontier of coding awaits.
Save up to 25% on the ICD-10, CPT®, and HCPCS coding resources you need.

 Visit OptumCoding.com and enter promo code **00000AD3** to save 25%

 Call 1.800.464.3649, option 1 and mention promo code **00000AD3** to save 20%

Contents

Introduction

Coding systems and claim forms are part of the reality of modern health care. This *Coding and Payment Guide* provides a comprehensive look at the coding and reimbursement systems used by behavioral health providers. It is organized topically and numerically, and can be used as a comprehensive coding and reimbursement resource and as a quick lookup resource to solve coding problems.

Coding systems grew out of the need for data collection. By having a standard notation for the procedures performed and for the diseases, injuries, and illnesses diagnosed, statisticians could identify effective treatments as well as broad practice patterns. Before long, these early coding systems emerged as the basis to pay claims. Coding systems and claim forms have evolved to become the basis of reimbursement for health care services. The correct application of codes and knowledge of payer policies correlates directly to payment.

The administrative simplification provisions of the Health Insurance Portability and Accountability Act (HIPAA) of 1996 required the standardization of the several hundred health care claim formats previously in existence as well as the establishment of standardized code sets for medical data including diagnoses, drugs, procedures, equipment, and supplies. The goal of the national standards is to reduce the administrative encumbrances of the existing system; simplify the way medical claims are paid, reducing costs; and promote the growth of electronic business in the health care industry.

This *Coding and Payment Guide* provides a comprehensive explanation of the coding and reimbursement systems used for behavioral health services.

Coding Systems

Coding systems seek to answer two questions: what was wrong with the patient (i.e., the diagnosis or diagnoses) and what was done to treat the patient (i.e., the procedures or services rendered).

Under the aegis of the federal government, a three-tiered coding system emerged for physician offices and outpatient facilities. Physicians' Current Procedural Terminology (CPT®) codes report procedures and physician services and comprises Level I of the system. A second level, known informally as HCPCS largely report supplies, nonphysician services, and pharmaceuticals. Dovetailing with each of these levels is the International Classification of Diseases, 10th Revision, Clinical Modification (ICD-10-CM) classification system that reports the diagnosis of illnesses, diseases, and injuries. Further explanations of each of these coding systems follows.

HCPCS Level I or CPT Codes

The Centers for Medicare and Medicaid Services (CMS), in conjunction with the American Medical Association (AMA), the American Dental Association (ADA), and several other professional groups, developed, adopted, and implemented a coding system describing services rendered to patients. Known as HCPCS Level I, the CPT coding system is the most commonly used system to report medical services and procedures. Copyright of CPT codes and descriptions is held by the AMA. This system reports outpatient and provider services.

The three categories of CPT codes predominantly describe medical services and procedures, and are adapted to provide a common billing

language that providers and payers can use for payment purposes. The codes are required for billing by both private and public insurance carriers, managed care companies, and workers' compensation programs. A requirement of HIPAA is that CPT codes are used for the reporting of physician and other health care services.

The AMA's CPT Editorial Panel reviews the coding system and adds, revises, and deletes codes and descriptions. The panel accepts information and feedback from providers about new codes and revisions to existing codes that could better reflect the services.

The majority of codes are found in Category I of the CPT coding system. These five-digit numeric codes describe procedures and services that are customarily performed in clinical practices.

CPT Category II codes are supplemental tracking codes that are primarily used when participating in the Physician Quality Reporting System (PQRS) established by Medicare and are intended to aid in the collection of data about quality of care. At the present time, participation in this program is optional and physicians should not report these codes if they elect not to participate. Category II codes are alphanumeric, consisting of four digits followed by an F and should never be used in lieu of a Category I CPT code. This series of codes is updated on a biannual basis (January 1 and July 1), with codes that are released becoming effective six months later (e.g., codes released on January 1 become effective July 1). Refer to the AMA CPT website at http://www.ama-assn.org/ama/pub/physician-resources/solutions-managing-your-practice/coding-billing-insurance/cpt/about-cpt/category-ii-codes.page.

Category III of the CPT coding system contains temporary tracking codes for new and emerging technologies that are meant to aid in the collection of data on these new services and procedures. Category III codes are indicated by four numeric digits followed by a T. Like Category II codes, Category III CPT codes are released twice a year (January 1 and July 1) and can be found on the on the AMA CPT website. Relative value units (RVUs) are not assigned for these codes, and payment is made at the discretion of the local payer. Once implemented, a service described by a Category III CPT code may eventually become a Category I code. The most current list of these codes can be found at http://www.ama-assn.org/ama/pub/physician-resources/solutions-managing-your-practice/coding-billing-insurance/cpt/about-cpt/category-iii-codes.page.

ICD-10-CM Codes

In response to ICD-9-CM's shortcomings, new coding systems were developed and have been implemented in the United States. The World Health Organization (WHO) created and adopted ICD-10 in 1994 and it has been used in much of the world since then. This system is the basis for the new U.S. diagnosis coding system, International Classification of Diseases, 10th Revision, Clinical Modification (ICD-10-CM) effective October 1, 2015.

The ICD-10-CM coding system is an alphanumeric system and allows for up to seven digits to be assigned to describe a disease or injury. Generally, the reason the patient seeks treatment should be sequenced first when multiple diagnoses are listed.

Overall, the 10th revision goes into greater clinical detail than ICD-9-CM and addresses information about previously classified diseases, as well as those diseases discovered since the last revision. Conditions are grouped with general epidemiological purposes and the evaluation of health care in mind. New features have been added, and conditions have been reorganized, although the format and conventions of the classification remain unchanged for the most part.

Some of these revisions include:

- Information relevant to ambulatory and managed care encounters
- Expanded injury codes
- Creation of combination diagnosis/symptom codes to reduce the number of codes needed to fully describe a condition
- The addition of sixth- and seventh-character subclassifications
- Incorporation of common fourth- and fifth-digit subclassifications
- Classifications specific to laterality
- Classification refinement for increased data granularity

This new structure also allows for further expansion than was possible with the ICD-9-CM classification system.

HCPCS Level II Codes

HCPCS Level II codes are commonly referred to as national codes or simply by the acronym HCPCS (Healthcare Common Procedure Coding System, pronounced hik piks). HCPCS codes are used to bill Medicare and Medicaid patients and are also used by some third-party payers.

HCPCS Level II codes, updated and published by CMS, are intended to supplement the CPT coding system by including codes for nonphysician services, durable medical equipment (DME), and office supplies. These Level II codes consist of one alphabetic character (A through V) followed by four numbers. Non-Medicare acceptance of HCPCS Level II codes is idiosyncratic. Providers should check with the payer before billing these codes. A complete list of the HCPCS Level II codes and the quarterly updates to this code set may be found at http://www.cms.gov/Medicare/Coding/HCPCS ReleaseCodeSets/HCPCS_Quarterly_Update.html.

Claim Forms

Institutional (facility) providers use the UB-04 claim form, also known as the CMS-1450 or the electronic 837I format, to file a Medicare Part A claim to Medicare contractors.

Noninstitutional providers and suppliers (private practice or other health care provider's offices) use the CMS-1500 form or the 837P electronic format to submit claims to Medicare contractors for Medicare Part B covered services. Medicare Part A coverage includes inpatient hospital, skilled nursing facilities (SNF), hospice, and home health. Medicare Part B coverage provides payment for medical supplies, physician, and outpatient services.

Not all services rendered by a facility are inpatient services. Providers working in facilities routinely render services on an outpatient basis. Outpatient services are provided in settings that include rehabilitation centers, certified outpatient rehabilitation facilities, SNFs, and hospitals. Outpatient and partial hospitalization facility claims might be submitted on either a CMS-1500 or UB-04, depending on the payer.

For professional component billing, most claims are filed using ICD-10-CM diagnosis codes to indicate the reason for the service, CPT codes to identify the service provided, and HCPCS Level II codes to report supplies on the CMS-1500 paper claim or the 837P electronic format.

Contents and Format of This Guide

CPT Procedure Codes

The chapter, "Procedure Codes," contains a numeric listing of procedure codes. Each page identifies the information associated with that procedure including an explanation of the service, coding tips, and associated diagnoses. Please note that this list of associated ICD-10-CM codes is not all inclusive. The procedure may be performed for reasons other than those listed that support the medical necessity of the service. Only those conditions supported by the medical record documentation should be reported.

Past editions of this book included separate chapters describing appropriate documentation and reimbursement practices to improve work flow and revenue cycle management. In this new edition of *Coding and Payment Guide*, the sections "Documentation Tips" and "Reimbursement Tips" have been added to each procedure code making that information more visible and useful.

The procedure code page contains related terms and the CMS Online Manual System references that designate the official references to the service, which is identified by the procedure code and found in the online manual system. The full excerpt from the online CMS Online Manual System pertaining to the reference is provided in the Medicare official regulatory information appendix. The full text of all of the Internet-Only Manuals (IOM) may be found at http://www.cms.gov/Regulations-and-Guidance/Guidance/Manuals/Internet-Only-Manuals-IOMs.html.

Finally, relative values and other Medicare information pertaining to the code is provided in a table at the end of the code information.

CCI Edits

Following the procedure code pages is a list of codes from the official *Centers for Medicare and Medicaid Services National Correct Coding Policy Manual for Part B Medicare Contractors* that are considered to be an integral part of the comprehensive or mutually exclusive coding system and should not be reported separately. Mutually exclusive codes are identified with an icon ❖.

To access the Correct Coding Initiative (CCI) edits please go to https://www.optumcoding.com/Product/Updates/specialty. Password **SPEC16DLC**. You will be updated via email every quarter when the newly released CCI edits are available so that you may remain current.

Indexes

Two indexes are provided in *Coding and Payment Guide*. The first is an index to the CPT procedure codes included in this book. The second is the complete ICD-10-CM index, which can be found at https://www.optumcoding.com/Product/Updates/specialty. Password **SPEC16DLC**.

The entire ICD-10-CM index is accessible online for those instances when the diagnosis code documented is not listed in the ICD-10-CM cross-codes provided.

Evaluation and Management

This section provides documentation guidelines and tables showing CPT evaluation and management (E/M) codes for different levels of care. The components that should be considered when selecting an E/M code are also included.

How to Use This Guide

When using this *Coding and Payment Guide* for code assignment, follow these important steps to improve accuracy and experience fewer overlooked diagnoses and services:

- **Step 1.** Carefully read the medical record documentation that describes the patient's diagnosis and the service provided. Remember, more than one diagnosis or service may be documented.

- **Step 2.** Locate the main term for the procedure or service documented in the CPT index. This will identify the procedure code that may be used to report this service.

- **Step 3.** Locate the procedure code in the chapter titled "Procedure Codes." Read the explanation and determine if that is the procedure performed and supported by the medical record documentation. The Terms to Know section may be used to ensure appropriate code assignment.

- **Step 4.** At this time review the additional CPT coding information found in the coding tips, IOM references, and CCI sections or the Medicare physician fee schedule references.

- **Step 5.** Peruse the list of ICD-10-CM codes to determine if the condition documented in the medical record is listed and the code identified. If the condition is not listed refer to the ICD-10-CM index or ICD-10-CM manual to locate the appropriate code.

- **Step 6.** Determine if any Medicare regulatory information is associated with this code and if so, an excerpt of this information may be found in the appendix titled, "Medicare Official Regulatory Information."

- **Step 7.** Finally, review the HCPCS Level II section to determine if there are applicable HCPCS Level II codes that may be reported. This section also includes HCPCS Level II modifiers as well as coding tips.

Sample Page and Key

On the following pages are a sample page from the book displaying the new format of *Coding and Payment Guide* with each element identified and explained on the opposite page.

80156-80157

1

80156   Carbamazepine; total

80157   free

Explanation

2

This drug, also known as Tegretol, is an enzyme inducer. Blood specimen collection is by venipuncture. CSF is obtained by spinal puncture, which is reported separately. Test specimens for total levels (80156) are frequently collected at the trough period, which is about 12 hours after the last dose when serum concentration is at its lowest. This is an effective approach to determine a therapeutic level of drug. Test specimens for free drug concentrations (80157) may be collected near peak levels about two to eight hours after ingestion. Methods include high performance liquid chromatography (HPLC) or gas liquid chromatography (GLC) for both types of analysis. This drug is absorbed slowly and erratically by the GI tract and a total concentration may be required, depending on the treatment underway. Methods include high performance liquid chromatography (HPLC) or gas liquid chromatography (GLC). Tegretol may be administered for such conditions as trigeminal neuralgia, epilepsy, and manic disorders. It is known for its anticonvulsant and pain management properties.

Coding Tips

3

This examination is quantitative. To report the professional services for drug management, see CPT code 90863, the appropriate level of E/M service, or the appropriate psychotherapy with E/M service code. Follow third-party payer guidelines when selecting the appropriate code for these services. If a specimen is transported to an outside laboratory, report 99000 for handling or conveyance.

Documentation Tips

4

Documentation must include the laboratory results to support reporting this service.

Reimbursement Tips

5

Medicare reimburses this service under the laboratory fee schedule.

Terms To Know

6

laboratory. Facility for the virological, microbiological, serological, chemical, immunohematological, hematological, biophysical, cytological, pathological, or other examination of materials derived from the human body for the purpose of providing information for the diagnosis, prevention, or treatment of any disease or impairment of or the assessment of the health of human beings. These examinations also include procedures to determine, measure, or otherwise describe the presence or absence of various substances or organisms in the body. Facilities that only collect or prepare specimens (or both) or act only as a mailing service and do not perform tests are not considered laboratories.

ICD-10-CM Diagnostic Codes

7

F30.11	Manic episode without psychotic symptoms, mild
F30.12	Manic episode without psychotic symptoms, moderate
F30.13	Manic episode, severe, without psychotic symptoms
F30.2	Manic episode, severe with psychotic symptoms
F30.3	Manic episode in partial remission
F30.4	Manic episode in full remission
F31.0	Bipolar disorder, current episode hypomanic
F31.11	Bipolar disorder, current episode manic without psychotic features, mild
F31.12	Bipolar disorder, current episode manic without psychotic features, moderate
F31.13	Bipolar disorder, current episode manic without psychotic features, severe
F31.2	Bipolar disorder, current episode manic severe with psychotic features
F31.31	Bipolar disorder, current episode depressed, mild
F31.32	Bipolar disorder, current episode depressed, moderate
F31.4	Bipolar disorder, current episode depressed, severe, without psychotic features
F31.5	Bipolar disorder, current episode depressed, severe, with psychotic features
F31.61	Bipolar disorder, current episode mixed, mild
F31.62	Bipolar disorder, current episode mixed, moderate
F31.63	Bipolar disorder, current episode mixed, severe, without psychotic features
F31.64	Bipolar disorder, current episode mixed, severe, with psychotic features
F31.71	Bipolar disorder, in partial remission, most recent episode hypomanic
F31.72	Bipolar disorder, in full remission, most recent episode hypomanic
F31.73	Bipolar disorder, in partial remission, most recent episode manic
F31.74	Bipolar disorder, in full remission, most recent episode manic
F31.75	Bipolar disorder, in partial remission, most recent episode depressed
F31.76	Bipolar disorder, in full remission, most recent episode depressed
F31.77	Bipolar disorder, in partial remission, most recent episode mixed
F31.78	Bipolar disorder, in full remission, most recent episode mixed
F31.89	Other bipolar disorder
G89.4	Chronic pain syndrome
T42.1X1A	Poisoning by iminostilbenes, accidental (unintentional), initial encounter
T42.1X2A	Poisoning by iminostilbenes, intentional self-harm, initial encounter
T42.1X3A	Poisoning by iminostilbenes, assault, initial encounter
T42.1X4A	Poisoning by iminostilbenes, undetermined, initial encounter
T42.1X5A	Adverse effect of iminostilbenes, initial encounter
T42.1X6A	Underdosing of iminostilbenes, initial encounter
Z02.83	Encounter for blood-alcohol and blood-drug test
Z51.81	Encounter for therapeutic drug level monitoring

Medicare Edits

8

	Fac RVU	Non-Fac RVU	FUD	Status	MUE
80156	0.0	0.0	N/A	X	2(3)
80157	0.0	0.0	N/A	X	2(3)

	Modifiers				Medicare References
80156	N/A	N/A	N/A	N/A	None
80157	N/A	N/A	N/A	N/A	
* with documentation					

1. CPT Codes and Descriptions

This edition of *Coding and Payment Guide for Behavioral Health Services* is updated with CPT codes for year 2015.

2. Explanation

Every CPT code or series of similar codes is presented with its official CPT code description. However, sometimes these descriptions do not provide the coder with sufficient information to make a proper code selection. In this *Coding and Payment Guide*, a step-by-step clinical description of the procedure is provided, in simple terms. Technical language that might be used by the physician is included and defined. *Coding and Payment Guide for Behavioral Health Services* describes the most common method of performing each procedure.

3. Coding Tips

Coding and reimbursement tips provide information on how the code should be used, provides related CPT codes, and offers help concerning common billing errors, modifier usage, and anesthesia. This information comes from consultants and technical editors at Optum360 and from the coding guidelines provided in the CPT book.

4. Documentation Tips

Provides tips to the coder regarding the information that should be noted in the medical record to support code assignment.

5. Reimbursement Tips

Medicare and other payer guidelines that could affect the reimbursement of this service or procedure are included in the Reimbursement Tips section.

6. Terms to Know

Some codes are accompanied by general information pertinent to the procedure, labeled "Terms to Know." This information is not critical to code selection, but is a useful supplement to coders hoping to expand their knowledge of the specialty.

7. ICD-10-CM Diagnostic Codes

The ICD-10-CM codes describing conditions that commonly support the medical necessity of the procedure or service are listed here. Please note that the list is not all inclusive and that the condition necessitating the service as described in the medical record should be identified on the claim even if it is not included in this list.

8. Medicare Information

Medicare edits are provided for most codes. These 2016 Medicare edits were current as of November 2015.

Relative Value Units
In a resource based relative value scale (RBRVS), services are ranked based on the relative costs of the resources required to provide those services as opposed to the average fee for the service, or average prevailing Medicare charge. The Medicare RBRVS defines three distinct components affecting the value of each service or procedure:

- Physician work component, reflecting the physician's time and skill

- Practice expense (PE) component, reflecting the physician's rent, staff, supplies, equipment, and other overhead

- Malpractice insurance component, reflecting the relative risk or liability associated with the service

There are two RVUs listed for each CPT code. The first RVU is for nonfacilities (Non-fac Total), which includes services provided in physician offices, patients' homes, or other nonhospital settings. The second RVU is for facilities (Fac Total), which represents services provided in hospitals, ambulatory surgery centers, or skilled nursing facilities.

Medicare Follow-Up Days (FUD)
Information on the Medicare global period is provided here. The global period is the time following a surgery during which routine care by the physician is considered postoperative and included in the surgical fee. Office visits or other routine care related to the original surgery cannot be separately reported if they occur during the global period.

Status
The Medicare status indicates if the service is separately payable by Medicare. The Medicare RBRVS includes:

A	Active code—separate payment may be made
B	Bundled code—payment is bundled into other service
C	Carrier priced—individual carrier will price the code
I	Not valid—Medicare uses another code for this service
N	Non-covered—service is not covered by Medicare
R	Restricted—special coverage instructions apply
T	Injections—separately payable if no other services on same date
X	Statutory exclusion—no RVUs or payment

Medically Unlikely Edits
This column provides the maximum number of units allowed by Medicare. However, it is also important to note that not every code has a Medically Unlikely Edit (MUE) available. Medicare has assigned some MUE values that are not available. If there is no value in the MUE column for a particular code, it may mean that CMS has not released information on that MUE. Watch the remittance advice for possible details on MUE denials related to those codes. If there is no published MUE, a dash will display in the field.

Beginning with the MUE release updated on July 2, 2014, an additional component of the MUE became effective. This edit is the MUE Adjudication Indicator (MAI). This edit is the result of an audit by the Office of the Inspector General (OIG) that identified inappropriate billing practices that bypassed the MUE edits. These included inappropriate reporting of bilateral services and split billing.

There are three MUE Adjudication Indicators.

1 Line Edit

2 Date of Service Edit: Policy

3 Date of Service Edit: Clinical

The MAI will be listed following the MUE value. For example code 11446 has an MUE value of 3 and an MAI value of 1. This will display in the MUE field as "3(1)."

Modifiers
Medicare identifies some modifiers that are required or appropriate to report with the CPT code. When the modifiers are not appropriate, it will be indicated with N/A. Four modifiers are included.

50 Bilateral Procedures
This modifier is used to identify when the same procedure is

performed bilaterally. Medicare requires one line with modifier 50 and the reimbursement is 50 percent of the allowable. Other payers may require two lines and will reduce the second procedure.

51   Multiple Procedure
     Medicare and other payers reduce the reimbursement of second and subsequent procedures performed at the same session to 50 percent of the allowable. For endoscopic procedures, the reimbursement is reduced by the value of the endoscopic base code.

62* Two Surgeons
     Medicare identifies procedures that may be performed by co-surgeons. The reimbursement is split between both providers. Both surgeons must report the same code when using this modifier.

80* Assistant Surgeon
     An assistant surgeon is allowed if modifier 80 is listed.

Reimbursement is usually 20 percent of the allowable. For Medicare it is 16 percent to account for the patient's co-pay amount.

* with documentation

Modifiers 62 and 80 may require supporting documentation to justify the co- or assistant surgeon.

Medicare Official Regulatory Information
Medicare official regulatory information provides official regulatory guidelines. Also known as the CMS Online Manual System, the Internet-only Manuals (IOM) contain official CMS information pertaining to program issuances, instructions, policies, and procedures based on statutes, regulations, guidelines, models, and directives. Optum360 has provided the reference for the surgery codes. The full text of guidelines can be found online at http://www.cms.gov/Regulations-and-Guidance/Guidance/Manuals/.

Procedure Codes

The Physicians' Current Procedural Terminology (CPT®) coding system was developed and is updated annually by the American Medical Association (AMA). The AMA owns and maintains the CPT coding system and publishes its updates annually under copyright. CPT codes predominantly describe medical services and procedures performed by physicians and nonphysician professionals. The codes are classified as Level I of the Healthcare Common Procedure Coding System (HCPCS).

In general, whenever possible, providers should consider using CPT codes to describe their services for several reasons. Foremost, providers can evaluate patient care by reviewing coded services and procedures. Secondly, procedural coding is a language understood in the provider and payer communities. Consequently, accurate coding can also help an insurer determine coverage eligibility for services provided.

Accurate coding consists of choosing the most appropriate code available for the service provided to the patient. However, the existence of a CPT or HCPCS code does not guarantee that a third-party payer will accept the code or that the service described by the code is covered.

Investigate codes that are denied or downcoded on a claim by the third-party payer, and resubmit with the correct codes if necessary.

Structure of the CPT Book

The CPT book has an introduction, eight main sections, 14 appendixes, and an index.

Category I Codes

The sections considered Category I are:

- Evaluation and Management
- Anesthesia
- Surgery
- Radiology, Nuclear Medicine, and Diagnostic Ultrasound
- Pathology and Laboratory
- Medicine

Category II Codes

Category II CPT codes are a set of codes used for supplemental tracking and performance measurements. Primarily these codes are used to report quality measures when participating in Medicare's Physician Quality Reporting System (PQRS). For more information about PQRS, see the CMS website at http://www.cms.gov/Medicare/Quality-Initiatives-Patient-Assessment-Instruments/PQRS/index.html

Category III Codes

Category III codes, which are considered temporary, have been added for reporting the use of new technologies that are not available to report in the existing Category I CPT code set.

CPT Coding Conventions

To code properly, coders must understand and follow the CPT conventions developed by the AMA.

Symbols

The following are several symbols used in the CPT book:

- A bullet (●) before the code means that the code is new to the CPT coding system in the current year.

- A triangle (▲) before the code means that the code narrative has been revised in the current year.

- Codes with a plus (+) symbol indicate an "add-on" code. Procedures described by add-on codes are always performed in addition to the primary procedure and should never be reported alone. This concept applies only to procedures or services performed by the same physician to describe any additional intraservice work, such as a procedure on additional digits or lesions, associated with the primary procedure.

- The symbols ►◄ indicate new or revised text other than that contained in the code descriptors.

- The symbol ⊘ designates a code that is exempt from the use of modifier 51. These codes have not been designated as add-on codes in the CPT book.

- The bull's eye symbol (⊙) indicates codes that have moderate sedation as an integral part of the procedure. Because conscious sedation is included in the service, it would be inappropriate to separately bill for this service using code 99141 or 99142. However, anesthesia services (CPT codes 00100–01999) may be billed separately when performed by a physician (or other qualified provider) other than the physician performing the procedure.

- The lightning bolt (⚡) symbol identifies vaccines that are pending FDA approval. These codes were assigned a CPT Category I code by the AMA in anticipation of future approval. Upon revision of the approval status by the FDA, the AMA will post notification on its website at http://www.ama-assn.org/ama/pub/physician-resources/solutions-managing-your-practice/coding-billing-insurance/cpt/about-cpt/category-i-vaccine-codes.page.

- The number (#) symbol indicates that a code is out of numeric order or "resequenced." The AMA employs a new numbering methodology of resequencing. According to the AMA there are instances where a new code is needed within an existing grouping of codes and an unused code number is not available. In the instance where the existing codes will not be changed or have minimal changes, the AMA will assign a code that is not in numeric sequence with the related codes. However, the code and description will appear in the CPT book with the other related codes.

- The symbol ○ is used to indicate a reinstated/recycled code number.

Unlisted Procedures and Modifiers

Unlisted Procedures

Not all medical services or procedures are assigned CPT codes. The code book does not contain codes for infrequently used, new, or experimental procedures. Each code section contains codes set aside specifically for reporting unlisted procedures.

Before choosing an unlisted procedure code, carefully review the CPT code list to ensure that a more specific code is not available. Also, check for a HCPCS Level II code if these codes are acceptable to the third-party payer. These codes are found at the end of the section or subsection of codes and most often end in "99." For example:

90899   Unlisted psychiatric service or procedure

Whenever an unlisted code is reported, it is necessary to include a descriptive narrative of the procedure performed in item 19 of the CMS-1500 claim form, as long as it can be adequately explained in the space provided.

Payers generally require additional documentation (e.g., progress notes, operative notes, consultation report, or history and physical) before considering claims with unlisted procedure codes.

Modifiers

The CPT coding system also includes modifiers that can be added to codes to describe extenuating or special circumstances or to provide additional information about a procedure that was performed, or a service or supply that was provided. Addition of the modifier does not alter the basic description for the service; it merely qualifies the circumstances under which the service was provided. Some third-party payers, such as Medicare, require modifier use in some circumstances. Circumstances that modify a service include the following:

- Procedures have both a technical and professional component

- More than one individual or setting was involved in the service

- Only part of a service was performed

- The service was delivered to more than one patient

- Adjunctive, complex, or bilateral procedures were performed

The following CPT modifiers are used most often by behavioral health providers:

22   Increased procedural services. When the work required to provide a service is substantially greater than typically required, it may be identified by adding modifier 22 to the usual procedure code. Documentation must support the substantial additional work and the reason for the additional work (ie, increased intensity, time, technical difficulty of procedure, severity of patient's condition, physical and mental effort required).

Note: This modifier should not be appended to an E/M service.

25   Significant, separately identifiable evaluation and management service by the same physician or other qualified health care professional on the same day of the procedure or other service. It may be necessary to indicate that on the day a procedure or service identified by a CPT code was performed, the patient's condition required a significant, separately identifiable E/M service above and beyond the other service provided or beyond the usual preoperative and postoperative care associated with the procedure that was performed. A significant, separately identifiable E/M service is defined or substantiated by documentation that satisfies the relevant criteria for the respective E/M service to be reported (see Evaluation and Management Services Guidelines for instructions on determining level of E/M service). The E/M service may be prompted by the symptom or condition for which the procedure and/or service was provided. As such, different diagnoses are not required for reporting of the E/M services on the same date. This circumstance may be reported by adding modifier 25 to the appropriate level of E/M service.

Note: This modifier is not used to report an E/M service that resulted in a decision to perform surgery. See modifier 57. For significant, separately identifiable non-E/M services, see modifier 59.

26   Professional component. Certain procedures are a combination of a physician or other qualified health care professional component and a technical component. When the physician or other qualified health care professional component is reported separately, the service may be identified by adding modifier 26 to the usual procedure number.

32   Mandated services. Services related to *mandated* consultation and/or related services (eg, third party payer, governmental, legislative or regulatory requirement) may be identified by adding modifier 32 to the basic procedure.

51   Multiple procedures. When multiple procedures, other than E/M services, physical medicine and rehabilitation services or provision of supplies (eg, vaccines), are performed at the same session by the same individual, the primary procedure or service may be reported as listed. The additional procedure(s) or service(s) may be identified by appending modifier 51 to the additional procedure or service code(s).

Note: This modifier should not be appended to designated add-on codes.

52   Reduced services. Under certain circumstances a service or procedure is partially reduced or eliminated at the discretion of the physician or other qualified health care professional. Under these circumstances the service provided can be identified by its usual procedure number and the addition of modifier 52, signifying that the service is reduced. This provides a means of reporting reduced services without disturbing the identification of the basic service.

Note: For hospital outpatient reporting of a previously scheduled procedure/service that is partially reduced or cancelled as a result of extenuating circumstances or those that threaten the well-being of the patient prior to or after administration of anesthesia, see modifiers 73 and 74 (see modifiers approved for ASC hospital outpatient use).

53   Discontinued procedure. Under certain circumstances, the physician or other qualified health care professional may elect to terminate a surgical or diagnostic procedure. Due to extenuating circumstances or those that threaten the well-being of the patient, it may be necessary to indicate that a surgical or diagnostic procedure was started but discontinued. This circumstance may be reported by adding modifier 53 to the code reported by the individual for the discontinued procedure.

Note: This modifier is not used to report the elective cancellation of a procedure prior to the patient's anesthesia induction and/or surgical preparation in the operating suite. For outpatient hospital/ambulatory surgery center (ASC) reporting of a previously scheduled procedure/service that is partially reduced or cancelled as a result of extenuating circumstances or those that threaten the well being of the patient prior to or after administration of anesthesia, see modifiers 73 and 74 (see modifiers approved for ASC hospital outpatient use).

59   Distinct procedural service. Under certain circumstances, it may be necessary to indicate that a procedure or service was distinct or independent from other non-E/M services performed on the same day. Modifier 59 is used to identify procedures/services, other than E/M services, that are not normally reported together, but are appropriate under the circumstances. Documentation must support a different session, different procedure or surgery, different site or organ system, separate incision/excision, separate lesion, or separate injury (or area of injury in extensive injuries) not ordinarily encountered or performed on the same day by the same individual. However, when another already established modifier is appropriate it should be used rather than modifier 59. Only if no more descriptive modifier is available, and the use of modifier 59 best explains the circumstances, should modifier 59 be used.

Note: Modifier 59 should not be appended to an E/M service. To report a separate and distinct E/M service with a non-E/M service performed on the same date, see modifier 25.

76   Repeat procedure or service by same physician or other qualified health care professional. It may be necessary to indicate that a procedure or service was repeated by the same physician or other qualified health care professional subsequent to the original procedure or service. This circumstance may be reported by adding modifier 76 to the repeated procedure or service.

Note: This modifier should not be appended to an E/M service.

77   Repeat procedure by another physician or other qualified health care professional. It may be necessary to indicate that a basic procedure or service was repeated by another physician or other qualified health care professional subsequent to the original procedure or service. This circumstance may be reported by adding modifier 77 to the repeated procedure or service.

Note: This modifier should not be appended to an E/M service.

Modifiers Approved for Hospital Outpatient Use

25   Significant, separately identifiable evaluation and management service by the same physician or other qualified health care professional on the same day of the procedure or other service. It may be necessary to indicate that on the day a procedure or service identified by a CPT code was performed, the patient's condition required a significant, separately identifiable E/M service above and beyond the other service provided or beyond the usual preoperative and postoperative care associated with the procedure that was performed. A significant, separately identifiable E/M service is defined or substantiated by documentation that satisfies the relevant criteria for the respective E/M service to be reported (see Evaluation and Management Services Guidelines for instructions on determining level of E/M service). The E/M service may be prompted by the symptom or condition for which the procedure and/or service was provided. As such, different diagnoses are not required for reporting of the E/M services on the same date. This circumstance may be reported by adding modifier 25 to the appropriate level of E/M service.

Note: This modifier is not used to report an E/M service that resulted in a decision to perform surgery. See modifier 57. For significant, separately identifiable non-E/M services, see modifier 59.

Optum360 Note: For OPPS services, this modifier may be used only with E/M service codes that have an OPPS status indicator of V (visit). In 2012, these code ranges under OPPS are: 90945, 92002–92014, 95250, 99201–99214, 99281–99284, 99460, 99463, G0101, G0175, G0246, G0248, G0249, G0380–G0383, and G0402.

The Outpatient Code Editor requires modifier 25 be used on an E/M code when it is reported with a procedure code that has a payment status indicator of "S" or "T." However, this does not preclude a provider from reporting this modifier with E/M codes that are assigned to a payment status indicator other than the "S" or "T" as long as the procedure meets the definition of "significant, separately identifiable E/M service." For significant, separately identifiable non-E/M services, see modifier 59.

27   Multiple outpatient hospital E/M encounters on the same date. For hospital outpatient reporting purposes, utilization of hospital resources related to separate and distinct E/M encounters performed in multiple outpatient hospital settings on the same date may be reported by adding modifier 27 to each appropriate level outpatient and/or emergency department E/M code(s). This modifier provides a means of reporting circumstances involving evaluation and management services provided by physician(s) in more than one (multiple) outpatient hospital setting(s) (eg, hospital emergency department, clinic).

Note: This modifier is not to be used for physician reporting of multiple E/M services performed by the same physician on the same date. For physician reporting of all outpatient evaluation and management services provided by the same physician on the same date and performed in multiple outpatient setting(s) (eg, hospital emergency department, clinic), see Evaluation and Management, Emergency Department, or Preventive Medicine Services codes.

Optum360 Note: For OPPS services, this modifier may be used only with E/M service codes that have an OPPS status indicator of V (visit). In 2012, these code ranges under OPPS are: 90945, 92002–92014, 95250, 99201–99214, 99281–99284, 99460, 99463, G0101, G0175, G0246, G0248, G0249, G0380–G0383, and G0402.

Hospitals use this modifier on the second and subsequent E/M code when more than one E/M service is provided to indicate that the E/M service is a separate and distinct E/M encounter from the service previously provided on the same day in the same or different hospital setting. Modifier 27 does not replace condition code (FLs 24–30) G0. Continue to report condition code G0 for multiple medical visits that occur on the same day in the same revenue center

52 **Reduced services.** Under certain circumstances a service or procedure is partially reduced or eliminated at the discretion of the physician or other qualified health care professional. Under these circumstances the service provided can be identified by its usual procedure number and the addition of modifier 52, signifying that the service is reduced. This provides a means of reporting reduced services without disturbing the identification of the basic service.

Note: For hospital outpatient reporting of a previously scheduled procedure/service that is partially reduced or cancelled as a result of extenuating circumstances or those that threaten the well-being of the patient prior to or after administration of anesthesia, see modifiers 73 and 74 (see modifiers approved for ASC hospital outpatient use).

Optum360 Note: For OPPS billing, modifier 52 is used to indicate partial reduction, cancellation, or discontinuation of services for which anesthesia is not planned. Report this modifier when the procedure was discontinued only after the patient was prepared and brought to the room where the procedure was to be performed.

When a radiology procedure is reduced, the correct reporting is to assign a code to the extent of the procedure performed. Modifier 52 (reduced services) is used only to report a radiology procedure that has been reduced when no other code exists to report what has been done. Report the intended code with modifier 52. For example, if the planned procedure is a two-view chest x-ray and only one view of the chest is performed, do not report CPT code 71020-52 (for x-ray chest, two views-reduced service). Instead, report CPT code 71010 (x-ray chest, single view). If a barium swallow is not completed because the patient cannot tolerate the barium, report CPT code 74270-52.

For hospital outpatient reporting when anesthesia is planned for a previously scheduled procedure or service that is discontinued, see modifiers 73 and 74.

59 **Distinct procedural service.** Under certain circumstances, it may be necessary to indicate that a procedure or service was distinct or independent from other non-E/M services performed on the same day. Modifier 59 is used to identify procedures/services, other than E/M services, that are not normally reported together, but are appropriate under the circumstances. Documentation must support a different session, different procedure or surgery, different site or organ system, separate incision/excision, separate lesion, or separate injury (or area of injury in extensive injuries) not ordinarily encountered or performed on the same day by the same individual. However, when another already established modifier is appropriate it should be used rather than modifier 59. Only if no more descriptive modifier is available, and the use of modifier 59 best explains the circumstances, should modifier 59 be used.

Note: Modifier 59 should not be appended to an E/M service. To report a separate and distinct E/M service with a non-E/M service performed on the same date, see modifier 25. See also page 684, Level II HCPCS/National Modifiers listing.

Optum360 Note: This modifier is allowable for radiology services. It may also be used with surgical or medical codes in appropriate circumstances When billing, report the first code without a modifier. On subsequent lines, report the code with the modifier.

73 **Discontinued outpatient hospital/ambulatory surgery center (ASC) procedure prior to the administration of anesthesia.** Due to extenuating circumstances or those that threaten the well being of the patient, the physician may cancel a surgical or diagnostic procedure subsequent to the patient's surgical preparation (including sedation when provided, and being taken to the room where the procedure is to be performed), but prior to the administration of anesthesia (local, regional block(s) or general). Under these circumstances, the intended service that is prepared for but cancelled can be reported by its usual procedure number and the addition of modifier 73.

Note: The elective cancellation of a service prior to the administration of anesthesia and/or surgical preparation of the patient should not be reported. For physician reporting of a discontinued procedure, see modifier 53.

Optum360 Note: Under OPPS, anesthesia includes general, local and regional block(s), moderate sedation/analgesia (conscious sedation), and deep sedation/analgesia. Modifier 73 is only used to indicate discontinued procedures for which anesthesia is planned or provided. This modifier is used to indicate that a procedure for which anesthesia was planned was terminated after the patient had been prepared for the procedure, but prior to administration of anesthesia. Preparation for the procedure includes procedural premedication when provided and being taken to the room where the procedure was to be performed. This modifier applies in extenuating circumstances and when the well-being of the patient is threatened.

Never report the elective cancellation of procedures. When one or more of the planned procedures is completed, report the completed procedure as usual. Any others that were planned and not started are not reported. When none of the procedures that were planned are completed, the first procedure that was planned to be done is reported with this modifier.

74 **Discontinued outpatient hospital/ambulatory surgery center (ASC) procedure prior to the administration of anesthesia.** Due to extenuating circumstances or those that threaten the well being of the patient, the physician may terminate a surgical or diagnostic procedure after the administration of anesthesia (local, regional block(s), general) or after the procedure was started (incision made, intubation started, scope inserted, etc.). Under these circumstances, the procedure started but terminated can be reported by its usual procedure number and the addition of modifier 74.

Note: The elective cancellation of a service prior to the administration of anesthesia and/or surgical preparation of the patient should not be reported. For physician reporting of a discontinued procedure, see modifier 53.

Optum360 Note: Under OPPS, anesthesia includes general, local and regional block(s), moderate sedation/analgesia (conscious sedation), and deep sedation/analgesia. Modifier 74 is only used to indicate discontinued procedures for which anesthesia is planned or provided. This modifier is used to indicate that a procedure for which anesthesia was planned was terminated after the induction of anesthesia or after the procedure was started (eg, incision made, intubation started, scope inserted). Use modifier 74 when the procedure was discontinued due to extenuating circumstances or to circumstances that threatened the well-being of the patient. Modifier 74 may also be used to indicate that a planned procedure was discontinued, partially reduced, or cancelled at the physician's discretion after the administration of anesthesia.

Never report the elective cancellation of procedures. If available, use a CPT code that classifies the extent of the procedure performed instead of reporting the intended procedure. When one or more of the planned procedures is completed, report the completed procedure as usual. Any others that were planned and not started are not reported. When none of the procedures that were planned are completed, the first procedure that was planned to be done is reported with this modifier.

76   **Repeat procedure or service by same physician or other qualified health care professional.** It may be necessary to indicate that a procedure or service was repeated by the same physician or other qualified health care professional subsequent to the original procedure or service. This circumstance may be reported by adding modifier 76 to the repeated procedure or service.

Note: This modifier should not be appended to an E/M service.

Optum360 Note: Report the procedures on two lines, first with the procedure code and then again with the procedure code and modifier.

77   **Repeat procedure by another physician or other qualified health care professional.** It may be necessary to indicate that a basic procedure or service was repeated by another physician or other qualified health care professional subsequent to the original procedure or service. This circumstance may be reported by adding modifier 77 to the repeated procedure or service.

Note: This modifier should not be appended to an E/M service.

Optum360 Note: Report the procedures on two lines, first with the procedure code and then again with the procedure code and modifier 77.

91   **Repeat clinical diagnostic laboratory test.** In the course of treatment of the patient, it may be necessary to repeat the same laboratory test on the same day to obtain subsequent (multiple) test results. Under these circumstances, the laboratory test performed can be identified by its usual procedure number and the addition of modifier 91.

Note: This modifier may not be used when tests are rerun to confirm initial results; due to testing problems with specimens or equipment; or for any other reason when a normal, one-time, reportable result is all that is required. This modifier may not be used when other code(s) describe a series of test results (eg, glucose tolerance tests, evocative/suppression testing). This modifier may only be used for laboratory test(s) performed more than once on the same day on the same patient.

Optum360 Note: Modifier 91 may be used only for laboratory tests paid under the clinical diagnostic laboratory fee schedule.

80155

80155   Caffeine

Explanation

Caffeine is the most widely consumed stimulant in the world and is found in beverages, foods, and medications. This drug may cause moderate to severe symptoms and/or caffeine toxicity. Blood specimen is collected via venipuncture. Test specimens are collected randomly rather than at trough level. A quantitative analysis of caffeine in the bloodstream does not influence medical management of the patient. This test is most commonly used on neonatal patients that are not responding to caffeine therapy or have suspected toxicity of caffeine. Method is enzyme immunoassay (EIA).

Coding Tips

This test is quantitative. If specimen is transported to an outside laboratory, report 99000 for handling or conveyance.

Documentation Tips

Documentation must include the laboratory results to support reporting this service.

Medical record documentation must, at a minimum, include signs and symptoms supporting the ordering of this service.

The seventh character A Initial encounter, is appropriate when documentation indicates that the health care provider is providing active treatment for the condition, even when provided by a different health care professional. Assign the seventh character D subsequent encounter, when the documentation indicates that the patient has completed the active phase of treatment and the health care provider is providing routine care (generally rehabilitation therapy) during the healing or recovery phase.

Reimbursement Tips

Medicare reimburses this service under the laboratory fee schedule.

Terms To Know

qualitative. To determine the nature of the component of substance.

quantitative. To determine the amount and nature of the components of a substance.

ICD-10-CM Diagnostic Codes

F15.180	Other stimulant abuse with stimulant-induced anxiety disorder
F15.182	Other stimulant abuse with stimulant-induced sleep disorder
F15.280	Other stimulant dependence with stimulant-induced anxiety disorder
F15.281	Other stimulant dependence with stimulant-induced sexual dysfunction
F15.282	Other stimulant dependence with stimulant-induced sleep disorder
F15.288	Other stimulant dependence with other stimulant-induced disorder
F15.29	Other stimulant dependence with unspecified stimulant-induced disorder
F15.980	Other stimulant use, unspecified with stimulant-induced anxiety disorder
F15.981	Other stimulant use, unspecified with stimulant-induced sexual dysfunction
F15.982	Other stimulant use, unspecified with stimulant-induced sleep disorder
F15.988	Other stimulant use, unspecified with other stimulant-induced disorder
F15.99	Other stimulant use, unspecified with unspecified stimulant-induced disorder
R00.0	Tachycardia, unspecified
R00.2	Palpitations
R07.9	Chest pain, unspecified
R09.89	Other specified symptoms and signs involving the circulatory and respiratory systems
R41.0	Disorientation, unspecified
R41.82	Altered mental status, unspecified
R56.9	Unspecified convulsions
T43.611A	Poisoning by caffeine, accidental (unintentional), initial encounter
T43.612A	Poisoning by caffeine, intentional self-harm, initial encounter
T43.613A	Poisoning by caffeine, assault, initial encounter
T43.614A	Poisoning by caffeine, undetermined, initial encounter
T43.615A	Adverse effect of caffeine, initial encounter
T43.616A	Underdosing of caffeine, initial encounter
Z02.83	Encounter for blood-alcohol and blood-drug test
Z51.81	Encounter for therapeutic drug level monitoring

Please note that this list of associated ICD-10-CM codes is not all-inclusive. The procedure may be performed for reasons other than those listed that support the medical necessity of the service. Only those conditions supported by the medical record documentation should be reported.

Medicare Edits

	Fac RVU	Non-Fac RVU	FUD	Status	MUE
80155	0.0	0.0	N/A	X	1(3)

	Modifiers				Medicare References
80155	N/A	N/A	N/A	N/A	None

* with documentation

80156-80157

80156   Carbamazepine; total
80157   free

Explanation

This drug, also known as Tegretol, is an enzyme inducer. Blood specimen collection is by venipuncture. CSF is obtained by spinal puncture, which is reported separately. Test specimens for total levels (80156) are frequently collected at the trough period, which is about 12 hours after the last dose when serum concentration is at its lowest. This is an effective approach to determine a therapeutic level of drug. Test specimens for free drug concentrations (80157) may be collected near peak levels about two to eight hours after ingestion. Methods include high performance liquid chromatography (HPLC) or gas liquid chromatography (GLC) for both types of analysis. This drug is absorbed slowly and erratically by the GI tract and a total concentration may be required, depending on the treatment underway. Methods include high performance liquid chromatography (HPLC) or gas liquid chromatography (GLC). Tegretol may be administered for such conditions as trigeminal neuralgia, epilepsy, and manic disorders. It is known for its anticonvulsant and pain management properties.

Coding Tips

This examination is quantitative. To report the professional services for drug management, see CPT code 90863, the appropriate level of evaluation and management (E/M) service, or the appropriate psychotherapy with E/M service code. Follow third-party payer guidelines when selecting the appropriate code for these services. If a specimen is transported to an outside laboratory, report 99000 for handling or conveyance.

Documentation Tips

Documentation must include the laboratory results to support reporting this service.

Reimbursement Tips

Medicare reimburses this service under the laboratory fee schedule.

Terms To Know

laboratory. Facility for the virological, microbiological, serological, chemical, immunohematological, hematological, biophysical, cytological, pathological, or other examination of materials derived from the human body for the purpose of providing information for the diagnosis, prevention, or treatment of any disease or impairment of or the assessment of the health of human beings. These examinations also include procedures to determine, measure, or otherwise describe the presence or absence of various substances or organisms in the body. Facilities that only collect or prepare specimens (or both) or act only as a mailing service and do not perform tests are not considered laboratories.

ICD-10-CM Diagnostic Codes

F30.11	Manic episode without psychotic symptoms, mild
F30.12	Manic episode without psychotic symptoms, moderate
F30.13	Manic episode, severe, without psychotic symptoms
F30.2	Manic episode, severe with psychotic symptoms
F30.3	Manic episode in partial remission
F30.4	Manic episode in full remission
F31.0	Bipolar disorder, current episode hypomanic
F31.11	Bipolar disorder, current episode manic without psychotic features, mild
F31.12	Bipolar disorder, current episode manic without psychotic features, moderate
F31.13	Bipolar disorder, current episode manic without psychotic features, severe
F31.2	Bipolar disorder, current episode manic severe with psychotic features
F31.31	Bipolar disorder, current episode depressed, mild
F31.32	Bipolar disorder, current episode depressed, moderate
F31.4	Bipolar disorder, current episode depressed, severe, without psychotic features
F31.5	Bipolar disorder, current episode depressed, severe, with psychotic features
F31.61	Bipolar disorder, current episode mixed, mild
F31.62	Bipolar disorder, current episode mixed, moderate
F31.63	Bipolar disorder, current episode mixed, severe, without psychotic features
F31.64	Bipolar disorder, current episode mixed, severe, with psychotic features
F31.71	Bipolar disorder, in partial remission, most recent episode hypomanic
F31.72	Bipolar disorder, in full remission, most recent episode hypomanic
F31.73	Bipolar disorder, in partial remission, most recent episode manic
F31.74	Bipolar disorder, in full remission, most recent episode manic
F31.75	Bipolar disorder, in partial remission, most recent episode depressed
F31.76	Bipolar disorder, in full remission, most recent episode depressed
F31.77	Bipolar disorder, in partial remission, most recent episode mixed
F31.78	Bipolar disorder, in full remission, most recent episode mixed
F31.89	Other bipolar disorder
G89.4	Chronic pain syndrome
T42.1X1A	Poisoning by iminostilbenes, accidental (unintentional), initial encounter
T42.1X2A	Poisoning by iminostilbenes, intentional self-harm, initial encounter
T42.1X3A	Poisoning by iminostilbenes, assault, initial encounter
T42.1X4A	Poisoning by iminostilbenes, undetermined, initial encounter
T42.1X5A	Adverse effect of iminostilbenes, initial encounter
T42.1X6A	Underdosing of iminostilbenes, initial encounter
Z02.83	Encounter for blood-alcohol and blood-drug test
Z51.81	Encounter for therapeutic drug level monitoring

Please note that this list of associated ICD-10-CM codes is not all-inclusive. The procedure may be performed for reasons other than those listed that support the medical necessity of the service. Only those conditions supported by the medical record documentation should be reported.

Medicare Edits

	Fac RVU	Non-Fac RVU	FUD	Status	MUE
80156	0.0	0.0	N/A	X	2(3)
80157	0.0	0.0	N/A	X	2(3)

	Modifiers				Medicare References
80156	N/A	N/A	N/A	N/A	None
80157	N/A	N/A	N/A	N/A	

* with documentation

80159

80159	Clozapine

Explanation

This drug, also known as Clozaril, is an atypical antipsychotic used to treat severe cases of schizophrenia in which the patient is a threat to themselves and/or others. It changes the activity of certain chemical processes in the brain. Agranulocytosis is the most common side effect and therefore white blood cell and absolute neutrophil count are required weekly for the first six months, biweekly for the second six months, and every four weeks after a year of being maintained on clozapine. Blood specimen is collected by venipuncture usually during the trough period. Methods include liquid chromatography and tandem mass spectrometry.

Coding Tips

This test is quantitative. If specimen is transported to an outside laboratory, report 99000 for handling or conveyance. Schizophrenia is not diagnosed unless there is characteristic disturbance of at least two of these areas: thought, perception, mood, conduct, and personality.

ICD-10-CM contains combination poisoning codes that include not only the poisoning itself and the type of poison involved, but also the associated intent (i.e., accidental, intentional self-harm, assault, and undetermined).

Documentation Tips

Documentation must include the laboratory results to support reporting this service.

Medical record documentation must, at a minimum, include signs and symptoms supporting the ordering of this service.

The seventh character A Initial encounter, is appropriate when documentation indicates that the health care provider is providing active treatment for the condition, even when provided by a different health care professional. Assign the seventh character D Subsequent encounter, when the documentation indicates that the patient has completed the active phase of treatment and the health care provider is providing routine care (generally rehabilitation therapy) during the healing or recovery phase.

Reimbursement Tips

Medicare reimburses this service under the laboratory fee schedule.

Terms To Know

quantitative. To determine the amount and nature of the components of a substance.

ICD-10-CM Diagnostic Codes

F20.0	Paranoid schizophrenia
F20.1	Disorganized schizophrenia
F20.2	Catatonic schizophrenia
F20.3	Undifferentiated schizophrenia
F20.5	Residual schizophrenia
F20.81	Schizophreniform disorder
F20.89	Other schizophrenia
F20.9	Schizophrenia, unspecified
F21	Schizotypal disorder
F25.0	Schizoaffective disorder, bipolar type
F25.1	Schizoaffective disorder, depressive type

F25.8	Other schizoaffective disorders	
F25.9	Schizoaffective disorder, unspecified	
T42.4X1A	Poisoning by benzodiazepines, accidental (unintentional), initial encounter	
T42.4X2A	Poisoning by benzodiazepines, intentional self-harm, initial encounter	
T42.4X3A	Poisoning by benzodiazepines, assault, initial encounter	
T42.4X4A	Poisoning by benzodiazepines, undetermined, initial encounter	
T42.4X5A	Adverse effect of benzodiazepines, initial encounter	
T42.4X6A	Underdosing of benzodiazepines, initial encounter	
Z02.83	Encounter for blood-alcohol and blood-drug test	
Z51.81	Encounter for therapeutic drug level monitoring	

Please note that this list of associated ICD-10-CM codes is not all-inclusive. The procedure may be performed for reasons other than those listed that support the medical necessity of the service. Only those conditions supported by the medical record documentation should be reported.

Medicare Edits

	Fac RVU	Non-Fac RVU	FUD	Status	MUE
80159	0.0	0.0	N/A	X	2(3)

	Modifiers				Medicare References
80159	N/A	N/A	N/A	N/A	None

* with documentation

(80164, 80165)

80164	Valproic acid (dipropylacetic acid); total
80165	free

Explanation

Valproic acid, also known as Depakene, is often used to treat seizures. Test specimens are frequently collected at the trough period, which is about 12 hours after the last dose when serum concentration is at its lowest. This is an effective approach to determine a therapeutic level of drug. Method is gas liquid chromatography (GLC), gas chromatography-mass spectrometry (GC-MS), and enzyme immunoassay (EIA). Report 80164 for total and 80165 for free.

Coding Tips

Codes 80164 and 80165 are resequenced codes and will not display in numeric order. This examination is quantitative. To report the professional services for drug management, see CPT code 90863, the appropriate level of evaluation and management (E/M) service, or the appropriate psychotherapy with E/M service code. Follow third-party payer guidelines when selecting the appropriate code for these services. If a specimen is transported to an outside laboratory, report 99000 for handling or conveyance.

Documentation Tips

Documentation must include the laboratory results to support reporting this service.

Medical record documentation must, at a minimum, include signs and symptoms supporting the ordering of this service.

Reimbursement Tips

Medicare reimburses this service under the laboratory fee schedule.

Terms To Know

bipolar disorder. Manic-depressive psychosis that has appeared in both the depressive and manic form, either alternating or separated by an interval of normality. Atypical: Episode of affective psychosis with some, but not all, of the features of the one form of the disorder in individuals who have had a previous episode of the other form of the disorder.

quantitative. To determine the amount and nature of the components of a substance.

therapeutic. Act meant to alleviate a medical or mental condition.

ICD-10-CM Diagnostic Codes

F30.11	Manic episode without psychotic symptoms, mild
F30.12	Manic episode without psychotic symptoms, moderate
F30.13	Manic episode, severe, without psychotic symptoms
F30.2	Manic episode, severe with psychotic symptoms
F30.3	Manic episode in partial remission
F30.4	Manic episode in full remission
F30.9	Manic episode, unspecified
F31.0	Bipolar disorder, current episode hypomanic
F31.10	Bipolar disorder, current episode manic without psychotic features, unspecified
F31.11	Bipolar disorder, current episode manic without psychotic features, mild
F31.12	Bipolar disorder, current episode manic without psychotic features, moderate

F31.13	Bipolar disorder, current episode manic without psychotic features, severe
F31.2	Bipolar disorder, current episode manic severe with psychotic features
F31.30	Bipolar disorder, current episode depressed, mild or moderate severity, unspecified
F31.31	Bipolar disorder, current episode depressed, mild
F31.32	Bipolar disorder, current episode depressed, moderate
F31.4	Bipolar disorder, current episode depressed, severe, without psychotic features
F31.5	Bipolar disorder, current episode depressed, severe, with psychotic features
F31.60	Bipolar disorder, current episode mixed, unspecified
F31.61	Bipolar disorder, current episode mixed, mild
F31.62	Bipolar disorder, current episode mixed, moderate
F31.63	Bipolar disorder, current episode mixed, severe, without psychotic features
F31.64	Bipolar disorder, current episode mixed, severe, with psychotic features
F31.70	Bipolar disorder, currently in remission, most recent episode unspecified
F31.71	Bipolar disorder, in partial remission, most recent episode hypomanic
F31.72	Bipolar disorder, in full remission, most recent episode hypomanic
F31.73	Bipolar disorder, in partial remission, most recent episode manic
F31.74	Bipolar disorder, in full remission, most recent episode manic
F31.75	Bipolar disorder, in partial remission, most recent episode depressed
F31.76	Bipolar disorder, in full remission, most recent episode depressed
F31.77	Bipolar disorder, in partial remission, most recent episode mixed
F31.78	Bipolar disorder, in full remission, most recent episode mixed
F31.89	Other bipolar disorder
F31.9	Bipolar disorder, unspecified
G40.001	Localization-related (focal) (partial) idiopathic epilepsy and epileptic syndromes with seizures of localized onset, not intractable, with status epilepticus
G40.009	Localization-related (focal) (partial) idiopathic epilepsy and epileptic syndromes with seizures of localized onset, not intractable, without status epilepticus
G40.011	Localization-related (focal) (partial) idiopathic epilepsy and epileptic syndromes with seizures of localized onset, intractable, with status epilepticus
G40.019	Localization-related (focal) (partial) idiopathic epilepsy and epileptic syndromes with seizures of localized onset, intractable, without status epilepticus
G40.101	Localization-related (focal) (partial) symptomatic epilepsy and epileptic syndromes with simple partial seizures, not intractable, with status epilepticus
G40.109	Localization-related (focal) (partial) symptomatic epilepsy and epileptic syndromes with simple partial seizures, not intractable, without status epilepticus
G40.111	Localization-related (focal) (partial) symptomatic epilepsy and epileptic syndromes with simple partial seizures, intractable, with status epilepticus
G40.201	Localization-related (focal) (partial) symptomatic epilepsy and epileptic syndromes with complex partial seizures, not intractable, with status epilepticus
G40.209	Localization-related (focal) (partial) symptomatic epilepsy and epileptic syndromes with complex partial seizures, not intractable, without status epilepticus
G40.211	Localization-related (focal) (partial) symptomatic epilepsy and epileptic syndromes with complex partial seizures, intractable, with status epilepticus
G40.219	Localization-related (focal) (partial) symptomatic epilepsy and epileptic syndromes with complex partial seizures, intractable, without status epilepticus
G40.301	Generalized idiopathic epilepsy and epileptic syndromes, not intractable, with status epilepticus
G40.309	Generalized idiopathic epilepsy and epileptic syndromes, not intractable, without status epilepticus
G40.311	Generalized idiopathic epilepsy and epileptic syndromes, intractable, with status epilepticus
G40.319	Generalized idiopathic epilepsy and epileptic syndromes, intractable, without status epilepticus
G40.401	Other generalized epilepsy and epileptic syndromes, not intractable, with status epilepticus
G40.409	Other generalized epilepsy and epileptic syndromes, not intractable, without status epilepticus
G40.411	Other generalized epilepsy and epileptic syndromes, intractable, with status epilepticus
G40.419	Other generalized epilepsy and epileptic syndromes, intractable, without status epilepticus
G40.901	Epilepsy, unspecified, not intractable, with status epilepticus
G40.909	Epilepsy, unspecified, not intractable, without status epilepticus
G40.911	Epilepsy, unspecified, intractable, with status epilepticus
G40.919	Epilepsy, unspecified, intractable, without status epilepticus
G43.001	Migraine without aura, not intractable, with status migrainosus
G43.009	Migraine without aura, not intractable, without status migrainosus
G43.011	Migraine without aura, intractable, with status migrainosus
G43.019	Migraine without aura, intractable, without status migrainosus
G43.101	Migraine with aura, not intractable, with status migrainosus
G43.109	Migraine with aura, not intractable, without status migrainosus
G43.111	Migraine with aura, intractable, with status migrainosus
G43.119	Migraine with aura, intractable, without status migrainosus
G43.401	Hemiplegic migraine, not intractable, with status migrainosus
G43.409	Hemiplegic migraine, not intractable, without status migrainosus
G43.419	Hemiplegic migraine, intractable, without status migrainosus
G43.501	Persistent migraine aura without cerebral infarction, not intractable, with status migrainosus
G43.509	Persistent migraine aura without cerebral infarction, not intractable, without status migrainosus
G43.511	Persistent migraine aura without cerebral infarction, intractable, with status migrainosus
G43.519	Persistent migraine aura without cerebral infarction, intractable, without status migrainosus
G43.601	Persistent migraine aura with cerebral infarction, not intractable, with status migrainosus
G43.609	Persistent migraine aura with cerebral infarction, not intractable, without status migrainosus

G43.611	Persistent migraine aura with cerebral infarction, intractable, with status migrainosus
G43.619	Persistent migraine aura with cerebral infarction, intractable, without status migrainosus
G43.701	Chronic migraine without aura, not intractable, with status migrainosus
G43.709	Chronic migraine without aura, not intractable, without status migrainosus
G43.711	Chronic migraine without aura, intractable, with status migrainosus
G43.719	Chronic migraine without aura, intractable, without status migrainosus
G43.801	Other migraine, not intractable, with status migrainosus
G43.809	Other migraine, not intractable, without status migrainosus
G43.811	Other migraine, intractable, with status migrainosus
G43.819	Other migraine, intractable, without status migrainosus
G43.821	Menstrual migraine, not intractable, with status migrainosus
G43.829	Menstrual migraine, not intractable, without status migrainosus
G43.831	Menstrual migraine, intractable, with status migrainosus
G43.839	Menstrual migraine, intractable, without status migrainosus
G43.901	Migraine, unspecified, not intractable, with status migrainosus
G43.909	Migraine, unspecified, not intractable, without status migrainosus
G43.911	Migraine, unspecified, intractable, with status migrainosus
G43.919	Migraine, unspecified, intractable, without status migrainosus
T42.6X1A	Poisoning by other antiepileptic and sedative-hypnotic drugs, accidental (unintentional), initial encounter
T42.6X2A	Poisoning by other antiepileptic and sedative-hypnotic drugs, intentional self-harm, initial encounter
T42.6X3A	Poisoning by other antiepileptic and sedative-hypnotic drugs, assault, initial encounter
T42.6X4A	Poisoning by other antiepileptic and sedative-hypnotic drugs, undetermined, initial encounter
T42.6X5A	Adverse effect of other antiepileptic and sedative-hypnotic drugs, initial encounter
T42.6X6A	Underdosing of other antiepileptic and sedative-hypnotic drugs, initial encounter
Z02.83	Encounter for blood-alcohol and blood-drug test
Z51.81	Encounter for therapeutic drug level monitoring

Please note that this list of associated ICD-10-CM codes is not all-inclusive. The procedure may be performed for reasons other than those listed that support the medical necessity of the service. Only those conditions supported by the medical record documentation should be reported.

Medicare Edits

	Fac RVU	Non-Fac RVU	FUD	Status	MUE
80164	0.0	0.0	N/A	X	2(3)
80165	0.0	0.0	N/A	X	2(3)

	Modifiers				Medicare References
80164	N/A	N/A	N/A	N/A	None
80165	N/A	N/A	N/A	N/A	

* with documentation

80173

80173   Haloperidol

Explanation

This drug, also known as Haldol, is a well-established tranquilizer with antipsychotic and other properties. Blood concentrations of haloperidol do not correspond well with therapeutic dosages; therefore, assays may be performed to establish compliance or to measure the body's ability to metabolize the drug. Methods may include high performance liquid chromatography (HPLC), gas liquid chromatography (GLC), and radioimmunoassay (RIA).

Coding Tips

This examination is quantitative. If a specimen is transported to an outside laboratory, report 99000 for handling or conveyance. To report the professional services for drug management, see CPT code 90863, the appropriate level of evaluation and management (E/M) service, or the appropriate psychotherapy with E/M service code. Follow third-party payer guidelines when selecting the appropriate code for these services.

ICD-10-CM contains combination poisoning codes that include not only the poisoning itself and the type of poison involved, but also the associated intent (i.e., accidental, intentional self-harm, assault, and undetermined).

Documentation Tips

Documentation must include the laboratory results to support reporting this service.

Medical record documentation must, at a minimum, include signs and symptoms supporting the ordering of this service.

The seventh character A Initial encounter, is appropriate when documentation indicates that the health care provider is providing active treatment for the condition, even when provided by a different health care professional. Assign the seventh character D Subsequent encounter, when the documentation indicates that the patient has completed the active phase of treatment and the health care provider is providing routine care (generally rehabilitation therapy) during the healing or recovery phase.

Reimbursement Tips

Medicare reimburses this service under the laboratory fee schedule.

Terms To Know

quantitative. To determine the amount and nature of the components of a substance.

ICD-10-CM Diagnostic Codes

F20.0	Paranoid schizophrenia
F20.1	Disorganized schizophrenia
F20.2	Catatonic schizophrenia
F20.3	Undifferentiated schizophrenia
F20.5	Residual schizophrenia
F20.81	Schizophreniform disorder
F20.89	Other schizophrenia
F20.9	Schizophrenia, unspecified
F21	Schizotypal disorder
F25.0	Schizoaffective disorder, bipolar type
F25.1	Schizoaffective disorder, depressive type

F25.8	Other schizoaffective disorders
F25.9	Schizoaffective disorder, unspecified
T43.4X1A	Poisoning by butyrophenone and thiothixene neuroleptics, accidental (unintentional), initial encounter
T43.4X2A	Poisoning by butyrophenone and thiothixene neuroleptics, intentional self-harm, initial encounter
T43.4X3A	Poisoning by butyrophenone and thiothixene neuroleptics, assault, initial encounter
T43.4X4A	Poisoning by butyrophenone and thiothixene neuroleptics, undetermined, initial encounter
T43.4X5A	Adverse effect of butyrophenone and thiothixene neuroleptics, initial encounter
T43.4X6A	Underdosing of butyrophenone and thiothixene neuroleptics, initial encounter
Z02.83	Encounter for blood-alcohol and blood-drug test
Z51.81	Encounter for therapeutic drug level monitoring

Please note that this list of associated ICD-10-CM codes is not all-inclusive. The procedure may be performed for reasons other than those listed that support the medical necessity of the service. Only those conditions supported by the medical record documentation should be reported.

Medicare Edits

	Fac RVU	Non-Fac RVU	FUD	Status	MUE
80173	0.0	0.0	N/A	X	2(3)

	Modifiers				Medicare References
80173	N/A	N/A	N/A	N/A	None

* with documentation

80178

80178	Lithium

Explanation

This drug may also be known as Eskalith. Lithium is a naturally occurring mineral and its salts may be used in the treatment of mental disorders, in particular bipolar depression. Steady state test specimens are frequently collected at the trough period, which is about 12 hours after the last dose when serum concentration is at its lowest. This is an effective approach to determine a therapeutic level of drug. Methods may include flame emission spectroscopy (FES), atomic absorption spectrophotometry (AAS), and ion-specific electrode (ISE).

Coding Tips

This examination is quantitative. To report the professional services for drug management, see CPT code 90863, the appropriate level of evaluation and management (E/M) service, or the appropriate psychotherapy with E/M service code. Follow third-party payer guidelines when selecting the appropriate code for these services. If a specimen is transported to an outside laboratory, report 99000 for handling or conveyance.

ICD-10-CM contains combination poisoning codes that include not only the poisoning itself and the type of poison involved, but also the associated intent (i.e., accidental, intentional self-harm, assault, and undetermined).

Documentation Tips

Documentation must include the laboratory results to support reporting this service.

Medical record documentation must, at a minimum, include signs and symptoms supporting the ordering of this service.

Reimbursement Tips

Medicare reimburses this service under the laboratory fee schedule.

Terms To Know

quantitative. To determine the amount and nature of the components of a substance.

ICD-10-CM Diagnostic Codes

F30.11	Manic episode without psychotic symptoms, mild
F30.12	Manic episode without psychotic symptoms, moderate
F30.13	Manic episode, severe, without psychotic symptoms
F30.2	Manic episode, severe with psychotic symptoms
F30.3	Manic episode in partial remission
F30.4	Manic episode in full remission
F30.8	Other manic episodes
F31.0	Bipolar disorder, current episode hypomanic
F31.10	Bipolar disorder, current episode manic without psychotic features, unspecified
F31.11	Bipolar disorder, current episode manic without psychotic features, mild
F31.12	Bipolar disorder, current episode manic without psychotic features, moderate
F31.13	Bipolar disorder, current episode manic without psychotic features, severe
F31.2	Bipolar disorder, current episode manic severe with psychotic features

F31.31	Bipolar disorder, current episode depressed, mild
F31.32	Bipolar disorder, current episode depressed, moderate
F31.4	Bipolar disorder, current episode depressed, severe, without psychotic features
F31.5	Bipolar disorder, current episode depressed, severe, with psychotic features
F31.61	Bipolar disorder, current episode mixed, mild
F31.62	Bipolar disorder, current episode mixed, moderate
F31.63	Bipolar disorder, current episode mixed, severe, without psychotic features
F31.64	Bipolar disorder, current episode mixed, severe, with psychotic features
F31.71	Bipolar disorder, in partial remission, most recent episode hypomanic
F31.72	Bipolar disorder, in full remission, most recent episode hypomanic
F31.73	Bipolar disorder, in partial remission, most recent episode manic
F31.74	Bipolar disorder, in full remission, most recent episode manic
F31.75	Bipolar disorder, in partial remission, most recent episode depressed
F31.76	Bipolar disorder, in full remission, most recent episode depressed
F31.77	Bipolar disorder, in partial remission, most recent episode mixed
F31.78	Bipolar disorder, in full remission, most recent episode mixed
F31.81	Bipolar II disorder
F31.89	Other bipolar disorder
F32.0	Major depressive disorder, single episode, mild
F32.1	Major depressive disorder, single episode, moderate
F32.2	Major depressive disorder, single episode, severe without psychotic features
F32.3	Major depressive disorder, single episode, severe with psychotic features
F32.4	Major depressive disorder, single episode, in partial remission
F32.5	Major depressive disorder, single episode, in full remission
F32.8	Other depressive episodes
F33.0	Major depressive disorder, recurrent, mild
F33.1	Major depressive disorder, recurrent, moderate
F33.2	Major depressive disorder, recurrent severe without psychotic features
F33.3	Major depressive disorder, recurrent, severe with psychotic symptoms
F33.41	Major depressive disorder, recurrent, in partial remission
F33.42	Major depressive disorder, recurrent, in full remission
F33.8	Other recurrent depressive disorders
F34.8	Other persistent mood [affective] disorders
T43.591A	Poisoning by other antipsychotics and neuroleptics, accidental (unintentional), initial encounter
T43.592A	Poisoning by other antipsychotics and neuroleptics, intentional self-harm, initial encounter
T43.593A	Poisoning by other antipsychotics and neuroleptics, assault, initial encounter
T43.594A	Poisoning by other antipsychotics and neuroleptics, undetermined, initial encounter
T43.595A	Adverse effect of other antipsychotics and neuroleptics, initial encounter
T43.596A	Underdosing of other antipsychotics and neuroleptics, initial encounter
T56.891A	Toxic effect of other metals, accidental (unintentional), initial encounter
T56.892A	Toxic effect of other metals, intentional self-harm, initial encounter
T56.893A	Toxic effect of other metals, assault, initial encounter
T56.894A	Toxic effect of other metals, undetermined, initial encounter
Z02.83	Encounter for blood-alcohol and blood-drug test
Z51.81	Encounter for therapeutic drug level monitoring

Please note that this list of associated ICD-10-CM codes is not all-inclusive. The procedure may be performed for reasons other than those listed that support the medical necessity of the service. Only those conditions supported by the medical record documentation should be reported.

Medicare Edits

	Fac RVU	Non-Fac RVU	FUD	Status	MUE
80178	0.0	0.0	N/A	X	2(3)

	Modifiers				Medicare References
80178	N/A	N/A	N/A	N/A	None

* with documentation

80183

80183   Oxcarbazepine

Explanation

Oxcarbazepine is also known as Trileptal and is an anticonvulsant and mood stabilizer used to treat epilepsy, motor tics, bipolar disorder, and anxiety. Test specimen is blood collected via venipuncture. This is an effective approach to determine a therapeutic level. Methods include tandem mass spectrometry or liquid chromatography.

Coding Tips

This code is for quantitative testing. If a specimen is transported to an outside laboratory, report 99000 for handling or conveyance.

ICD-10-CM contains combination poisoning codes that include not only the poisoning itself and the type of poison involved, but also the associated intent (i.e., accidental, intentional self-harm, assault, and undetermined).

Documentation Tips

Documentation must include the laboratory results to support reporting this service.

Medical record documentation must, at a minimum, include signs and symptoms supporting the ordering of this service.

Reimbursement Tips

Medicare reimburses this service under the laboratory fee schedule.

Terms To Know

quantitative. To determine the amount and nature of the components of a substance.

ICD-10-CM Diagnostic Codes

F30.11	Manic episode without psychotic symptoms, mild
F30.12	Manic episode without psychotic symptoms, moderate
F30.13	Manic episode, severe, without psychotic symptoms
F30.2	Manic episode, severe with psychotic symptoms
F30.3	Manic episode in partial remission
F30.4	Manic episode in full remission
F30.8	Other manic episodes
F31.0	Bipolar disorder, current episode hypomanic
F31.10	Bipolar disorder, current episode manic without psychotic features, unspecified
F31.11	Bipolar disorder, current episode manic without psychotic features, mild
F31.12	Bipolar disorder, current episode manic without psychotic features, moderate
F31.13	Bipolar disorder, current episode manic without psychotic features, severe
F31.2	Bipolar disorder, current episode manic severe with psychotic features
F31.31	Bipolar disorder, current episode depressed, mild
F31.32	Bipolar disorder, current episode depressed, moderate
F31.4	Bipolar disorder, current episode depressed, severe, without psychotic features
F31.5	Bipolar disorder, current episode depressed, severe, with psychotic features
F31.61	Bipolar disorder, current episode mixed, mild
F31.62	Bipolar disorder, current episode mixed, moderate
F31.63	Bipolar disorder, current episode mixed, severe, without psychotic features
F31.64	Bipolar disorder, current episode mixed, severe, with psychotic features
F31.71	Bipolar disorder, in partial remission, most recent episode hypomanic
F31.72	Bipolar disorder, in full remission, most recent episode hypomanic
F31.73	Bipolar disorder, in partial remission, most recent episode manic
F31.74	Bipolar disorder, in full remission, most recent episode manic
F31.75	Bipolar disorder, in partial remission, most recent episode depressed
F31.76	Bipolar disorder, in full remission, most recent episode depressed
F31.77	Bipolar disorder, in partial remission, most recent episode mixed
F31.78	Bipolar disorder, in full remission, most recent episode mixed
F31.81	Bipolar II disorder
F31.89	Other bipolar disorder
F32.0	Major depressive disorder, single episode, mild
F32.1	Major depressive disorder, single episode, moderate
F32.2	Major depressive disorder, single episode, severe without psychotic features
F32.3	Major depressive disorder, single episode, severe with psychotic features
F32.4	Major depressive disorder, single episode, in partial remission
F32.5	Major depressive disorder, single episode, in full remission
F32.8	Other depressive episodes
F33.0	Major depressive disorder, recurrent, mild
F33.1	Major depressive disorder, recurrent, moderate
F33.2	Major depressive disorder, recurrent severe without psychotic features
F33.3	Major depressive disorder, recurrent, severe with psychotic symptoms
F33.41	Major depressive disorder, recurrent, in partial remission
F33.42	Major depressive disorder, recurrent, in full remission
F33.8	Other recurrent depressive disorders
F34.8	Other persistent mood [affective] disorders
F39	Unspecified mood [affective] disorder
F95.8	Other tic disorders
F95.9	Tic disorder, unspecified
G40.001	Localization-related (focal) (partial) idiopathic epilepsy and epileptic syndromes with seizures of localized onset, not intractable, with status epilepticus
G40.009	Localization-related (focal) (partial) idiopathic epilepsy and epileptic syndromes with seizures of localized onset, not intractable, without status epilepticus
G40.011	Localization-related (focal) (partial) idiopathic epilepsy and epileptic syndromes with seizures of localized onset, intractable, with status epilepticus
G40.019	Localization-related (focal) (partial) idiopathic epilepsy and epileptic syndromes with seizures of localized onset, intractable, without status epilepticus

G40.101	Localization-related (focal) (partial) symptomatic epilepsy and epileptic syndromes with simple partial seizures, not intractable, with status epilepticus
G40.109	Localization-related (focal) (partial) symptomatic epilepsy and epileptic syndromes with simple partial seizures, not intractable, without status epilepticus
G40.111	Localization-related (focal) (partial) symptomatic epilepsy and epileptic syndromes with simple partial seizures, intractable, with status epilepticus
G40.119	Localization-related (focal) (partial) symptomatic epilepsy and epileptic syndromes with simple partial seizures, intractable, without status epilepticus
G40.201	Localization-related (focal) (partial) symptomatic epilepsy and epileptic syndromes with complex partial seizures, not intractable, with status epilepticus
G40.209	Localization-related (focal) (partial) symptomatic epilepsy and epileptic syndromes with complex partial seizures, not intractable, without status epilepticus
G40.211	Localization-related (focal) (partial) symptomatic epilepsy and epileptic syndromes with complex partial seizures, intractable, with status epilepticus
G40.219	Localization-related (focal) (partial) symptomatic epilepsy and epileptic syndromes with complex partial seizures, intractable, without status epilepticus
G40.301	Generalized idiopathic epilepsy and epileptic syndromes, not intractable, with status epilepticus
G40.309	Generalized idiopathic epilepsy and epileptic syndromes, not intractable, without status epilepticus
G40.311	Generalized idiopathic epilepsy and epileptic syndromes, intractable, with status epilepticus
G40.319	Generalized idiopathic epilepsy and epileptic syndromes, intractable, without status epilepticus
G40.401	Other generalized epilepsy and epileptic syndromes, not intractable, with status epilepticus
G40.409	Other generalized epilepsy and epileptic syndromes, not intractable, without status epilepticus
G40.411	Other generalized epilepsy and epileptic syndromes, intractable, with status epilepticus
G40.419	Other generalized epilepsy and epileptic syndromes, intractable, without status epilepticus
G40.501	Epileptic seizures related to external causes, not intractable, with status epilepticus
G40.509	Epileptic seizures related to external causes, not intractable, without status epilepticus
G40.811	Lennox-Gastaut syndrome, not intractable, with status epilepticus
G40.812	Lennox-Gastaut syndrome, not intractable, without status epilepticus
G40.813	Lennox-Gastaut syndrome, intractable, with status epilepticus
G40.814	Lennox-Gastaut syndrome, intractable, without status epilepticus
G40.919	Epilepsy, unspecified, intractable, without status epilepticus
G40.A01	Absence epileptic syndrome, not intractable, with status epilepticus
G40.A09	Absence epileptic syndrome, not intractable, without status epilepticus
G40.A11	Absence epileptic syndrome, intractable, with status epilepticus
G40.A19	Absence epileptic syndrome, intractable, without status epilepticus

G40.B01	Juvenile myoclonic epilepsy, not intractable, with status epilepticus
G40.B09	Juvenile myoclonic epilepsy, not intractable, without status epilepticus
G40.B11	Juvenile myoclonic epilepsy, intractable, with status epilepticus
G40.B19	Juvenile myoclonic epilepsy, intractable, without status epilepticus
T42.1X1A	Poisoning by iminostilbenes, accidental (unintentional), initial encounter
T42.1X2A	Poisoning by iminostilbenes, intentional self-harm, initial encounter
T42.1X3A	Poisoning by iminostilbenes, assault, initial encounter
T42.1X4A	Poisoning by iminostilbenes, undetermined, initial encounter
T42.1X5A	Adverse effect of iminostilbenes, initial encounter
T42.1X6A	Underdosing of iminostilbenes, initial encounter
Z02.83	Encounter for blood-alcohol and blood-drug test
Z51.81	Encounter for therapeutic drug level monitoring

Please note that this list of associated ICD-10-CM codes is not all-inclusive. The procedure may be performed for reasons other than those listed that support the medical necessity of the service. Only those conditions supported by the medical record documentation should be reported.

Medicare Edits

	Fac RVU	Non-Fac RVU	FUD	Status	MUE
80183	0.0	0.0	N/A	X	1(3)

	Modifiers				Medicare References
80183	N/A	N/A	N/A	N/A	None

* with documentation

(80300, 80301)

80300 Drug screen, any number of drug classes from Drug Class List A; any number of non-TLC devices or procedures, (eg, immunoassay) capable of being read by direct optical observation, including instrumented-assisted when performed (eg, dipsticks, cups, cards, cartridges), per date of service

80301 single drug class method, by instrumented test systems (eg, discrete multichannel chemistry analyzers utilizing immunoassay or enzyme assay), per date of service

Explanation

These tests may be requested as drug screens for multiple drug classes within Drug Class List A. A number of different methods are available to screen for single drugs or drug classes, including simple drug screening kits that rely on immunoassay, multiplexed screening kits, urine cups, test cards, or test strips for detection. Presumptive tests may be confirmed with a definitive test that will designate the drug. Specimen type varies. Report 80300 for any number of drug classes. Report 80301 for single drug class analysis utilizing instrumental testing systems. Both codes are reported by date of service.

Coding Tips

These codes are resequenced codes and will not display in numeric order. These codes are used to report those drugs contained in Drug Class List A of the CPT manual. These codes are reported once per date of service, regardless of the number of procedures or direct observation drug class procedures or results are performed. To report definitive drug testing, see codes 80300–80377. To report therapeutic drug testing, see codes 80150–80299.

ICD-10-CM contains combination poisoning codes that include not only the poisoning itself and the type of poison involved, but also the associated intent (i.e., accidental, intentional self-harm, assault, and undetermined).

Documentation Tips

Documentation must include the laboratory results to support reporting this service.

Medical record documentation must, at a minimum, include signs and symptoms supporting the ordering of this service.

Reimbursement Tips

Medicare reimburses this service under the laboratory fee schedule.

ICD-10-CM Diagnostic Codes

The application of this code is too broad to adequately present ICD-10-CM diagnostic code links here. Refer to your ICD-10-CM book.

Medicare Edits

	Fac RVU	Non-Fac RVU	FUD	Status	MUE
80300	0.0	0.0	N/A	I	-
80301	0.0	0.0	N/A	I	-

	Modifiers				Medicare References
80300	N/A	N/A	N/A	N/A	None
80301	N/A	N/A	N/A	N/A	

* with documentation

(80303, 80304)

80303 Drug screen, any number of drug classes, presumptive, single or multiple drug class method; thin layer chromatography procedure(s) (TLC) (eg, acid, neutral, alkaloid plate), per date of service

80304 not otherwise specified presumptive procedure (eg, TOF, MALDI, LDTD, DESI, DART), each procedure

Explanation

These tests may be requested as drug screens for multiple drug classes. In 80303, the screening test must be performed by a chromatographic technique that has good sensitivity, although it may not be as specific as a confirmatory test. Thin-layer chromatography is a common chromatographic technique for drug screening tests. It is performed by applying a thin layer adsorbent to a rectangular plate in the stationary phase. The specimen is applied to the plate and the end of the plate is placed in a solvent. As the solvent rises along the adsorbent on the plate, the different components of the specimen are carried along at varying rates and deposited along the plate. The different components can be separately visualized and analyzed. In 80304, a number of different but not otherwise specified presumptive procedures (e.g., TOF, MALDI, LDTD, DESI, DART) are available to screen for multiple drug classes and is reported per each procedure. Presumptive tests may be confirmed with a definitive test. Specimen type varies.

Coding Tips

These codes are resequenced codes and will not display in numeric order. Code 80303 should be reported once per date of service. Code 80304 should be reported once per procedure performed and, therefore, maybe reported with multiple units of service.

ICD-10-CM contains combination poisoning codes that include not only the poisoning itself and the type of poison involved, but also the associated intent (i.e., accidental, intentional self-harm, assault, and undetermined).

Documentation Tips

Documentation must include the laboratory results to support reporting this service.

Medical record documentation must, at a minimum, include signs and symptoms supporting the ordering of this service.

Reimbursement Tips

Medicare reimburses this service under the laboratory fee schedule.

ICD-10-CM Diagnostic Codes

The application of this code is too broad to adequately present ICD-10-CM diagnostic code links here. Refer to your ICD-10-CM book.

Medicare Edits

	Fac RVU	Non-Fac RVU	FUD	Status	MUE
80303	0.0	0.0	N/A	I	-
80304	0.0	0.0	N/A	I	-

	Modifiers				Medicare References
80303	N/A	N/A	N/A	N/A	None
80304	N/A	N/A	N/A	N/A	

* with documentation

(80320, 80321, 80322)

80320   Alcohols

80321   Alcohol biomarkers; 1 or 2

80322   3 or more

Explanation

Alcohol biomarkers are physiological signs of exposure to, or ingestion of, alcohol and may suggest the possibility of an alcohol use disorder. There are two categories of alcohol biomarkers: direct and indirect. Indirect alcohol biomarkers typically screen for specific types of liver serum elevations that may occur as the result of heavy drinking; other indirect biomarkers may include identification of changes in red blood cells that may indicate nutritional problems from alcohol use. Direct alcohol biomarkers such as the breathalyzer evaluate the blood alcohol concentration. Other direct biomarkers, also known as analytes of alcohol metabolism, include tests for EtG (ethyl glucuronide) and EtS (ethyl sulfate), which are most commonly measured in urine. These tests may register a positive result even with low level alcohol exposure and remain detectable over a several day period. Specimen may be blood (serum) or urine. Method is commonly enzymatic rate analysis (alcohol dehydrogenase). Report 80320 when testing for alcohols; 80321 when testing one or two biomarkers; and 80322 when testing three or more biomarkers.

Coding Tips

These codes are resequenced codes and will not display in numeric order. To report alcohol breath test, see 82075. For presumptive testing, see the appropriate code from the 80300–80304 range.

ICD-10-CM contains combination poisoning codes that include not only the poisoning itself and the type of poison involved, but also the associated intent (i.e., accidental, intentional self-harm, assault, and undetermined).

Documentation Tips

Documentation must include the laboratory results to support reporting this service.

Medical record documentation must, at a minimum, include signs and symptoms supporting the ordering of this service.

Reimbursement Tips

Medicare reimburses this service under the laboratory fee schedule.

Terms To Know

qualitative. To determine the nature of the component of substance.

quantitative. To determine the amount and nature of the components of a substance.

ICD-10-CM Diagnostic Codes

F10.10	Alcohol abuse, uncomplicated
F10.120	Alcohol abuse with intoxication, uncomplicated
F10.121	Alcohol abuse with intoxication delirium
F10.129	Alcohol abuse with intoxication, unspecified
F10.14	Alcohol abuse with alcohol-induced mood disorder
F10.150	Alcohol abuse with alcohol-induced psychotic disorder with delusions
F10.151	Alcohol abuse with alcohol-induced psychotic disorder with hallucinations
F10.159	Alcohol abuse with alcohol-induced psychotic disorder, unspecified
F10.180	Alcohol abuse with alcohol-induced anxiety disorder
F10.181	Alcohol abuse with alcohol-induced sexual dysfunction
F10.182	Alcohol abuse with alcohol-induced sleep disorder
F10.188	Alcohol abuse with other alcohol-induced disorder
F10.19	Alcohol abuse with unspecified alcohol-induced disorder
F10.20	Alcohol dependence, uncomplicated
F10.21	Alcohol dependence, in remission
F10.220	Alcohol dependence with intoxication, uncomplicated
F10.221	Alcohol dependence with intoxication delirium
F10.229	Alcohol dependence with intoxication, unspecified
F10.230	Alcohol dependence with withdrawal, uncomplicated
F10.231	Alcohol dependence with withdrawal delirium
F10.232	Alcohol dependence with withdrawal with perceptual disturbance
F10.239	Alcohol dependence with withdrawal, unspecified
F10.24	Alcohol dependence with alcohol-induced mood disorder
F10.250	Alcohol dependence with alcohol-induced psychotic disorder with delusions
F10.251	Alcohol dependence with alcohol-induced psychotic disorder with hallucinations
F10.259	Alcohol dependence with alcohol-induced psychotic disorder, unspecified
F10.26	Alcohol dependence with alcohol-induced persisting amnestic disorder
F10.27	Alcohol dependence with alcohol-induced persisting dementia
F10.280	Alcohol dependence with alcohol-induced anxiety disorder
F10.281	Alcohol dependence with alcohol-induced sexual dysfunction
F10.282	Alcohol dependence with alcohol-induced sleep disorder
F10.288	Alcohol dependence with other alcohol-induced disorder
F10.29	Alcohol dependence with unspecified alcohol-induced disorder
F10.920	Alcohol use, unspecified with intoxication, uncomplicated
F10.921	Alcohol use, unspecified with intoxication delirium
F10.929	Alcohol use, unspecified with intoxication, unspecified
F10.94	Alcohol use, unspecified with alcohol-induced mood disorder
F10.950	Alcohol use, unspecified with alcohol-induced psychotic disorder with delusions
F10.951	Alcohol use, unspecified with alcohol-induced psychotic disorder with hallucinations
F10.959	Alcohol use, unspecified with alcohol-induced psychotic disorder, unspecified
F10.96	Alcohol use, unspecified with alcohol-induced persisting amnestic disorder
F10.97	Alcohol use, unspecified with alcohol-induced persisting dementia
F10.980	Alcohol use, unspecified with alcohol-induced anxiety disorder
F10.981	Alcohol use, unspecified with alcohol-induced sexual dysfunction
F10.982	Alcohol use, unspecified with alcohol-induced sleep disorder
F10.988	Alcohol use, unspecified with other alcohol-induced disorder
F10.99	Alcohol use, unspecified with unspecified alcohol-induced disorder
T51.0X1A	Toxic effect of ethanol, accidental (unintentional), initial encounter
T51.0X2A	Toxic effect of ethanol, intentional self-harm, initial encounter
T51.0X3A	Toxic effect of ethanol, assault, initial encounter

T51.0X4A   Toxic effect of ethanol, undetermined, initial encounter

T51.2X1A   Toxic effect of 2-Propanol, accidental (unintentional), initial encounter

T51.2X2A   Toxic effect of 2-Propanol, intentional self-harm, initial encounter

T51.2X3A   Toxic effect of 2-Propanol, assault, initial encounter

T51.2X4A   Toxic effect of 2-Propanol, undetermined, initial encounter

T51.8X1A   Toxic effect of other alcohols, accidental (unintentional), initial encounter

T51.8X2A   Toxic effect of other alcohols, intentional self-harm, initial encounter

T51.8X3A   Toxic effect of other alcohols, assault, initial encounter

T51.8X4A   Toxic effect of other alcohols, undetermined, initial encounter

T51.91XA   Toxic effect of unspecified alcohol, accidental (unintentional), initial encounter

T51.92XA   Toxic effect of unspecified alcohol, intentional self-harm, initial encounter

T51.93XA   Toxic effect of unspecified alcohol, assault, initial encounter

T51.94XA   Toxic effect of unspecified alcohol, undetermined, initial encounter

Z02.83   Encounter for blood-alcohol and blood-drug test

Please note that this list of associated ICD-10-CM codes is not all-inclusive. The procedure may be performed for reasons other than those listed that support the medical necessity of the service. Only those conditions supported by the medical record documentation should be reported.

Medicare Edits

	Fac RVU	Non-Fac RVU	FUD	Status	MUE
80320	0.0	0.0	N/A	I	-
80321	0.0	0.0	N/A	I	-
80322	0.0	0.0	N/A	I	-

	Modifiers				Medicare References
80320	N/A	N/A	N/A	N/A	None
80321	N/A	N/A	N/A	N/A	
80322	N/A	N/A	N/A	N/A	

* with documentation

(80324, 80325, 80326)

80324	Amphetamines; 1 or 2
80325	3 or 4
80326	5 or more

Explanation

These tests may be requested as a qualitative, quantitative, or combination analysis of amphetamine/methamphetamine. Methods used for analysis include gas-liquid chromatography (GLC) and gas chromatometry/mass spectrometry (GC/MS). This is a definitive drug test, meaning testing methods would not be performed by enzymatic or immunoassays. Report 80324 for one to two analytes; 80325 for three to four analytes; and 80326 for five or more analytes.

Coding Tips

These codes are resequenced codes and will not display in numeric order. For presumptive drug testing, see 80300–90301 or 80303–80304.

ICD-10-CM contains combination poisoning codes that include not only the poisoning itself and the type of poison involved, but also the associated intent (i.e., accidental, intentional self-harm, assault, and undetermined).

Documentation Tips

Documentation must include the laboratory results to support reporting this service.

Medical record documentation must, at a minimum, include signs and symptoms supporting the ordering of this service.

Reimbursement Tips

Medicare reimburses this service under the laboratory fee schedule.

Terms To Know

qualitative. To determine the nature of the component of substance.

quantitative. To determine the amount and nature of the components of a substance.

ICD-10-CM Diagnostic Codes

F15.10	Other stimulant abuse, uncomplicated
F15.120	Other stimulant abuse with intoxication, uncomplicated
F15.121	Other stimulant abuse with intoxication delirium
F15.122	Other stimulant abuse with intoxication with perceptual disturbance
F15.129	Other stimulant abuse with intoxication, unspecified
F15.14	Other stimulant abuse with stimulant-induced mood disorder
F15.150	Other stimulant abuse with stimulant-induced psychotic disorder with delusions
F15.151	Other stimulant abuse with stimulant-induced psychotic disorder with hallucinations
F15.159	Other stimulant abuse with stimulant-induced psychotic disorder, unspecified
F15.180	Other stimulant abuse with stimulant-induced anxiety disorder
F15.181	Other stimulant abuse with stimulant-induced sexual dysfunction
F15.182	Other stimulant abuse with stimulant-induced sleep disorder
F15.188	Other stimulant abuse with other stimulant-induced disorder
F15.19	Other stimulant abuse with unspecified stimulant-induced disorder

F15.20	Other stimulant dependence, uncomplicated	
F15.21	Other stimulant dependence, in remission	
F15.220	Other stimulant dependence with intoxication, uncomplicated	
F15.221	Other stimulant dependence with intoxication delirium	
F15.222	Other stimulant dependence with intoxication with perceptual disturbance	
F15.229	Other stimulant dependence with intoxication, unspecified	
F15.23	Other stimulant dependence with withdrawal	
F15.24	Other stimulant dependence with stimulant-induced mood disorder	
F15.250	Other stimulant dependence with stimulant-induced psychotic disorder with delusions	
F15.251	Other stimulant dependence with stimulant-induced psychotic disorder with hallucinations	
F15.259	Other stimulant dependence with stimulant-induced psychotic disorder, unspecified	
F15.280	Other stimulant dependence with stimulant-induced anxiety disorder	
F15.281	Other stimulant dependence with stimulant-induced sexual dysfunction	
F15.282	Other stimulant dependence with stimulant-induced sleep disorder	
F15.288	Other stimulant dependence with other stimulant-induced disorder	
F15.29	Other stimulant dependence with unspecified stimulant-induced disorder	
F15.90	Other stimulant use, unspecified, uncomplicated	
F15.920	Other stimulant use, unspecified with intoxication, uncomplicated	
F15.921	Other stimulant use, unspecified with intoxication delirium	
F15.922	Other stimulant use, unspecified with intoxication with perceptual disturbance	
F15.929	Other stimulant use, unspecified with intoxication, unspecified	
F15.93	Other stimulant use, unspecified with withdrawal	
F15.94	Other stimulant use, unspecified with stimulant-induced mood disorder	
F15.950	Other stimulant use, unspecified with stimulant-induced psychotic disorder with delusions	
F15.951	Other stimulant use, unspecified with stimulant-induced psychotic disorder with hallucinations	
F15.959	Other stimulant use, unspecified with stimulant-induced psychotic disorder, unspecified	
F15.980	Other stimulant use, unspecified with stimulant-induced anxiety disorder	
F15.981	Other stimulant use, unspecified with stimulant-induced sexual dysfunction	
F15.982	Other stimulant use, unspecified with stimulant-induced sleep disorder	
F15.988	Other stimulant use, unspecified with other stimulant-induced disorder	
F15.99	Other stimulant use, unspecified with unspecified stimulant-induced disorder	
T43.621A	Poisoning by amphetamines, accidental (unintentional), initial encounter	
T43.622A	Poisoning by amphetamines, intentional self-harm, initial encounter	

T43.623A	Poisoning by amphetamines, assault, initial encounter
T43.624A	Poisoning by amphetamines, undetermined, initial encounter
T43.625A	Adverse effect of amphetamines, initial encounter
Z02.83	Encounter for blood-alcohol and blood-drug test

Please note that this list of associated ICD-10-CM codes is not all-inclusive. The procedure may be performed for reasons other than those listed that support the medical necessity of the service. Only those conditions supported by the medical record documentation should be reported.

Medicare Edits

	Fac RVU	Non-Fac RVU	FUD	Status	MUE
80324	0.0	0.0	N/A	I	-
80325	0.0	0.0	N/A	I	-
80326	0.0	0.0	N/A	I	-

	Modifiers				Medicare References
80324	N/A	N/A	N/A	N/A	None
80325	N/A	N/A	N/A	N/A	
80326	N/A	N/A	N/A	N/A	

* with documentation

(80332, 80333, 80334)

80332	Antidepressants, serotonergic class; 1 or 2
80333	3-5
80334	6 or more

Explanation

Serotonergic antidepressants work by blocking the reabsorption of the neurotransmitter serotonin, a chemical that assists the brain in sending and receiving messages and in turn boosts mood. They are labeled as selective serotonin reuptake inhibitors (SSRI) because they tend to chiefly target serotonin as opposed to other neurotransmitters such as norepinephrine. Test specimens are frequently collected at the trough period, which is about 12 hours after the last dose when serum concentration is at its lowest. This approach is effective in determining a therapeutic drug level. Drug overdose may be the reason for the test as well. Definitive methods include liquid or gas chromatography with mass spectrometry, excluding immunoassays and enzymatic methods. These drugs are widely recognized as the most commonly prescribed antidepressants used to treat moderate to severe depression and are considered fairly safe with fewer side effects than other antidepressant classes. Report 80332 for one or two serotonergic antidepressants; 80333 for three to five; and 80334 for six or more.

Coding Tips

These codes are resequenced codes and will not display in numeric order. For presumptive drug testing, see the appropriate code from the 80300–80304 range of codes.

ICD-10-CM contains combination poisoning codes that include not only the poisoning itself and the type of poison involved, but also the associated intent (i.e., accidental, intentional self-harm, assault, and undetermined).

Documentation Tips

Documentation must include the laboratory results to support reporting this service.

Medical record documentation must, at a minimum, include signs and symptoms supporting the ordering of this service.

Reimbursement Tips

Medicare reimburses this service under the laboratory fee schedule.

ICD-10-CM Diagnostic Codes

F32.0	Major depressive disorder, single episode, mild
F32.1	Major depressive disorder, single episode, moderate
F32.2	Major depressive disorder, single episode, severe without psychotic features
F32.3	Major depressive disorder, single episode, severe with psychotic features
F32.4	Major depressive disorder, single episode, in partial remission
F32.5	Major depressive disorder, single episode, in full remission
F32.8	Other depressive episodes
F32.9	Major depressive disorder, single episode, unspecified
F33.0	Major depressive disorder, recurrent, mild
F33.1	Major depressive disorder, recurrent, moderate
F33.2	Major depressive disorder, recurrent severe without psychotic features
F33.3	Major depressive disorder, recurrent, severe with psychotic symptoms
F33.40	Major depressive disorder, recurrent, in remission, unspecified
F33.41	Major depressive disorder, recurrent, in partial remission
F33.42	Major depressive disorder, recurrent, in full remission
F33.8	Other recurrent depressive disorders
F33.9	Major depressive disorder, recurrent, unspecified
T43.211A	Poisoning by selective serotonin and norepinephrine reuptake inhibitors, accidental (unintentional), initial encounter
T43.212A	Poisoning by selective serotonin and norepinephrine reuptake inhibitors, intentional self-harm, initial encounter
T43.213A	Poisoning by selective serotonin and norepinephrine reuptake inhibitors, assault, initial encounter
T43.214A	Poisoning by selective serotonin and norepinephrine reuptake inhibitors, undetermined, initial encounter
T43.221A	Poisoning by selective serotonin reuptake inhibitors, accidental (unintentional), initial encounter
T43.222A	Poisoning by selective serotonin reuptake inhibitors, intentional self-harm, initial encounter
T43.223A	Poisoning by selective serotonin reuptake inhibitors, assault, initial encounter
T43.224A	Poisoning by selective serotonin reuptake inhibitors, undetermined, initial encounter
T43.291A	Poisoning by other antidepressants, accidental (unintentional), initial encounter
T43.292A	Poisoning by other antidepressants, intentional self-harm, initial encounter
T43.293A	Poisoning by other antidepressants, assault, initial encounter
T43.294A	Poisoning by other antidepressants, undetermined, initial encounter
Z02.83	Encounter for blood-alcohol and blood-drug test

Please note that this list of associated ICD-10-CM codes is not all-inclusive. The procedure may be performed for reasons other than those listed that support the medical necessity of the service. Only those conditions supported by the medical record documentation should be reported.

Medicare Edits

	Fac RVU	Non-Fac RVU	FUD	Status	MUE
80332	0.0	0.0	N/A	I	-
80333	0.0	0.0	N/A	I	-
80334	0.0	0.0	N/A	I	-

	Modifiers				Medicare References
80332	N/A	N/A	N/A	N/A	None
80333	N/A	N/A	N/A	N/A	
80334	N/A	N/A	N/A	N/A	

* with documentation

(80335, 80336, 80337)

80335	Antidepressants, tricyclic and other cyclicals; 1 or 2
80336	3-5
80337	6 or more

Explanation

Tricyclic and tetracyclic antidepressants work by blocking the absorption of neurotransmitters serotonin and norepinephrine, making a greater number of these chemicals available in the brain. These chemicals assist the brain in sending and receiving messages, which in turn boosts mood. They are labeled as tricyclic or tetracyclic based on the number of rings in their chemical structure: three (tri) or four (tetra). Test specimens are frequently collected at the trough period, which is about 12 hours after the last dose when serum concentration is at its lowest. This approach is effective in determining a therapeutic drug level. Drug overdose may be the reason for the test as well. Method is typically high performance liquid chromatography (HPLC) or gas liquid chromatography (GLC). These drugs may be prescribed for disorders outside of depressive states, such as chronic pain. While they are effective as an antidepressant, they have mostly been replaced with antidepressants that are known to have fewer side effects. Report 80335 for one or two tricyclic and other cyclical antidepressants; 88336 for three to five; and 88337 for six or more. Report 80338 for testing of antidepressants not classified to a specific class or type.

Coding Tips

These codes are resequenced codes and will not display in numeric order. For presumptive drug testing, see the appropriate code from the 80300–80304 range of codes.

ICD-10-CM contains combination poisoning codes that include not only the poisoning itself and the type of poison involved, but also the associated intent (I.e., accidental, intentional self-harm, assault, and undetermined).

Documentation Tips

Documentation must include the laboratory results to support reporting this service.

Medical record documentation must, at a minimum, include signs and symptoms supporting the ordering of this service.

Reimbursement Tips

Medicare reimburses this service under the laboratory fee schedule.

ICD-10-CM Diagnostic Codes

F06.31	Mood disorder due to known physiological condition with depressive features
F06.32	Mood disorder due to known physiological condition with major depressive-like episode
F31.0	Bipolar disorder, current episode hypomanic
F31.11	Bipolar disorder, current episode manic without psychotic features, mild
F31.12	Bipolar disorder, current episode manic without psychotic features, moderate
F31.13	Bipolar disorder, current episode manic without psychotic features, severe
F31.2	Bipolar disorder, current episode manic severe with psychotic features
F31.31	Bipolar disorder, current episode depressed, mild
F31.32	Bipolar disorder, current episode depressed, moderate
F31.4	Bipolar disorder, current episode depressed, severe, without psychotic features
F31.5	Bipolar disorder, current episode depressed, severe, with psychotic features
F31.61	Bipolar disorder, current episode mixed, mild
F31.62	Bipolar disorder, current episode mixed, moderate
F31.63	Bipolar disorder, current episode mixed, severe, without psychotic features
F31.64	Bipolar disorder, current episode mixed, severe, with psychotic features
F31.71	Bipolar disorder, in partial remission, most recent episode hypomanic
F31.72	Bipolar disorder, in full remission, most recent episode hypomanic
F31.73	Bipolar disorder, in partial remission, most recent episode manic
F31.74	Bipolar disorder, in full remission, most recent episode manic
F31.75	Bipolar disorder, in partial remission, most recent episode depressed
F31.76	Bipolar disorder, in full remission, most recent episode depressed
F31.77	Bipolar disorder, in partial remission, most recent episode mixed
F31.78	Bipolar disorder, in full remission, most recent episode mixed
F31.81	Bipolar II disorder
F31.89	Other bipolar disorder
F32.0	Major depressive disorder, single episode, mild
F32.1	Major depressive disorder, single episode, moderate
F32.2	Major depressive disorder, single episode, severe without psychotic features
F32.3	Major depressive disorder, single episode, severe with psychotic features
F32.4	Major depressive disorder, single episode, in partial remission
F32.5	Major depressive disorder, single episode, in full remission
F32.8	Other depressive episodes
F33.0	Major depressive disorder, recurrent, mild
F33.1	Major depressive disorder, recurrent, moderate
F33.2	Major depressive disorder, recurrent severe without psychotic features
F33.3	Major depressive disorder, recurrent, severe with psychotic symptoms
F33.41	Major depressive disorder, recurrent, in partial remission
F33.42	Major depressive disorder, recurrent, in full remission
F33.8	Other recurrent depressive disorders
F34.1	Dysthymic disorder
F41.1	Generalized anxiety disorder
F42	Obsessive-compulsive disorder
F43.11	Post-traumatic stress disorder, acute
F43.12	Post-traumatic stress disorder, chronic
F43.21	Adjustment disorder with depressed mood
F43.23	Adjustment disorder with mixed anxiety and depressed mood
F60.5	Obsessive-compulsive personality disorder
T43.011A	Poisoning by tricyclic antidepressants, accidental (unintentional), initial encounter
T43.012A	Poisoning by tricyclic antidepressants, intentional self-harm, initial encounter

T43.013A	Poisoning by tricyclic antidepressants, assault, initial encounter	
T43.015A	Adverse effect of tricyclic antidepressants, initial encounter	
T43.021A	Poisoning by tetracyclic antidepressants, accidental (unintentional), initial encounter	
T43.022A	Poisoning by tetracyclic antidepressants, intentional self-harm, initial encounter	
T43.023A	Poisoning by tetracyclic antidepressants, assault, initial encounter	
T43.025A	Adverse effect of tetracyclic antidepressants, initial encounter	
T43.1X1A	Poisoning by monoamine-oxidase-inhibitor antidepressants, accidental (unintentional), initial encounter	
T43.1X2A	Poisoning by monoamine-oxidase-inhibitor antidepressants, intentional self-harm, initial encounter	
T43.1X3A	Poisoning by monoamine-oxidase-inhibitor antidepressants, assault, initial encounter	
T43.1X5A	Adverse effect of monoamine-oxidase-inhibitor antidepressants, initial encounter	
T43.201A	Poisoning by unspecified antidepressants, accidental (unintentional), initial encounter	
T43.202A	Poisoning by unspecified antidepressants, intentional self-harm, initial encounter	
T43.203A	Poisoning by unspecified antidepressants, assault, initial encounter	
T43.205A	Adverse effect of unspecified antidepressants, initial encounter	
T43.291A	Poisoning by other antidepressants, accidental (unintentional), initial encounter	
T43.292A	Poisoning by other antidepressants, intentional self-harm, initial encounter	
T43.293A	Poisoning by other antidepressants, assault, initial encounter	
T43.295A	Adverse effect of other antidepressants, initial encounter	
Z02.83	Encounter for blood-alcohol and blood-drug test	

Please note that this list of associated ICD-10-CM codes is not all-inclusive. The procedure may be performed for reasons other than those listed that support the medical necessity of the service. Only those conditions supported by the medical record documentation should be reported.

Medicare Edits

	Fac RVU	Non-Fac RVU	FUD	Status	MUE
80335	0.0	0.0	N/A	I	-
80336	0.0	0.0	N/A	I	-
80337	0.0	0.0	N/A	I	-

	Modifiers				Medicare References
80335	N/A	N/A	N/A	N/A	None
80336	N/A	N/A	N/A	N/A	
80337	N/A	N/A	N/A	N/A	

* with documentation

(80338)

80338	Antidepressants, not otherwise specified

Explanation

Some antidepressants work by increasing the levels of neurotransmitters that are associated with depression. These chemicals assist the brain in sending and receiving messages, which in turn boosts mood. Each type or class of antidepressants affects neurotransmitters in somewhat different ways. This code describes testing of antidepressants not classified to a specific class or type. Test specimens are frequently collected at the trough period, which is about 12 hours after the last dose when serum concentration is at its lowest. This effective approach helps determine a therapeutic level of drug. Drug overdose may be the reason for the test as well. Method is typically high performance liquid chromatography (HPLC) or gas liquid chromatography (GLC). These drugs may be prescribed for disorders outside of depressive states, such as chronic pain. While they are effective as an antidepressant, they have mostly been replaced with antidepressants that are known to have fewer side effects.

Coding Tips

This code is a resequenced code and will not display in numeric order. For presumptive drug testing, see the appropriate code from the 80300–80304 range of codes.

ICD-10-CM contains combination poisoning codes that include not only the poisoning itself and the type of poison involved, but also the associated intent (i.e., accidental, intentional self-harm, assault, and undetermined).

Documentation Tips

Documentation must include the laboratory results to support reporting this service.

Medical record documentation must, at a minimum, include signs and symptoms supporting the ordering of this service.

Reimbursement Tips

Medicare reimburses this service under the laboratory fee schedule.

Terms To Know

qualitative. To determine the nature of the component of substance.

quantitative. To determine the amount and nature of the components of a substance.

ICD-10-CM Diagnostic Codes

F06.31	Mood disorder due to known physiological condition with depressive features
F06.32	Mood disorder due to known physiological condition with major depressive-like episode
F31.0	Bipolar disorder, current episode hypomanic
F31.11	Bipolar disorder, current episode manic without psychotic features, mild
F31.12	Bipolar disorder, current episode manic without psychotic features, moderate
F31.13	Bipolar disorder, current episode manic without psychotic features, severe
F31.2	Bipolar disorder, current episode manic severe with psychotic features
F31.31	Bipolar disorder, current episode depressed, mild

F31.32	Bipolar disorder, current episode depressed, moderate
F31.4	Bipolar disorder, current episode depressed, severe, without psychotic features
F31.5	Bipolar disorder, current episode depressed, severe, with psychotic features
F31.61	Bipolar disorder, current episode mixed, mild
F31.62	Bipolar disorder, current episode mixed, moderate
F31.63	Bipolar disorder, current episode mixed, severe, without psychotic features
F31.64	Bipolar disorder, current episode mixed, severe, with psychotic features
F31.71	Bipolar disorder, in partial remission, most recent episode hypomanic
F31.72	Bipolar disorder, in full remission, most recent episode hypomanic
F31.73	Bipolar disorder, in partial remission, most recent episode manic
F31.74	Bipolar disorder, in full remission, most recent episode manic
F31.75	Bipolar disorder, in partial remission, most recent episode depressed
F31.76	Bipolar disorder, in full remission, most recent episode depressed
F31.77	Bipolar disorder, in partial remission, most recent episode mixed
F31.78	Bipolar disorder, in full remission, most recent episode mixed
F31.81	Bipolar II disorder
F31.89	Other bipolar disorder
F32.0	Major depressive disorder, single episode, mild
F32.1	Major depressive disorder, single episode, moderate
F32.2	Major depressive disorder, single episode, severe without psychotic features
F32.3	Major depressive disorder, single episode, severe with psychotic features
F32.4	Major depressive disorder, single episode, in partial remission
F32.5	Major depressive disorder, single episode, in full remission
F32.8	Other depressive episodes
F33.0	Major depressive disorder, recurrent, mild
F33.1	Major depressive disorder, recurrent, moderate
F33.2	Major depressive disorder, recurrent severe without psychotic features
F33.3	Major depressive disorder, recurrent, severe with psychotic symptoms
F33.41	Major depressive disorder, recurrent, in partial remission
F33.42	Major depressive disorder, recurrent, in full remission
F33.8	Other recurrent depressive disorders
F34.1	Dysthymic disorder
F41.1	Generalized anxiety disorder
F42	Obsessive-compulsive disorder
F43.11	Post-traumatic stress disorder, acute
F43.12	Post-traumatic stress disorder, chronic
F43.21	Adjustment disorder with depressed mood
F43.23	Adjustment disorder with mixed anxiety and depressed mood
F60.5	Obsessive-compulsive personality disorder
T43.011A	Poisoning by tricyclic antidepressants, accidental (unintentional), initial encounter
T43.012A	Poisoning by tricyclic antidepressants, intentional self-harm, initial encounter

T43.013A	Poisoning by tricyclic antidepressants, assault, initial encounter
T43.015A	Adverse effect of tricyclic antidepressants, initial encounter
T43.021A	Poisoning by tetracyclic antidepressants, accidental (unintentional), initial encounter
T43.022A	Poisoning by tetracyclic antidepressants, intentional self-harm, initial encounter
T43.023A	Poisoning by tetracyclic antidepressants, assault, initial encounter
T43.025A	Adverse effect of tetracyclic antidepressants, initial encounter
T43.1X1A	Poisoning by monoamine-oxidase-inhibitor antidepressants, accidental (unintentional), initial encounter
T43.1X2A	Poisoning by monoamine-oxidase-inhibitor antidepressants, intentional self-harm, initial encounter
T43.1X3A	Poisoning by monoamine-oxidase-inhibitor antidepressants, assault, initial encounter
T43.1X5A	Adverse effect of monoamine-oxidase-inhibitor antidepressants, initial encounter
T43.201A	Poisoning by unspecified antidepressants, accidental (unintentional), initial encounter
T43.202A	Poisoning by unspecified antidepressants, intentional self-harm, initial encounter
T43.203A	Poisoning by unspecified antidepressants, assault, initial encounter
T43.205A	Adverse effect of unspecified antidepressants, initial encounter
T43.211A	Poisoning by selective serotonin and norepinephrine reuptake inhibitors, accidental (unintentional), initial encounter
T43.212A	Poisoning by selective serotonin and norepinephrine reuptake inhibitors, intentional self-harm, initial encounter
T43.213A	Poisoning by selective serotonin and norepinephrine reuptake inhibitors, assault, initial encounter
T43.215A	Adverse effect of selective serotonin and norepinephrine reuptake inhibitors, initial encounter
T43.221A	Poisoning by selective serotonin reuptake inhibitors, accidental (unintentional), initial encounter
T43.222A	Poisoning by selective serotonin reuptake inhibitors, intentional self-harm, initial encounter
T43.223A	Poisoning by selective serotonin reuptake inhibitors, assault, initial encounter
T43.225A	Adverse effect of selective serotonin reuptake inhibitors, initial encounter
T43.291A	Poisoning by other antidepressants, accidental (unintentional), initial encounter
T43.292A	Poisoning by other antidepressants, intentional self-harm, initial encounter
T43.293A	Poisoning by other antidepressants, assault, initial encounter
T43.295A	Adverse effect of other antidepressants, initial encounter
Z02.83	Encounter for blood-alcohol and blood-drug test

Please note that this list of associated ICD-10-CM codes is not all-inclusive. The procedure may be performed for reasons other than those listed that support the medical necessity of the service. Only those conditions supported by the medical record documentation should be reported.

Medicare Edits

	Fac RVU	Non-Fac RVU	FUD	Status	MUE
80338	0.0	0.0	N/A	I	-

	Modifiers				Medicare References
80338	N/A	N/A	N/A	N/A	None

* with documentation

(80342, 80343, 80344)

80342	Antipsychotics, not otherwise specified; 1-3
80343	4-6
80344	7 or more

Explanation

Derivatives of phenothiazine are numerous and most are classified as antipsychotics. A common one is chlorpromazine. Methods may include high performance liquid chromatography (HPLC), thin-layer chromatography (TLC), gas chromatography (GC), or fluorometry for blood and thin-layer chromatography (TLC), gas-liquid chromatography (GLC), or radioimmunoassay (RIA) for urine. These tests are performed to evaluate the amount of phenothiazine present. Report 80342 for one to three analytes; 80343 for four to six analytes; and 80344 for seven or more analytes.

Coding Tips

These codes are resequenced codes and will not display in numeric order. For presumptive drug testing, see the appropriate code from the 80300–80304 code range.

ICD-10-CM contains combination poisoning codes that include not only the poisoning itself and the type of poison involved, but also the associated intent (i.e., accidental, intentional self-harm, assault, and undetermined).

Documentation Tips

Documentation must include the laboratory results to support reporting this service.

Medical record documentation must, at a minimum, include signs and symptoms supporting the ordering of this service.

Reimbursement Tips

Medicare reimburses this service under the laboratory fee schedule.

Terms To Know

qualitative. To determine the nature of the component of substance.

quantitative. To determine the amount and nature of the components of a substance.

ICD-10-CM Diagnostic Codes

F20.0	Paranoid schizophrenia
F20.1	Disorganized schizophrenia
F20.2	Catatonic schizophrenia
F20.3	Undifferentiated schizophrenia
F20.5	Residual schizophrenia
F20.81	Schizophreniform disorder
F20.89	Other schizophrenia
F21	Schizotypal disorder
F22	Delusional disorders
F23	Brief psychotic disorder
F24	Shared psychotic disorder
F25.0	Schizoaffective disorder, bipolar type
F25.1	Schizoaffective disorder, depressive type
F25.8	Other schizoaffective disorders
F28	Other psychotic disorder not due to a substance or known physiological condition

F31.0	Bipolar disorder, current episode hypomanic
F31.10	Bipolar disorder, current episode manic without psychotic features, unspecified
F31.11	Bipolar disorder, current episode manic without psychotic features, mild
F31.12	Bipolar disorder, current episode manic without psychotic features, moderate
F31.13	Bipolar disorder, current episode manic without psychotic features, severe
F31.2	Bipolar disorder, current episode manic severe with psychotic features
F31.31	Bipolar disorder, current episode depressed, mild
F31.32	Bipolar disorder, current episode depressed, moderate
F31.4	Bipolar disorder, current episode depressed, severe, without psychotic features
F31.5	Bipolar disorder, current episode depressed, severe, with psychotic features
F31.61	Bipolar disorder, current episode mixed, mild
F31.62	Bipolar disorder, current episode mixed, moderate
F31.63	Bipolar disorder, current episode mixed, severe, without psychotic features
F31.64	Bipolar disorder, current episode mixed, severe, with psychotic features
F31.71	Bipolar disorder, in partial remission, most recent episode hypomanic
F31.72	Bipolar disorder, in full remission, most recent episode hypomanic
F31.73	Bipolar disorder, in partial remission, most recent episode manic
F31.74	Bipolar disorder, in full remission, most recent episode manic
F31.75	Bipolar disorder, in partial remission, most recent episode depressed
F31.76	Bipolar disorder, in full remission, most recent episode depressed
F31.77	Bipolar disorder, in partial remission, most recent episode mixed
F31.78	Bipolar disorder, in full remission, most recent episode mixed
F31.81	Bipolar II disorder
F31.89	Other bipolar disorder
F32.0	Major depressive disorder, single episode, mild
F32.1	Major depressive disorder, single episode, moderate
F32.2	Major depressive disorder, single episode, severe without psychotic features
F32.3	Major depressive disorder, single episode, severe with psychotic features
F32.4	Major depressive disorder, single episode, in partial remission
F32.5	Major depressive disorder, single episode, in full remission
F32.8	Other depressive episodes
F33.0	Major depressive disorder, recurrent, mild
F33.1	Major depressive disorder, recurrent, moderate
F33.2	Major depressive disorder, recurrent severe without psychotic features
F33.3	Major depressive disorder, recurrent, severe with psychotic symptoms
F33.41	Major depressive disorder, recurrent, in partial remission
F33.42	Major depressive disorder, recurrent, in full remission
F33.8	Other recurrent depressive disorders

F41.0	Panic disorder [episodic paroxysmal anxiety] without agoraphobia
F41.1	Generalized anxiety disorder
F41.3	Other mixed anxiety disorders
F41.8	Other specified anxiety disorders
T43.501A	Poisoning by unspecified antipsychotics and neuroleptics, accidental (unintentional), initial encounter
T43.502A	Poisoning by unspecified antipsychotics and neuroleptics, intentional self-harm, initial encounter
T43.503A	Poisoning by unspecified antipsychotics and neuroleptics, assault, initial encounter
T43.505A	Adverse effect of unspecified antipsychotics and neuroleptics, initial encounter
T43.506A	Underdosing of unspecified antipsychotics and neuroleptics, initial encounter
T43.591A	Poisoning by other antipsychotics and neuroleptics, accidental (unintentional), initial encounter
T43.592A	Poisoning by other antipsychotics and neuroleptics, intentional self-harm, initial encounter
T43.593A	Poisoning by other antipsychotics and neuroleptics, assault, initial encounter
T43.595A	Adverse effect of other antipsychotics and neuroleptics, initial encounter
T43.596A	Underdosing of other antipsychotics and neuroleptics, initial encounter
Z02.83	Encounter for blood-alcohol and blood-drug test

Please note that this list of associated ICD-10-CM codes is not all-inclusive. The procedure may be performed for reasons other than those listed that support the medical necessity of the service. Only those conditions supported by the medical record documentation should be reported.

Medicare Edits

	Fac RVU	Non-Fac RVU	FUD	Status	MUE
80342	0.0	0.0	N/A	I	-
80343	0.0	0.0	N/A	I	-
80344	0.0	0.0	N/A	I	-

	Modifiers				Medicare References
80342	N/A	N/A	N/A	N/A	None
80343	N/A	N/A	N/A	N/A	
80344	N/A	N/A	N/A	N/A	

* with documentation

(80345)

80345   Barbiturates

Explanation

This test may be requested as a qualitative, quantitative, or combination analysis for barbiturates. Barbiturates are a type of depressant drug that cause relaxation and sleepiness. Methods used for analysis include gas-liquid chromatography (GLC) and gas chromatometry/mass spectrometry (GC/MS). This is a definitive drug test, meaning methods of testing would not be performed by enzymatic or immunoassays.

Coding Tips

This code is a resequenced code and will not display in numeric order. For presumptive drug testing, see the appropriate code from the 80300–80304 code range.

ICD-10-CM contains combination poisoning codes that include not only the poisoning itself and the type of poison involved, but also the associated intent (i.e., accidental, intentional self-harm, assault, and undetermined).

Documentation Tips

Documentation must include the laboratory results to support reporting this service.

Medical record documentation must, at a minimum, include signs and symptoms supporting the ordering of this service.

Reimbursement Tips

Medicare reimburses this service under the laboratory fee schedule.

Terms To Know

qualitative. To determine the nature of the component of substance.

quantitative. To determine the amount and nature of the components of a substance.

ICD-10-CM Diagnostic Codes

F13.10	Sedative, hypnotic or anxiolytic abuse, uncomplicated
F13.120	Sedative, hypnotic or anxiolytic abuse with intoxication, uncomplicated
F13.121	Sedative, hypnotic or anxiolytic abuse with intoxication delirium
F13.129	Sedative, hypnotic or anxiolytic abuse with intoxication, unspecified
F13.14	Sedative, hypnotic or anxiolytic abuse with sedative, hypnotic or anxiolytic-induced mood disorder
F13.150	Sedative, hypnotic or anxiolytic abuse with sedative, hypnotic or anxiolytic-induced psychotic disorder with delusions
F13.151	Sedative, hypnotic or anxiolytic abuse with sedative, hypnotic or anxiolytic-induced psychotic disorder with hallucinations
F13.159	Sedative, hypnotic or anxiolytic abuse with sedative, hypnotic or anxiolytic-induced psychotic disorder, unspecified
F13.180	Sedative, hypnotic or anxiolytic abuse with sedative, hypnotic or anxiolytic-induced anxiety disorder
F13.181	Sedative, hypnotic or anxiolytic abuse with sedative, hypnotic or anxiolytic-induced sexual dysfunction
F13.182	Sedative, hypnotic or anxiolytic abuse with sedative, hypnotic or anxiolytic-induced sleep disorder
F13.188	Sedative, hypnotic or anxiolytic abuse with other sedative, hypnotic or anxiolytic-induced disorder

F13.19	Sedative, hypnotic or anxiolytic abuse with unspecified sedative, hypnotic or anxiolytic-induced disorder
F13.20	Sedative, hypnotic or anxiolytic dependence, uncomplicated
F13.21	Sedative, hypnotic or anxiolytic dependence, in remission
F13.220	Sedative, hypnotic or anxiolytic dependence with intoxication, uncomplicated
F13.221	Sedative, hypnotic or anxiolytic dependence with intoxication delirium
F13.229	Sedative, hypnotic or anxiolytic dependence with intoxication, unspecified
F13.230	Sedative, hypnotic or anxiolytic dependence with withdrawal, uncomplicated
F13.231	Sedative, hypnotic or anxiolytic dependence with withdrawal delirium
F13.232	Sedative, hypnotic or anxiolytic dependence with withdrawal with perceptual disturbance
F13.239	Sedative, hypnotic or anxiolytic dependence with withdrawal, unspecified
F13.24	Sedative, hypnotic or anxiolytic dependence with sedative, hypnotic or anxiolytic-induced mood disorder
F13.250	Sedative, hypnotic or anxiolytic dependence with sedative, hypnotic or anxiolytic-induced psychotic disorder with delusions
F13.251	Sedative, hypnotic or anxiolytic dependence with sedative, hypnotic or anxiolytic-induced psychotic disorder with hallucinations
F13.259	Sedative, hypnotic or anxiolytic dependence with sedative, hypnotic or anxiolytic-induced psychotic disorder, unspecified
F13.26	Sedative, hypnotic or anxiolytic dependence with sedative, hypnotic or anxiolytic-induced persisting amnestic disorder
F13.27	Sedative, hypnotic or anxiolytic dependence with sedative, hypnotic or anxiolytic-induced persisting dementia
F13.280	Sedative, hypnotic or anxiolytic dependence with sedative, hypnotic or anxiolytic-induced anxiety disorder
F13.281	Sedative, hypnotic or anxiolytic dependence with sedative, hypnotic or anxiolytic-induced sexual dysfunction
F13.282	Sedative, hypnotic or anxiolytic dependence with sedative, hypnotic or anxiolytic-induced sleep disorder
F13.288	Sedative, hypnotic or anxiolytic dependence with other sedative, hypnotic or anxiolytic-induced disorder
F13.29	Sedative, hypnotic or anxiolytic dependence with unspecified sedative, hypnotic or anxiolytic-induced disorder
F13.90	Sedative, hypnotic, or anxiolytic use, unspecified, uncomplicated
F13.920	Sedative, hypnotic or anxiolytic use, unspecified with intoxication, uncomplicated
F13.921	Sedative, hypnotic or anxiolytic use, unspecified with intoxication delirium
F13.929	Sedative, hypnotic or anxiolytic use, unspecified with intoxication, unspecified
F13.930	Sedative, hypnotic or anxiolytic use, unspecified with withdrawal, uncomplicated
F13.931	Sedative, hypnotic or anxiolytic use, unspecified with withdrawal delirium
F13.932	Sedative, hypnotic or anxiolytic use, unspecified with withdrawal with perceptual disturbances
F13.939	Sedative, hypnotic or anxiolytic use, unspecified with withdrawal, unspecified

F13.94	Sedative, hypnotic or anxiolytic use, unspecified with sedative, hypnotic or anxiolytic-induced mood disorder
F13.950	Sedative, hypnotic or anxiolytic use, unspecified with sedative, hypnotic or anxiolytic-induced psychotic disorder with delusions
F13.951	Sedative, hypnotic or anxiolytic use, unspecified with sedative, hypnotic or anxiolytic-induced psychotic disorder with hallucinations
F13.959	Sedative, hypnotic or anxiolytic use, unspecified with sedative, hypnotic or anxiolytic-induced psychotic disorder, unspecified
F13.96	Sedative, hypnotic or anxiolytic use, unspecified with sedative, hypnotic or anxiolytic-induced persisting amnestic disorder
F13.97	Sedative, hypnotic or anxiolytic use, unspecified with sedative, hypnotic or anxiolytic-induced persisting dementia
F13.980	Sedative, hypnotic or anxiolytic use, unspecified with sedative, hypnotic or anxiolytic-induced anxiety disorder
F13.981	Sedative, hypnotic or anxiolytic use, unspecified with sedative, hypnotic or anxiolytic-induced sexual dysfunction
F13.982	Sedative, hypnotic or anxiolytic use, unspecified with sedative, hypnotic or anxiolytic-induced sleep disorder
F13.988	Sedative, hypnotic or anxiolytic use, unspecified with other sedative, hypnotic or anxiolytic-induced disorder
F13.99	Sedative, hypnotic or anxiolytic use, unspecified with unspecified sedative, hypnotic or anxiolytic-induced disorder
T42.3X1A	Poisoning by barbiturates, accidental (unintentional), initial encounter
T42.3X2A	Poisoning by barbiturates, intentional self-harm, initial encounter
T42.3X3A	Poisoning by barbiturates, assault, initial encounter
T42.3X4A	Poisoning by barbiturates, undetermined, initial encounter
T42.3X5A	Adverse effect of barbiturates, initial encounter
Z02.83	Encounter for blood-alcohol and blood-drug test

Please note that this list of associated ICD-10-CM codes is not all-inclusive. The procedure may be performed for reasons other than those listed that support the medical necessity of the service. Only those conditions supported by the medical record documentation should be reported.

Medicare Edits

	Fac RVU	Non-Fac RVU	FUD	Status	MUE
80345	0.0	0.0	N/A	I	-

	Modifiers				Medicare References
80345	N/A	N/A	N/A	N/A	None

* with documentation

(80346, 80347)

80346	Benzodiazepines; 1-12
80347	13 or more

Explanation

This test may be requested as Dalmane, quantitative analysis. Flurazepam is a benzodiazepine with sedative and hypnotic effects. Method is gas chromatography (GC), gas chromatography-mass spectrometry (GC-MS), high performance liquid chromatography (HPLC), or thin layer chromatography (TLC). This test measures (quantitates) the amount of the drug present. Report 80346 for one to 12 analytes and 80347 for 13 or more analytes.

Coding Tips

These codes are resequenced codes and will not display in numeric order. For presumptive drug testing, see the appropriate code from the 80300–80304 code range.

ICD-10-CM contains combination poisoning codes that include not only the poisoning itself and the type of poison involved, but also the associated intent (i.e., accidental, intentional self-harm, assault, and undetermined).

Documentation Tips

Documentation must include the laboratory results to support reporting this service.

Medical record documentation must, at a minimum, include signs and symptoms supporting the ordering of this service.

Reimbursement Tips

Medicare reimburses this service under the laboratory fee schedule.

ICD-10-CM Diagnostic Codes

F10.20	Alcohol dependence, uncomplicated
F10.21	Alcohol dependence, in remission
F10.220	Alcohol dependence with intoxication, uncomplicated
F10.221	Alcohol dependence with intoxication delirium
F10.230	Alcohol dependence with withdrawal, uncomplicated
F10.231	Alcohol dependence with withdrawal delirium
F10.232	Alcohol dependence with withdrawal with perceptual disturbance
F10.24	Alcohol dependence with alcohol-induced mood disorder
F10.250	Alcohol dependence with alcohol-induced psychotic disorder with delusions
F10.251	Alcohol dependence with alcohol-induced psychotic disorder with hallucinations
F10.26	Alcohol dependence with alcohol-induced persisting amnestic disorder
F10.27	Alcohol dependence with alcohol-induced persisting dementia
F10.280	Alcohol dependence with alcohol-induced anxiety disorder
F10.281	Alcohol dependence with alcohol-induced sexual dysfunction
F10.282	Alcohol dependence with alcohol-induced sleep disorder
F10.288	Alcohol dependence with other alcohol-induced disorder
F41.0	Panic disorder [episodic paroxysmal anxiety] without agoraphobia
F41.1	Generalized anxiety disorder
F41.3	Other mixed anxiety disorders

F41.8	Other specified anxiety disorders
G47.00	Insomnia, unspecified
G47.01	Insomnia due to medical condition
G47.09	Other insomnia
R56.9	Unspecified convulsions
T42.4X1A	Poisoning by benzodiazepines, accidental (unintentional), initial encounter
T42.4X2A	Poisoning by benzodiazepines, intentional self-harm, initial encounter
T42.4X3A	Poisoning by benzodiazepines, assault, initial encounter
T42.4X4A	Poisoning by benzodiazepines, undetermined, initial encounter
T42.4X5A	Adverse effect of benzodiazepines, initial encounter
Z02.83	Encounter for blood-alcohol and blood-drug test

Please note that this list of associated ICD-10-CM codes is not all-inclusive. The procedure may be performed for reasons other than those listed that support the medical necessity of the service. Only those conditions supported by the medical record documentation should be reported.

Medicare Edits

	Fac RVU	Non-Fac RVU	FUD	Status	MUE
80346	0.0	0.0	N/A	I	-
80347	0.0	0.0	N/A	I	-

	Modifiers				Medicare References
80346	N/A	N/A	N/A	N/A	None
80347	N/A	N/A	N/A	N/A	

* with documentation

(80348)

80348   Buprenorphine

Explanation

This test may be requested as a qualitative, quantitative, or combination analysis of buprenorphine (also known as Suboxone or Subutex), which is prescribed to treat opioid dependence. The main use of this test is to monitor patients to determine if they are following dependence therapy. The specimen is urine. Methods used for analysis include gas-liquid chromatography (GLC) and gas chromatometry/mass spectrometry (GC/MS). This is a definitive drug test, meaning methods of testing would not be performed by enzymatic or immunoassays.

Coding Tips

These codes are resequenced codes and will not display in numeric order. For presumptive drug testing, see the appropriate code from the 80300–80304 code range.

ICD-10-CM contains combination poisoning codes that include not only the poisoning itself and the type of poison involved, but also the associated intent (i.e., accidental, intentional self-harm, assault, and undetermined).

Documentation Tips

Documentation must include the laboratory results to support reporting this service.

Medical record documentation must, at a minimum, include signs and symptoms supporting the ordering of this service.

Reimbursement Tips

Medicare reimburses this service under the laboratory fee schedule.

ICD-10-CM Diagnostic Codes

F11.10	Opioid abuse, uncomplicated
F11.120	Opioid abuse with intoxication, uncomplicated
F11.121	Opioid abuse with intoxication delirium
F11.122	Opioid abuse with intoxication with perceptual disturbance
F11.14	Opioid abuse with opioid-induced mood disorder
F11.150	Opioid abuse with opioid-induced psychotic disorder with delusions
F11.151	Opioid abuse with opioid-induced psychotic disorder with hallucinations
F11.181	Opioid abuse with opioid-induced sexual dysfunction
F11.182	Opioid abuse with opioid-induced sleep disorder
F11.188	Opioid abuse with other opioid-induced disorder
F11.20	Opioid dependence, uncomplicated
F11.21	Opioid dependence, in remission
F11.220	Opioid dependence with intoxication, uncomplicated
F11.221	Opioid dependence with intoxication delirium
F11.222	Opioid dependence with intoxication with perceptual disturbance
F11.23	Opioid dependence with withdrawal
F11.24	Opioid dependence with opioid-induced mood disorder
F11.250	Opioid dependence with opioid-induced psychotic disorder with delusions
F11.251	Opioid dependence with opioid-induced psychotic disorder with hallucinations

F11.281	Opioid dependence with opioid-induced sexual dysfunction
F11.282	Opioid dependence with opioid-induced sleep disorder
F11.288	Opioid dependence with other opioid-induced disorder
F11.90	Opioid use, unspecified, uncomplicated
F11.920	Opioid use, unspecified with intoxication, uncomplicated
F11.921	Opioid use, unspecified with intoxication delirium
F11.922	Opioid use, unspecified with intoxication with perceptual disturbance
F11.93	Opioid use, unspecified with withdrawal
F11.94	Opioid use, unspecified with opioid-induced mood disorder
F11.950	Opioid use, unspecified with opioid-induced psychotic disorder with delusions
F11.951	Opioid use, unspecified with opioid-induced psychotic disorder with hallucinations
F11.981	Opioid use, unspecified with opioid-induced sexual dysfunction
F11.982	Opioid use, unspecified with opioid-induced sleep disorder
F11.988	Opioid use, unspecified with other opioid-induced disorder
T40.2X1A	Poisoning by other opioids, accidental (unintentional), initial encounter
T40.2X2A	Poisoning by other opioids, intentional self-harm, initial encounter
T40.2X3A	Poisoning by other opioids, assault, initial encounter
T40.2X5A	Adverse effect of other opioids, initial encounter
T40.4X1A	Poisoning by other synthetic narcotics, accidental (unintentional), initial encounter
T40.4X2A	Poisoning by other synthetic narcotics, intentional self-harm, initial encounter
T40.4X3A	Poisoning by other synthetic narcotics, assault, initial encounter
T40.4X5A	Adverse effect of other synthetic narcotics, initial encounter
T40.601A	Poisoning by unspecified narcotics, accidental (unintentional), initial encounter
T40.602A	Poisoning by unspecified narcotics, intentional self-harm, initial encounter
T40.603A	Poisoning by unspecified narcotics, assault, initial encounter
T40.605A	Adverse effect of unspecified narcotics, initial encounter
T40.691A	Poisoning by other narcotics, accidental (unintentional), initial encounter
T40.692A	Poisoning by other narcotics, intentional self-harm, initial encounter
T40.693A	Poisoning by other narcotics, assault, initial encounter
T40.695A	Adverse effect of other narcotics, initial encounter
Z02.83	Encounter for blood-alcohol and blood-drug test

Please note that this list of associated ICD-10-CM codes is not all-inclusive. The procedure may be performed for reasons other than those listed that support the medical necessity of the service. Only those conditions supported by the medical record documentation should be reported.

Medicare Edits

	Fac RVU	Non-Fac RVU	FUD	Status	MUE
80348	0.0	0.0	N/A	I	-

	Modifiers				Medicare References
80348	N/A	N/A	N/A	N/A	None

* with documentation

(80349, 80350, 80351, 80352)

80349	Cannabinoids, natural
80350	Cannabinoids, synthetic; 1-3
80351	4-6
80352	7 or more

Explanation

These tests may be requested as qualitative, quantitative, or combination analysis of cannabinoids. Naturally occurring cannabinoids are found in the resin composition of the cannabis plant. Synthetic drugs have been constructed that follow the same courses within the brain, but work differently than the natural version. Methods used for analysis include gas-liquid chromatography (GLC) and gas chromatometry/mass spectrometry (GC/MS). Specimen is urine. This is a definitive drug test, meaning methods of testing would not be performed by enzymatic or immunoassays. Report 80349 when testing for natural cannabinoids; 80350 when testing for one to three synthetic cannabinoids; 80351 when testing for four to six synthetic cannabinoids; and 80352 when testing for seven or more.

Coding Tips

These codes are resequenced codes and will not display in numeric order. For presumptive drug testing, see the appropriate code from the 80300–80304 code range.

ICD-10-CM contains combination poisoning codes that include not only the poisoning itself and the type of poison involved, but also the associated intent (i.e., accidental, intentional self-harm, assault, and undetermined).

Documentation Tips

Documentation must include the laboratory results to support reporting this service.

Medical record documentation must, at a minimum, include signs and symptoms supporting the ordering of this service.

Reimbursement Tips

Medicare reimburses this service under the laboratory fee schedule.

Terms To Know

qualitative. To determine the nature of the component of substance.

quantitative. To determine the amount and nature of the components of a substance.

ICD-10-CM Diagnostic Codes

F12.10	Cannabis abuse, uncomplicated
F12.120	Cannabis abuse with intoxication, uncomplicated
F12.121	Cannabis abuse with intoxication delirium
F12.122	Cannabis abuse with intoxication with perceptual disturbance
F12.129	Cannabis abuse with intoxication, unspecified
F12.150	Cannabis abuse with psychotic disorder with delusions
F12.159	Cannabis abuse with psychotic disorder, unspecified
F12.180	Cannabis abuse with cannabis-induced anxiety disorder
F12.188	Cannabis abuse with other cannabis-induced disorder
F12.19	Cannabis abuse with unspecified cannabis-induced disorder
F12.20	Cannabis dependence, uncomplicated
F12.21	Cannabis dependence, in remission
F12.220	Cannabis dependence with intoxication, uncomplicated
F12.221	Cannabis dependence with intoxication delirium
F12.222	Cannabis dependence with intoxication with perceptual disturbance
F12.229	Cannabis dependence with intoxication, unspecified
F12.250	Cannabis dependence with psychotic disorder with delusions
F12.251	Cannabis dependence with psychotic disorder with hallucinations
F12.259	Cannabis dependence with psychotic disorder, unspecified
F12.280	Cannabis dependence with cannabis-induced anxiety disorder
F12.288	Cannabis dependence with other cannabis-induced disorder
F12.29	Cannabis dependence with unspecified cannabis-induced disorder
F12.90	Cannabis use, unspecified, uncomplicated
F12.920	Cannabis use, unspecified with intoxication, uncomplicated
F12.921	Cannabis use, unspecified with intoxication delirium
F12.922	Cannabis use, unspecified with intoxication with perceptual disturbance
F12.929	Cannabis use, unspecified with intoxication, unspecified
F12.950	Cannabis use, unspecified with psychotic disorder with delusions
F12.959	Cannabis use, unspecified with psychotic disorder, unspecified
F12.980	Cannabis use, unspecified with anxiety disorder
F12.988	Cannabis use, unspecified with other cannabis-induced disorder
F12.99	Cannabis use, unspecified with unspecified cannabis-induced disorder
T40.7X1A	Poisoning by cannabis (derivatives), accidental (unintentional), initial encounter
T40.7X2A	Poisoning by cannabis (derivatives), intentional self-harm, initial encounter
T40.7X3A	Poisoning by cannabis (derivatives), assault, initial encounter
T40.7X4A	Poisoning by cannabis (derivatives), undetermined, initial encounter
T40.7X5A	Adverse effect of cannabis (derivatives), initial encounter
Z02.83	Encounter for blood-alcohol and blood-drug test

Please note that this list of associated ICD-10-CM codes is not all-inclusive. The procedure may be performed for reasons other than those listed that support the medical necessity of the service. Only those conditions supported by the medical record documentation should be reported.

Medicare Edits

	Fac RVU	Non-Fac RVU	FUD	Status	MUE
80349	0.0	0.0	N/A	I	-
80350	0.0	0.0	N/A	I	-
80351	0.0	0.0	N/A	I	-
80352	0.0	0.0	N/A	I	-

	Modifiers				Medicare References
80349	N/A	N/A	N/A	N/A	None
80350	N/A	N/A	N/A	N/A	
80351	N/A	N/A	N/A	N/A	
80352	N/A	N/A	N/A	N/A	

* with documentation

(80353)

80353   Cocaine

Explanation

Cocaine is a refined derivative of the coca plant and is a frequently abused drug. Specimen can be blood or urine. This test may be requested as a qualitative, quantitative, or combination analysis for cocaine. Methods used for analysis include gas-liquid chromatography (GLC) and gas chromatometry/mass spectrometry (GC/MS). This is a definitive drug test, meaning methods of testing would not be performed by enzymatic or immunoassays.

Coding Tips

This code is a resequenced code and will not display in numeric order. For presumptive drug testing, see the appropriate code from the 80300–80304 code range.

ICD-10-CM contains combination poisoning codes that include not only the poisoning itself and the type of poison involved, but also the associated intent (i.e., accidental, intentional self-harm, assault, and undetermined).

Documentation Tips

Documentation must include the laboratory results to support reporting this service.

Medical record documentation must, at a minimum, include signs and symptoms supporting the ordering of this service.

Reimbursement Tips

Medicare reimburses this service under the laboratory fee schedule.

Terms To Know

qualitative. To determine the nature of the component of substance.
quantitative. To determine the amount and nature of the components of a substance.

ICD-10-CM Diagnostic Codes

F14.10	Cocaine abuse, uncomplicated
F14.120	Cocaine abuse with intoxication, uncomplicated
F14.122	Cocaine abuse with intoxication with perceptual disturbance
F14.159	Cocaine abuse with cocaine-induced psychotic disorder, unspecified
F14.180	Cocaine abuse with cocaine-induced anxiety disorder
F14.181	Cocaine abuse with cocaine-induced sexual dysfunction
F14.188	Cocaine abuse with other cocaine-induced disorder
F14.20	Cocaine dependence, uncomplicated
F14.21	Cocaine dependence, in remission
F14.220	Cocaine dependence with intoxication, uncomplicated
F14.221	Cocaine dependence with intoxication delirium
F14.222	Cocaine dependence with intoxication with perceptual disturbance
F14.229	Cocaine dependence with intoxication, unspecified
F14.23	Cocaine dependence with withdrawal
F14.24	Cocaine dependence with cocaine-induced mood disorder
F14.250	Cocaine dependence with cocaine-induced psychotic disorder with delusions

F14.251	Cocaine dependence with cocaine-induced psychotic disorder with hallucinations
F14.259	Cocaine dependence with cocaine-induced psychotic disorder, unspecified
F14.280	Cocaine dependence with cocaine-induced anxiety disorder
F14.281	Cocaine dependence with cocaine-induced sexual dysfunction
F14.282	Cocaine dependence with cocaine-induced sleep disorder
F14.288	Cocaine dependence with other cocaine-induced disorder
F14.29	Cocaine dependence with unspecified cocaine-induced disorder
F14.90	Cocaine use, unspecified, uncomplicated
F14.922	Cocaine use, unspecified with intoxication with perceptual disturbance
F14.959	Cocaine use, unspecified with cocaine-induced psychotic disorder, unspecified
F14.980	Cocaine use, unspecified with cocaine-induced anxiety disorder
F14.981	Cocaine use, unspecified with cocaine-induced sexual dysfunction
F14.988	Cocaine use, unspecified with other cocaine-induced disorder
F14.99	Cocaine use, unspecified with unspecified cocaine-induced disorder
T40.5X1A	Poisoning by cocaine, accidental (unintentional), initial encounter
T40.5X2A	Poisoning by cocaine, intentional self-harm, initial encounter
T40.5X3A	Poisoning by cocaine, assault, initial encounter
T40.5X4A	Poisoning by cocaine, undetermined, initial encounter
T40.5X5A	Adverse effect of cocaine, initial encounter
Z02.83	Encounter for blood-alcohol and blood-drug test

Please note that this list of associated ICD-10-CM codes is not all-inclusive. The procedure may be performed for reasons other than those listed that support the medical necessity of the service. Only those conditions supported by the medical record documentation should be reported.

Medicare Edits

	Fac RVU	Non-Fac RVU	FUD	Status	MUE
80353	0.0	0.0	N/A	I	-

	Modifiers				Medicare References
80353	N/A	N/A	N/A	N/A	None

* with documentation

(80354)

80354   Fentanyl

Explanation

This test may be requested as a qualitative, quantitative, or combination analysis of fentanyl. This drug is classified as an opiate and due to the sensation that is similar to heroin, it may be abused. It is prescribed for symptoms coinciding with chronic pain, often administered when other pain meds fail. The half-life varies depending on method of delivery. Methods used for analysis include gas-liquid chromatography (GLC) and gas chromatometry/mass spectrometry (GC/MS). This is a definitive drug test, meaning methods of testing would not be performed by enzymatic or immunoassays. Specimen is serum, plasma, or urine.

Coding Tips

This code is a resequenced code and will not display in numeric order. For presumptive drug testing, see the appropriate code from the 80300–80304 code range.

ICD-10-CM contains combination poisoning codes that include not only the poisoning itself and the type of poison involved, but also the associated intent (i.e., accidental, intentional self-harm, assault, and undetermined).

Documentation Tips

Documentation must include the laboratory results to support reporting this service.

Medical record documentation must, at a minimum, include signs and symptoms supporting the ordering of this service.

Reimbursement Tips

Medicare reimburses this service under the laboratory fee schedule.

Terms To Know

qualitative. To determine the nature of the component of substance.
quantitative. To determine the amount and nature of the components of a substance.

ICD-10-CM Diagnostic Codes

F11.10	Opioid abuse, uncomplicated
F11.120	Opioid abuse with intoxication, uncomplicated
F11.121	Opioid abuse with intoxication delirium
F11.122	Opioid abuse with intoxication with perceptual disturbance
F11.14	Opioid abuse with opioid-induced mood disorder
F11.150	Opioid abuse with opioid-induced psychotic disorder with delusions
F11.151	Opioid abuse with opioid-induced psychotic disorder with hallucinations
F11.181	Opioid abuse with opioid-induced sexual dysfunction
F11.182	Opioid abuse with opioid-induced sleep disorder
F11.188	Opioid abuse with other opioid-induced disorder
F11.20	Opioid dependence, uncomplicated
F11.21	Opioid dependence, in remission
F11.220	Opioid dependence with intoxication, uncomplicated
F11.221	Opioid dependence with intoxication delirium
F11.222	Opioid dependence with intoxication with perceptual disturbance
F11.23	Opioid dependence with withdrawal
F11.24	Opioid dependence with opioid-induced mood disorder
F11.250	Opioid dependence with opioid-induced psychotic disorder with delusions
F11.251	Opioid dependence with opioid-induced psychotic disorder with hallucinations
F11.281	Opioid dependence with opioid-induced sexual dysfunction
F11.282	Opioid dependence with opioid-induced sleep disorder
F11.288	Opioid dependence with other opioid-induced disorder
F11.90	Opioid use, unspecified, uncomplicated
F11.920	Opioid use, unspecified with intoxication, uncomplicated
F11.921	Opioid use, unspecified with intoxication delirium
F11.922	Opioid use, unspecified with intoxication with perceptual disturbance
F11.93	Opioid use, unspecified with withdrawal
F11.94	Opioid use, unspecified with opioid-induced mood disorder
F11.950	Opioid use, unspecified with opioid-induced psychotic disorder with delusions
F11.951	Opioid use, unspecified with opioid-induced psychotic disorder with hallucinations
F11.981	Opioid use, unspecified with opioid-induced sexual dysfunction
F11.982	Opioid use, unspecified with opioid-induced sleep disorder
F11.988	Opioid use, unspecified with other opioid-induced disorder
G89.21	Chronic pain due to trauma
G89.22	Chronic post-thoracotomy pain
G89.28	Other chronic postprocedural pain
G89.29	Other chronic pain
G89.3	Neoplasm related pain (acute) (chronic)
G89.4	Chronic pain syndrome
T40.2X1A	Poisoning by other opioids, accidental (unintentional), initial encounter
T40.2X2A	Poisoning by other opioids, intentional self-harm, initial encounter
T40.2X3A	Poisoning by other opioids, assault, initial encounter
T40.2X5A	Adverse effect of other opioids, initial encounter
T40.4X1A	Poisoning by other synthetic narcotics, accidental (unintentional), initial encounter
T40.4X2A	Poisoning by other synthetic narcotics, intentional self-harm, initial encounter
T40.4X3A	Poisoning by other synthetic narcotics, assault, initial encounter
T40.4X5A	Adverse effect of other synthetic narcotics, initial encounter
Z02.83	Encounter for blood-alcohol and blood-drug test

Please note that this list of associated ICD-10-CM codes is not all-inclusive. The procedure may be performed for reasons other than those listed that support the medical necessity of the service. Only those conditions supported by the medical record documentation should be reported.

Medicare Edits

	Fac RVU	Non-Fac RVU	FUD	Status	MUE
80354	0.0	0.0	N/A	I	-

	Modifiers				Medicare References
80354	N/A	N/A	N/A	N/A	None

* with documentation

(80356)

80356   Heroin metabolite

Explanation

This test may be requested as a qualitative, quantitative, or combination analysis for heroin metabolite. Heroin is a manufactured opiate with a morphine base and is difficult to determine through body fluids. The half-life is just a few minutes, but in analysis, the proportion of morphine to codeine found in the specimen can assist in determining heroin versus codeine. Methods used for analysis include gas-liquid chromatography (GLC) and gas chromatometry/mass spectrometry (GC/MS). This is a definitive drug test, meaning methods of testing would not be performed by enzymatic or immunoassays.

Coding Tips

This code is a resequenced code and will not display in numeric order. For presumptive drug testing, see the appropriate code from the 80300–80304 code range.

ICD-10-CM contains combination poisoning codes that include not only the poisoning itself and the type of poison involved, but also the associated intent (i.e., accidental, intentional self-harm, assault, and undetermined).

Documentation Tips

Documentation must include the laboratory results to support reporting this service.

Medical record documentation must, at a minimum, include signs and symptoms supporting the ordering of this service.

Reimbursement Tips

Medicare reimburses this service under the laboratory fee schedule.

Terms To Know

qualitative. To determine the nature of the component of substance.
quantitative. To determine the amount and nature of the components of a substance.

ICD-10-CM Diagnostic Codes

F11.10	Opioid abuse, uncomplicated
F11.120	Opioid abuse with intoxication, uncomplicated
F11.121	Opioid abuse with intoxication delirium
F11.122	Opioid abuse with intoxication with perceptual disturbance
F11.14	Opioid abuse with opioid-induced mood disorder
F11.150	Opioid abuse with opioid-induced psychotic disorder with delusions
F11.151	Opioid abuse with opioid-induced psychotic disorder with hallucinations
F11.181	Opioid abuse with opioid-induced sexual dysfunction
F11.182	Opioid abuse with opioid-induced sleep disorder
F11.188	Opioid abuse with other opioid-induced disorder
F11.20	Opioid dependence, uncomplicated
F11.21	Opioid dependence, in remission
F11.220	Opioid dependence with intoxication, uncomplicated
F11.221	Opioid dependence with intoxication delirium
F11.222	Opioid dependence with intoxication with perceptual disturbance

F11.23	Opioid dependence with withdrawal
F11.24	Opioid dependence with opioid-induced mood disorder
F11.250	Opioid dependence with opioid-induced psychotic disorder with delusions
F11.251	Opioid dependence with opioid-induced psychotic disorder with hallucinations
F11.281	Opioid dependence with opioid-induced sexual dysfunction
F11.282	Opioid dependence with opioid-induced sleep disorder
F11.288	Opioid dependence with other opioid-induced disorder
F11.90	Opioid use, unspecified, uncomplicated
F11.920	Opioid use, unspecified with intoxication, uncomplicated
F11.921	Opioid use, unspecified with intoxication delirium
F11.922	Opioid use, unspecified with intoxication with perceptual disturbance
F11.93	Opioid use, unspecified with withdrawal
F11.94	Opioid use, unspecified with opioid-induced mood disorder
F11.950	Opioid use, unspecified with opioid-induced psychotic disorder with delusions
F11.951	Opioid use, unspecified with opioid-induced psychotic disorder with hallucinations
F11.981	Opioid use, unspecified with opioid-induced sexual dysfunction
F11.982	Opioid use, unspecified with opioid-induced sleep disorder
F11.988	Opioid use, unspecified with other opioid-induced disorder
T40.1X1A	Poisoning by heroin, accidental (unintentional), initial encounter
T40.1X2A	Poisoning by heroin, intentional self-harm, initial encounter
T40.1X3A	Poisoning by heroin, assault, initial encounter
T40.2X1A	Poisoning by other opioids, accidental (unintentional), initial encounter
T40.2X2A	Poisoning by other opioids, intentional self-harm, initial encounter
T40.2X3A	Poisoning by other opioids, assault, initial encounter
T40.2X5A	Adverse effect of other opioids, initial encounter
Z02.83	Encounter for blood-alcohol and blood-drug test

Please note that this list of associated ICD-10-CM codes is not all-inclusive. The procedure may be performed for reasons other than those listed that support the medical necessity of the service. Only those conditions supported by the medical record documentation should be reported.

Medicare Edits

	Fac RVU	Non-Fac RVU	FUD	Status	MUE
80356	0.0	0.0	N/A	I	-

	Modifiers				Medicare References
80356	N/A	N/A	N/A	N/A	None

* with documentation

(80357)

| 80357 | Ketamine and norketamine |

Explanation

This test may be requested as a qualitative, quantitative, or combination analysis for ketamine and/or norketamine. Ketamine is used for anesthesia, but is also sold/abused based on hallucinogenic properties. It has a half-life of three to four hours. Ketamine and norketamine can be found in urine specimens up to two days after use. Methods used for analysis include gas-liquid chromatography (GLC) and gas chromatometry/mass spectrometry (GC/MS). This is a definitive drug test, meaning methods of testing would not be performed by enzymatic or immunoassays.

Coding Tips

This code is a resequenced code and will not display in numeric order. For presumptive drug testing, see the appropriate code from the 80300–80304 code range.

ICD-10-CM contains combination poisoning codes that include not only the poisoning itself and the type of poison involved, but also the associated intent (i.e., accidental, intentional self-harm, assault, and undetermined).

Documentation Tips

Documentation must include the laboratory results to support reporting this service.

Medical record documentation must, at a minimum, include signs and symptoms supporting the ordering of this service.

Reimbursement Tips

Medicare reimburses this service under the laboratory fee schedule.

Terms To Know

qualitative. To determine the nature of the component of substance.

quantitative. To determine the amount and nature of the components of a substance.

ICD-10-CM Diagnostic Codes

F13.10	Sedative, hypnotic or anxiolytic abuse, uncomplicated
F13.120	Sedative, hypnotic or anxiolytic abuse with intoxication, uncomplicated
F13.121	Sedative, hypnotic or anxiolytic abuse with intoxication delirium
F13.14	Sedative, hypnotic or anxiolytic abuse with sedative, hypnotic or anxiolytic-induced mood disorder
F13.150	Sedative, hypnotic or anxiolytic abuse with sedative, hypnotic or anxiolytic-induced psychotic disorder with delusions
F13.151	Sedative, hypnotic or anxiolytic abuse with sedative, hypnotic or anxiolytic-induced psychotic disorder with hallucinations
F13.180	Sedative, hypnotic or anxiolytic abuse with sedative, hypnotic or anxiolytic-induced anxiety disorder
F13.181	Sedative, hypnotic or anxiolytic abuse with sedative, hypnotic or anxiolytic-induced sexual dysfunction
F13.182	Sedative, hypnotic or anxiolytic abuse with sedative, hypnotic or anxiolytic-induced sleep disorder
F13.188	Sedative, hypnotic or anxiolytic abuse with other sedative, hypnotic or anxiolytic-induced disorder
F13.20	Sedative, hypnotic or anxiolytic dependence, uncomplicated
F13.21	Sedative, hypnotic or anxiolytic dependence, in remission

F13.220	Sedative, hypnotic or anxiolytic dependence with intoxication, uncomplicated
F13.221	Sedative, hypnotic or anxiolytic dependence with intoxication delirium
F13.230	Sedative, hypnotic or anxiolytic dependence with withdrawal, uncomplicated
F13.231	Sedative, hypnotic or anxiolytic dependence with withdrawal delirium
F13.232	Sedative, hypnotic or anxiolytic dependence with withdrawal with perceptual disturbance
F13.24	Sedative, hypnotic or anxiolytic dependence with sedative, hypnotic or anxiolytic-induced mood disorder
F13.250	Sedative, hypnotic or anxiolytic dependence with sedative, hypnotic or anxiolytic-induced psychotic disorder with delusions
F13.251	Sedative, hypnotic or anxiolytic dependence with sedative, hypnotic or anxiolytic-induced psychotic disorder with hallucinations
F13.26	Sedative, hypnotic or anxiolytic dependence with sedative, hypnotic or anxiolytic-induced persisting amnestic disorder
F13.27	Sedative, hypnotic or anxiolytic dependence with sedative, hypnotic or anxiolytic-induced persisting dementia
F13.280	Sedative, hypnotic or anxiolytic dependence with sedative, hypnotic or anxiolytic-induced anxiety disorder
F13.281	Sedative, hypnotic or anxiolytic dependence with sedative, hypnotic or anxiolytic-induced sexual dysfunction
F13.282	Sedative, hypnotic or anxiolytic dependence with sedative, hypnotic or anxiolytic-induced sleep disorder
F13.288	Sedative, hypnotic or anxiolytic dependence with other sedative, hypnotic or anxiolytic-induced disorder
F13.90	Sedative, hypnotic, or anxiolytic use, unspecified, uncomplicated
F13.920	Sedative, hypnotic or anxiolytic use, unspecified with intoxication, uncomplicated
F13.921	Sedative, hypnotic or anxiolytic use, unspecified with intoxication delirium
F13.929	Sedative, hypnotic or anxiolytic use, unspecified with intoxication, unspecified
F13.930	Sedative, hypnotic or anxiolytic use, unspecified with withdrawal, uncomplicated
F13.931	Sedative, hypnotic or anxiolytic use, unspecified with withdrawal delirium
F13.932	Sedative, hypnotic or anxiolytic use, unspecified with withdrawal with perceptual disturbances
F13.94	Sedative, hypnotic or anxiolytic use, unspecified with sedative, hypnotic or anxiolytic-induced mood disorder
F13.950	Sedative, hypnotic or anxiolytic use, unspecified with sedative, hypnotic or anxiolytic-induced psychotic disorder with delusions
F13.951	Sedative, hypnotic or anxiolytic use, unspecified with sedative, hypnotic or anxiolytic-induced psychotic disorder with hallucinations
F13.96	Sedative, hypnotic or anxiolytic use, unspecified with sedative, hypnotic or anxiolytic-induced persisting amnestic disorder
F13.97	Sedative, hypnotic or anxiolytic use, unspecified with sedative, hypnotic or anxiolytic-induced persisting dementia
F13.980	Sedative, hypnotic or anxiolytic use, unspecified with sedative, hypnotic or anxiolytic-induced anxiety disorder
F13.981	Sedative, hypnotic or anxiolytic use, unspecified with sedative, hypnotic or anxiolytic-induced sexual dysfunction
F13.982	Sedative, hypnotic or anxiolytic use, unspecified with sedative, hypnotic or anxiolytic-induced sleep disorder
F13.988	Sedative, hypnotic or anxiolytic use, unspecified with other sedative, hypnotic or anxiolytic-induced disorder
T41.291A	Poisoning by other general anesthetics, accidental (unintentional), initial encounter
T41.292A	Poisoning by other general anesthetics, intentional self-harm, initial encounter
T41.293A	Poisoning by other general anesthetics, assault, initial encounter
T41.295A	Adverse effect of other general anesthetics, initial encounter
Z02.83	Encounter for blood-alcohol and blood-drug test

Please note that this list of associated ICD-10-CM codes is not all-inclusive. The procedure may be performed for reasons other than those listed that support the medical necessity of the service. Only those conditions supported by the medical record documentation should be reported.

Medicare Edits

	Fac RVU	Non-Fac RVU	FUD	Status	MUE
80357	0.0	0.0	N/A	I	-

	Modifiers				Medicare References
80357	N/A	N/A	N/A	N/A	None

* with documentation

(80358)

80358   Methadone

Explanation

This test may be requested as a qualitative, quantitative, or combination analysis for methadone. This test is used to measure toxicity and the determination of methadone in the system in cases of drug abuse. The specimen is a random urine sample. This agent is widely used in the detoxification of opiate addicts. Methods used for analysis include gas-liquid chromatography (GLC) and gas chromatometry/mass spectrometry (GC/MS). This is a definitive drug test, meaning methods of testing would not be performed by enzymatic or immunoassays.

Coding Tips

This code is a resequenced code and will not display in numeric order. For presumptive drug testing, see the appropriate code from the 80300–80304 code range.

ICD-10-CM contains combination poisoning codes that include not only the poisoning itself and the type of poison involved, but also the associated intent (i.e., accidental, intentional self-harm, assault, and undetermined).

Documentation Tips

Documentation must include the laboratory results to support reporting this service.

Medical record documentation must, at a minimum, include signs and symptoms supporting the ordering of this service.

Reimbursement Tips

Medicare reimburses this service under the laboratory fee schedule.

Terms To Know

qualitative. To determine the nature of the component of substance.
quantitative. To determine the amount and nature of the components of a substance.

ICD-10-CM Diagnostic Codes

F11.10	Opioid abuse, uncomplicated
F11.120	Opioid abuse with intoxication, uncomplicated
F11.121	Opioid abuse with intoxication delirium
F11.122	Opioid abuse with intoxication with perceptual disturbance
F11.129	Opioid abuse with intoxication, unspecified
F11.14	Opioid abuse with opioid-induced mood disorder
F11.150	Opioid abuse with opioid-induced psychotic disorder with delusions
F11.151	Opioid abuse with opioid-induced psychotic disorder with hallucinations
F11.159	Opioid abuse with opioid-induced psychotic disorder, unspecified
F11.181	Opioid abuse with opioid-induced sexual dysfunction
F11.182	Opioid abuse with opioid-induced sleep disorder
F11.188	Opioid abuse with other opioid-induced disorder
F11.19	Opioid abuse with unspecified opioid-induced disorder
F11.20	Opioid dependence, uncomplicated
F11.21	Opioid dependence, in remission
F11.220	Opioid dependence with intoxication, uncomplicated
F11.221	Opioid dependence with intoxication delirium

F11.222	Opioid dependence with intoxication with perceptual disturbance
F11.229	Opioid dependence with intoxication, unspecified
F11.23	Opioid dependence with withdrawal
F11.24	Opioid dependence with opioid-induced mood disorder
F11.250	Opioid dependence with opioid-induced psychotic disorder with delusions
F11.251	Opioid dependence with opioid-induced psychotic disorder with hallucinations
F11.259	Opioid dependence with opioid-induced psychotic disorder, unspecified
F11.281	Opioid dependence with opioid-induced sexual dysfunction
F11.282	Opioid dependence with opioid-induced sleep disorder
F11.288	Opioid dependence with other opioid-induced disorder
F11.29	Opioid dependence with unspecified opioid-induced disorder
F11.90	Opioid use, unspecified, uncomplicated
F11.920	Opioid use, unspecified with intoxication, uncomplicated
F11.921	Opioid use, unspecified with intoxication delirium
F11.922	Opioid use, unspecified with intoxication with perceptual disturbance
F11.929	Opioid use, unspecified with intoxication, unspecified
F11.93	Opioid use, unspecified with withdrawal
F11.94	Opioid use, unspecified with opioid-induced mood disorder
F11.950	Opioid use, unspecified with opioid-induced psychotic disorder with delusions
F11.951	Opioid use, unspecified with opioid-induced psychotic disorder with hallucinations
F11.959	Opioid use, unspecified with opioid-induced psychotic disorder, unspecified
F11.981	Opioid use, unspecified with opioid-induced sexual dysfunction
F11.982	Opioid use, unspecified with opioid-induced sleep disorder
F11.988	Opioid use, unspecified with other opioid-induced disorder
F11.99	Opioid use, unspecified with unspecified opioid-induced disorder
T40.2X1A	Poisoning by other opioids, accidental (unintentional), initial encounter
T40.2X2A	Poisoning by other opioids, intentional self-harm, initial encounter
T40.2X3A	Poisoning by other opioids, assault, initial encounter
T40.2X4A	Poisoning by other opioids, undetermined, initial encounter
T40.2X5A	Adverse effect of other opioids, initial encounter
T40.3X1A	Poisoning by methadone, accidental (unintentional), initial encounter
T40.3X2A	Poisoning by methadone, intentional self-harm, initial encounter
T40.3X3A	Poisoning by methadone, assault, initial encounter
T40.3X4A	Poisoning by methadone, undetermined, initial encounter
T40.3X5A	Adverse effect of methadone, initial encounter
T40.4X1A	Poisoning by other synthetic narcotics, accidental (unintentional), initial encounter
T40.4X2A	Poisoning by other synthetic narcotics, intentional self-harm, initial encounter
T40.4X3A	Poisoning by other synthetic narcotics, assault, initial encounter
T40.4X4A	Poisoning by other synthetic narcotics, undetermined, initial encounter
T40.4X5A	Adverse effect of other synthetic narcotics, initial encounter

T40.601A	Poisoning by unspecified narcotics, accidental (unintentional), initial encounter
T40.602A	Poisoning by unspecified narcotics, intentional self-harm, initial encounter
T40.603A	Poisoning by unspecified narcotics, assault, initial encounter
T40.604A	Poisoning by unspecified narcotics, undetermined, initial encounter
T40.605A	Adverse effect of unspecified narcotics, initial encounter
T40.691A	Poisoning by other narcotics, accidental (unintentional), initial encounter
T40.692A	Poisoning by other narcotics, intentional self-harm, initial encounter
T40.693A	Poisoning by other narcotics, assault, initial encounter
T40.694A	Poisoning by other narcotics, undetermined, initial encounter
T40.695A	Adverse effect of other narcotics, initial encounter
Z02.83	Encounter for blood-alcohol and blood-drug test

Please note that this list of associated ICD-10-CM codes is not all-inclusive. The procedure may be performed for reasons other than those listed that support the medical necessity of the service. Only those conditions supported by the medical record documentation should be reported.

Medicare Edits

	Fac RVU	Non-Fac RVU	FUD	Status	MUE
80358	0.0	0.0	N/A	I	-

	Modifiers				Medicare References
80358	N/A	N/A	N/A	N/A	None

* with documentation

(80359)

80359	Methylenedioxyamphetamines (MDA, MDEA, MDMA)

Explanation

This test may be requested as a qualitative, quantitative, or combination analysis of amphetamine/methamphetamine. Methods used for analysis include gas-liquid chromatography (GLC) and gas chromatometry/mass spectrometry (GC/MS). This is a definitive drug test, meaning methods of testing would not be performed by enzymatic or immunoassays. Specimen can be blood or urine.

Coding Tips

This code is a resequenced code and will not display in numeric order. For presumptive drug testing, see the appropriate code from the 80300–80304 code range.

ICD-10-CM contains combination poisoning codes that include not only the poisoning itself and the type of poison involved, but also the associated intent (i.e., accidental, intentional self-harm, assault, and undetermined).

Documentation Tips

Documentation must include the laboratory results to support reporting this service.

Medical record documentation must, at a minimum, include signs and symptoms supporting the ordering of this service.

Reimbursement Tips

Medicare reimburses this service under the laboratory fee schedule.

ICD-10-CM Diagnostic Codes

F15.10	Other stimulant abuse, uncomplicated
F15.120	Other stimulant abuse with intoxication, uncomplicated
F15.121	Other stimulant abuse with intoxication delirium
F15.122	Other stimulant abuse with intoxication with perceptual disturbance
F15.14	Other stimulant abuse with stimulant-induced mood disorder
F15.150	Other stimulant abuse with stimulant-induced psychotic disorder with delusions
F15.151	Other stimulant abuse with stimulant-induced psychotic disorder with hallucinations
F15.180	Other stimulant abuse with stimulant-induced anxiety disorder
F15.181	Other stimulant abuse with stimulant-induced sexual dysfunction
F15.182	Other stimulant abuse with stimulant-induced sleep disorder
F15.188	Other stimulant abuse with other stimulant-induced disorder
F15.20	Other stimulant dependence, uncomplicated
F15.21	Other stimulant dependence, in remission
F15.220	Other stimulant dependence with intoxication, uncomplicated
F15.221	Other stimulant dependence with intoxication delirium
F15.222	Other stimulant dependence with intoxication with perceptual disturbance
F15.23	Other stimulant dependence with withdrawal
F15.24	Other stimulant dependence with stimulant-induced mood disorder
F15.250	Other stimulant dependence with stimulant-induced psychotic disorder with delusions

F15.251	Other stimulant dependence with stimulant-induced psychotic disorder with hallucinations	
F15.280	Other stimulant dependence with stimulant-induced anxiety disorder	
F15.281	Other stimulant dependence with stimulant-induced sexual dysfunction	
F15.282	Other stimulant dependence with stimulant-induced sleep disorder	
F15.288	Other stimulant dependence with other stimulant-induced disorder	
F15.90	Other stimulant use, unspecified, uncomplicated	
F15.920	Other stimulant use, unspecified with intoxication, uncomplicated	
F15.921	Other stimulant use, unspecified with intoxication delirium	
F15.922	Other stimulant use, unspecified with intoxication with perceptual disturbance	
F15.93	Other stimulant use, unspecified with withdrawal	
F15.94	Other stimulant use, unspecified with stimulant-induced mood disorder	
F15.950	Other stimulant use, unspecified with stimulant-induced psychotic disorder with delusions	
F15.951	Other stimulant use, unspecified with stimulant-induced psychotic disorder with hallucinations	
F15.980	Other stimulant use, unspecified with stimulant-induced anxiety disorder	
F15.981	Other stimulant use, unspecified with stimulant-induced sexual dysfunction	
F15.982	Other stimulant use, unspecified with stimulant-induced sleep disorder	
F15.988	Other stimulant use, unspecified with other stimulant-induced disorder	
T43.621A	Poisoning by amphetamines, accidental (unintentional), initial encounter	
T43.622A	Poisoning by amphetamines, intentional self-harm, initial encounter	
T43.623A	Poisoning by amphetamines, assault, initial encounter	
T43.625A	Adverse effect of amphetamines, initial encounter	
Z02.83	Encounter for blood-alcohol and blood-drug test	

Please note that this list of associated ICD-10-CM codes is not all-inclusive. The procedure may be performed for reasons other than those listed that support the medical necessity of the service. Only those conditions supported by the medical record documentation should be reported.

Medicare Edits

	Fac RVU	Non-Fac RVU	FUD	Status	MUE
80359	0.0	0.0	N/A	I	-

	Modifiers				Medicare References
80359	N/A	N/A	N/A	N/A	None

* with documentation

(80360)

80360 Methylphenidate

Explanation

This test may be requested as a qualitative, quantitative, or combination analysis for methylphenidate (Ritalin). This test would be ordered to monitor therapy in patients with attention deficit hyperactivity disorder (ADHD). Methods used for analysis include gas-liquid chromatography (GLC) and gas chromatometry/mass spectrometry (GC/MS). This is a definitive drug test, meaning methods of testing would not be performed by enzymatic or immunoassays.

Coding Tips

This code is a resequenced code and will not display in numeric order. For presumptive drug testing, see the appropriate code from the 80300–80304 code range.

ICD-10-CM contains combination poisoning codes that include not only the poisoning itself and the type of poison involved, but also the associated intent (i.e., accidental, intentional self-harm, assault, and undetermined).

Documentation Tips

Documentation must include the laboratory results to support reporting this service.

Medical record documentation must, at a minimum, include signs and symptoms supporting the ordering of this service.

Reimbursement Tips

Medicare reimburses this service under the laboratory fee schedule.

Terms To Know

qualitative. To determine the nature of the component of substance.

quantitative. To determine the amount and nature of the components of a substance.

ICD-10-CM Diagnostic Codes

F15.10	Other stimulant abuse, uncomplicated
F15.120	Other stimulant abuse with intoxication, uncomplicated
F15.121	Other stimulant abuse with intoxication delirium
F15.122	Other stimulant abuse with intoxication with perceptual disturbance
F15.129	Other stimulant abuse with intoxication, unspecified
F15.14	Other stimulant abuse with stimulant-induced mood disorder
F15.150	Other stimulant abuse with stimulant-induced psychotic disorder with delusions
F15.151	Other stimulant abuse with stimulant-induced psychotic disorder with hallucinations
F15.159	Other stimulant abuse with stimulant-induced psychotic disorder, unspecified
F15.180	Other stimulant abuse with stimulant-induced anxiety disorder
F15.181	Other stimulant abuse with stimulant-induced sexual dysfunction
F15.182	Other stimulant abuse with stimulant-induced sleep disorder
F15.188	Other stimulant abuse with other stimulant-induced disorder
F15.19	Other stimulant abuse with unspecified stimulant-induced disorder
F15.20	Other stimulant dependence, uncomplicated

F15.21	Other stimulant dependence, in remission
F15.220	Other stimulant dependence with intoxication, uncomplicated
F15.221	Other stimulant dependence with intoxication delirium
F15.222	Other stimulant dependence with intoxication with perceptual disturbance
F15.229	Other stimulant dependence with intoxication, unspecified
F15.23	Other stimulant dependence with withdrawal
F15.24	Other stimulant dependence with stimulant-induced mood disorder
F15.250	Other stimulant dependence with stimulant-induced psychotic disorder with delusions
F15.251	Other stimulant dependence with stimulant-induced psychotic disorder with hallucinations
F15.259	Other stimulant dependence with stimulant-induced psychotic disorder, unspecified
F15.280	Other stimulant dependence with stimulant-induced anxiety disorder
F15.281	Other stimulant dependence with stimulant-induced sexual dysfunction
F15.282	Other stimulant dependence with stimulant-induced sleep disorder
F15.288	Other stimulant dependence with other stimulant-induced disorder
F15.29	Other stimulant dependence with unspecified stimulant-induced disorder
F15.90	Other stimulant use, unspecified, uncomplicated
F15.920	Other stimulant use, unspecified with intoxication, uncomplicated
F15.921	Other stimulant use, unspecified with intoxication delirium
F15.922	Other stimulant use, unspecified with intoxication with perceptual disturbance
F15.929	Other stimulant use, unspecified with intoxication, unspecified
F15.93	Other stimulant use, unspecified with withdrawal
F15.94	Other stimulant use, unspecified with stimulant-induced mood disorder
F15.950	Other stimulant use, unspecified with stimulant-induced psychotic disorder with delusions
F15.951	Other stimulant use, unspecified with stimulant-induced psychotic disorder with hallucinations
F15.959	Other stimulant use, unspecified with stimulant-induced psychotic disorder, unspecified
F15.980	Other stimulant use, unspecified with stimulant-induced anxiety disorder
F15.981	Other stimulant use, unspecified with stimulant-induced sexual dysfunction
F15.982	Other stimulant use, unspecified with stimulant-induced sleep disorder
F15.988	Other stimulant use, unspecified with other stimulant-induced disorder
F15.99	Other stimulant use, unspecified with unspecified stimulant-induced disorder
F90.0	Attention-deficit hyperactivity disorder, predominantly inattentive type
F90.1	Attention-deficit hyperactivity disorder, predominantly hyperactive type
F90.2	Attention-deficit hyperactivity disorder, combined type

F90.8	Attention-deficit hyperactivity disorder, other type
F90.9	Attention-deficit hyperactivity disorder, unspecified type
T43.631A	Poisoning by methylphenidate, accidental (unintentional), initial encounter
T43.632A	Poisoning by methylphenidate, intentional self-harm, initial encounter
T43.633A	Poisoning by methylphenidate, assault, initial encounter
T43.634A	Poisoning by methylphenidate, undetermined, initial encounter
T43.635A	Adverse effect of methylphenidate, initial encounter
Z02.83	Encounter for blood-alcohol and blood-drug test

Please note that this list of associated ICD-10-CM codes is not all-inclusive. The procedure may be performed for reasons other than those listed that support the medical necessity of the service. Only those conditions supported by the medical record documentation should be reported.

Medicare Edits

	Fac RVU	Non-Fac RVU	FUD	Status	MUE
80360	0.0	0.0	N/A	I	-

	Modifiers				Medicare References
80360	N/A	N/A	N/A	N/A	None

* with documentation

(80361)

80361   Opiates, 1 or more

Explanation

These tests may be requested as qualitative, quantitative, or combination analyses for opiates and opioids/opiate analogs. These tests measure the amount of a given opiate present and may be ordered to measure toxicity or possible drug abuse of opiates, such as morphine, Percodan, and meperidine (Demerol). These drugs are prescribed for treatment of chronic pain, but recent studies are evaluating the benefits of this type of therapy given the complex side effects and chronic conditions that can be caused by long-term use of these drugs. Methods used for analysis include gas-liquid chromatography (GLC) and gas chromatometry/mass spectrometry (GC/MS). This is a definitive drug test, meaning methods of testing would not be performed by enzymatic or immunoassays. Report 80361 when testing for one or more opiates; 80362 when testing for one to two opioids and/or opiate analogs; 80363 when testing for three to four opioids and/or opiate analogs; and 80364 when testing for five or more opioids and/or opiate analogs.

Coding Tips

This code is a resequenced code and will not display in numeric order. For presumptive drug testing, see the appropriate code from the 80300–80304 code range.

ICD-10-CM contains combination poisoning codes that include not only the poisoning itself and the type of poison involved, but also the associated intent (i.e., accidental, intentional self-harm, assault, and undetermined).

Documentation Tips

Documentation must include the laboratory results to support reporting this service.

Medical record documentation must, at a minimum, include signs and symptoms supporting the ordering of this service.

Reimbursement Tips

Medicare reimburses this service under the laboratory fee schedule.

Terms To Know

qualitative. To determine the nature of the component of substance.
quantitative. To determine the amount and nature of the components of a substance.

ICD-10-CM Diagnostic Codes

F11.10	Opioid abuse, uncomplicated
F11.120	Opioid abuse with intoxication, uncomplicated
F11.121	Opioid abuse with intoxication delirium
F11.122	Opioid abuse with intoxication with perceptual disturbance
F11.14	Opioid abuse with opioid-induced mood disorder
F11.150	Opioid abuse with opioid-induced psychotic disorder with delusions
F11.151	Opioid abuse with opioid-induced psychotic disorder with hallucinations
F11.181	Opioid abuse with opioid-induced sexual dysfunction
F11.182	Opioid abuse with opioid-induced sleep disorder
F11.188	Opioid abuse with other opioid-induced disorder
F11.20	Opioid dependence, uncomplicated
F11.21	Opioid dependence, in remission
F11.220	Opioid dependence with intoxication, uncomplicated
F11.221	Opioid dependence with intoxication delirium
F11.222	Opioid dependence with intoxication with perceptual disturbance
F11.23	Opioid dependence with withdrawal
F11.24	Opioid dependence with opioid-induced mood disorder
F11.250	Opioid dependence with opioid-induced psychotic disorder with delusions
F11.251	Opioid dependence with opioid-induced psychotic disorder with hallucinations
F11.281	Opioid dependence with opioid-induced sexual dysfunction
F11.282	Opioid dependence with opioid-induced sleep disorder
F11.288	Opioid dependence with other opioid-induced disorder
F11.90	Opioid use, unspecified, uncomplicated
F11.920	Opioid use, unspecified with intoxication, uncomplicated
F11.921	Opioid use, unspecified with intoxication delirium
F11.922	Opioid use, unspecified with intoxication with perceptual disturbance
F11.93	Opioid use, unspecified with withdrawal
F11.94	Opioid use, unspecified with opioid-induced mood disorder
F11.950	Opioid use, unspecified with opioid-induced psychotic disorder with delusions
F11.951	Opioid use, unspecified with opioid-induced psychotic disorder with hallucinations
F11.981	Opioid use, unspecified with opioid-induced sexual dysfunction
F11.982	Opioid use, unspecified with opioid-induced sleep disorder
F11.988	Opioid use, unspecified with other opioid-induced disorder
T40.2X1A	Poisoning by other opioids, accidental (unintentional), initial encounter
T40.2X2A	Poisoning by other opioids, intentional self-harm, initial encounter
T40.2X3A	Poisoning by other opioids, assault, initial encounter
T40.2X5A	Adverse effect of other opioids, initial encounter
Z02.83	Encounter for blood-alcohol and blood-drug test

Please note that this list of associated ICD-10-CM codes is not all-inclusive. The procedure may be performed for reasons other than those listed that support the medical necessity of the service. Only those conditions supported by the medical record documentation should be reported.

Medicare Edits

	Fac RVU	Non-Fac RVU	FUD	Status	MUE
80361	0.0	0.0	N/A	I	-

	Modifiers				Medicare References
80361	N/A	N/A	N/A	N/A	None

* with documentation

(80362, 80363, 80364)

80362	Opioids and opiate analogs; 1 or 2
80363	3 or 4
80364	5 or more

Explanation

These tests may be requested as qualitative, quantitative, or combination analyses for opioids/opiate analogs. These tests measure the toxicity or possible drug abuse of opiates, such as morphine, Percodan, and meperidine (Demerol). These drugs are prescribed for treatment of chronic pain, but recent studies are evaluating the benefits of this type of therapy given the complex side effects and chronic conditions that can be caused by long-term use of these drugs. Methods used for analysis include gas-liquid chromatography (GLC) and gas chromatometry/mass spectrometry (GC/MS). This is a definitive drug test, meaning methods of testing would not be performed by enzymatic or immunoassays. Report 80361 when testing for one or more opiates; 80362 when testing for one to two opioids and/or opiate analogs; 80363 when testing for three to four opioids and/or opiate analogs; and 80364 when testing for five or more opioids and/or opiate analogs.

Coding Tips

These codes are resequenced codes and will not display in numeric order. For presumptive drug testing, see the appropriate code from the 80300–80304 code range.

ICD-10-CM contains combination poisoning codes that include not only the poisoning itself and the type of poison involved, but also the associated intent (i.e., accidental, intentional self-harm, assault, and undetermined).

Documentation Tips

Documentation must include the laboratory results to support reporting this service.

Medical record documentation must, at a minimum, include signs and symptoms supporting the ordering of this service.

Reimbursement Tips

Medicare reimburses this service under the laboratory fee schedule.

Terms To Know

qualitative. To determine the nature of the component of substance.

quantitative. To determine the amount and nature of the components of a substance.

ICD-10-CM Diagnostic Codes

F11.10	Opioid abuse, uncomplicated
F11.120	Opioid abuse with intoxication, uncomplicated
F11.121	Opioid abuse with intoxication delirium
F11.122	Opioid abuse with intoxication with perceptual disturbance
F11.14	Opioid abuse with opioid-induced mood disorder
F11.150	Opioid abuse with opioid-induced psychotic disorder with delusions
F11.151	Opioid abuse with opioid-induced psychotic disorder with hallucinations
F11.181	Opioid abuse with opioid-induced sexual dysfunction
F11.182	Opioid abuse with opioid-induced sleep disorder
F11.188	Opioid abuse with other opioid-induced disorder

F11.20	Opioid dependence, uncomplicated
F11.21	Opioid dependence, in remission
F11.220	Opioid dependence with intoxication, uncomplicated
F11.221	Opioid dependence with intoxication delirium
F11.222	Opioid dependence with intoxication with perceptual disturbance
F11.23	Opioid dependence with withdrawal
F11.24	Opioid dependence with opioid-induced mood disorder
F11.250	Opioid dependence with opioid-induced psychotic disorder with delusions
F11.251	Opioid dependence with opioid-induced psychotic disorder with hallucinations
F11.281	Opioid dependence with opioid-induced sexual dysfunction
F11.282	Opioid dependence with opioid-induced sleep disorder
F11.288	Opioid dependence with other opioid-induced disorder
F11.90	Opioid use, unspecified, uncomplicated
F11.920	Opioid use, unspecified with intoxication, uncomplicated
F11.921	Opioid use, unspecified with intoxication delirium
F11.922	Opioid use, unspecified with intoxication with perceptual disturbance
F11.93	Opioid use, unspecified with withdrawal
F11.94	Opioid use, unspecified with opioid-induced mood disorder
F11.950	Opioid use, unspecified with opioid-induced psychotic disorder with delusions
F11.951	Opioid use, unspecified with opioid-induced psychotic disorder with hallucinations
F11.959	Opioid use, unspecified with opioid-induced psychotic disorder, unspecified
F11.981	Opioid use, unspecified with opioid-induced sexual dysfunction
F11.982	Opioid use, unspecified with opioid-induced sleep disorder
F11.988	Opioid use, unspecified with other opioid-induced disorder
T40.2X1A	Poisoning by other opioids, accidental (unintentional), initial encounter
T40.2X2A	Poisoning by other opioids, intentional self-harm, initial encounter
T40.2X3A	Poisoning by other opioids, assault, initial encounter
T40.2X5A	Adverse effect of other opioids, initial encounter
Z02.83	Encounter for blood-alcohol and blood-drug test

Please note that this list of associated ICD-10-CM codes is not all-inclusive. The procedure may be performed for reasons other than those listed that support the medical necessity of the service. Only those conditions supported by the medical record documentation should be reported.

Medicare Edits

	Fac RVU	Non-Fac RVU	FUD	Status	MUE
80362	0.0	0.0	N/A	I	-
80363	0.0	0.0	N/A	I	-
80364	0.0	0.0	N/A	I	-

	Modifiers				Medicare References
80362	N/A	N/A	N/A	N/A	None
80363	N/A	N/A	N/A	N/A	
80364	N/A	N/A	N/A	N/A	

* with documentation

(80365)

80365 Oxycodone

Explanation

This test may be requested as a qualitative, quantitative, or combination analysis of oxycodone and can detect several opiates. Methods used for analysis include gas-liquid chromatography (GLC) and gas chromatometry/mass spectrometry (GC/MS). This is a definitive drug test, meaning methods of testing would not be performed by enzymatic or immunoassays. Specimen can be blood or urine.

Coding Tips

This code is a resequenced code and will not display in numeric order. For presumptive drug testing, see the appropriate code from the 80300–80304 code range.

ICD-10-CM contains combination poisoning codes that include not only the poisoning itself and the type of poison involved, but also the associated intent (i.e., accidental, intentional self-harm, assault, and undetermined).

Documentation Tips

Documentation must include the laboratory results to support reporting this service.

Medical record documentation must, at a minimum, include signs and symptoms supporting the ordering of this service.

Reimbursement Tips

Medicare reimburses this service under the laboratory fee schedule.

Terms To Know

qualitative. To determine the nature of the component of substance.

quantitative. To determine the amount and nature of the components of a substance.

ICD-10-CM Diagnostic Codes

F11.10	Opioid abuse, uncomplicated
F11.120	Opioid abuse with intoxication, uncomplicated
F11.121	Opioid abuse with intoxication delirium
F11.122	Opioid abuse with intoxication with perceptual disturbance
F11.129	Opioid abuse with intoxication, unspecified
F11.14	Opioid abuse with opioid-induced mood disorder
F11.150	Opioid abuse with opioid-induced psychotic disorder with delusions
F11.151	Opioid abuse with opioid-induced psychotic disorder with hallucinations
F11.159	Opioid abuse with opioid-induced psychotic disorder, unspecified
F11.181	Opioid abuse with opioid-induced sexual dysfunction
F11.182	Opioid abuse with opioid-induced sleep disorder
F11.188	Opioid abuse with other opioid-induced disorder
F11.19	Opioid abuse with unspecified opioid-induced disorder
F11.20	Opioid dependence, uncomplicated
F11.21	Opioid dependence, in remission
F11.220	Opioid dependence with intoxication, uncomplicated
F11.221	Opioid dependence with intoxication delirium
F11.222	Opioid dependence with intoxication with perceptual disturbance
F11.229	Opioid dependence with intoxication, unspecified
F11.23	Opioid dependence with withdrawal
F11.24	Opioid dependence with opioid-induced mood disorder
F11.250	Opioid dependence with opioid-induced psychotic disorder with delusions
F11.251	Opioid dependence with opioid-induced psychotic disorder with hallucinations
F11.259	Opioid dependence with opioid-induced psychotic disorder, unspecified
F11.281	Opioid dependence with opioid-induced sexual dysfunction
F11.282	Opioid dependence with opioid-induced sleep disorder
F11.288	Opioid dependence with other opioid-induced disorder
F11.29	Opioid dependence with unspecified opioid-induced disorder
F11.90	Opioid use, unspecified, uncomplicated
F11.920	Opioid use, unspecified with intoxication, uncomplicated
F11.921	Opioid use, unspecified with intoxication delirium
F11.922	Opioid use, unspecified with intoxication with perceptual disturbance
F11.929	Opioid use, unspecified with intoxication, unspecified
F11.93	Opioid use, unspecified with withdrawal
F11.94	Opioid use, unspecified with opioid-induced mood disorder
F11.950	Opioid use, unspecified with opioid-induced psychotic disorder with delusions
F11.951	Opioid use, unspecified with opioid-induced psychotic disorder with hallucinations
F11.959	Opioid use, unspecified with opioid-induced psychotic disorder, unspecified
F11.981	Opioid use, unspecified with opioid-induced sexual dysfunction
F11.982	Opioid use, unspecified with opioid-induced sleep disorder
F11.988	Opioid use, unspecified with other opioid-induced disorder
F11.99	Opioid use, unspecified with unspecified opioid-induced disorder
T40.2X1A	Poisoning by other opioids, accidental (unintentional), initial encounter
T40.2X2A	Poisoning by other opioids, intentional self-harm, initial encounter
T40.2X3A	Poisoning by other opioids, assault, initial encounter
T40.2X4A	Poisoning by other opioids, undetermined, initial encounter
T40.2X5A	Adverse effect of other opioids, initial encounter
Z02.83	Encounter for blood-alcohol and blood-drug test

Please note that this list of associated ICD-10-CM codes is not all-inclusive. The procedure may be performed for reasons other than those listed that support the medical necessity of the service. Only those conditions supported by the medical record documentation should be reported.

Medicare Edits

	Fac RVU	Non-Fac RVU	FUD	Status	MUE
80365	0.0	0.0	N/A	I	-

	Modifiers				Medicare References
80365	N/A	N/A	N/A	N/A	None

* with documentation

(80367)

80367 Propoxyphene

Explanation

This test may be requested as a qualitative, quantitative, or combination analysis of propoxyphene. This is an opiate and was prescribed for pain relief; however, the FDA suggested removal of this drug in 2010 due to toxic effects it can have on the heart. At that time, all products containing propoxyphene were discontinued. Methods used for analysis include gas-liquid chromatography (GLC) and gas chromatometry/mass spectrometry (GC/MS). This is a definitive drug test, meaning methods of testing would not be performed by enzymatic or immunoassays. Specimen is plasma, serum, or urine.

Coding Tips

This code is a resequenced code and will not display in numeric order. For presumptive drug testing, see the appropriate code from the 80300–80304 code range.

ICD-10-CM contains combination poisoning codes that include not only the poisoning itself and the type of poison involved, but also the associated intent (i.e., accidental, intentional self-harm, assault, and undetermined).

Documentation Tips

Documentation must include the laboratory results to support reporting this service.

Medical record documentation must, at a minimum, include signs and symptoms supporting the ordering of this service.

Reimbursement Tips

Medicare reimburses this service under the laboratory fee schedule.

Terms To Know

qualitative. To determine the nature of the component of substance.
quantitative. To determine the amount and nature of the components of a substance.

ICD-10-CM Diagnostic Codes

F11.10	Opioid abuse, uncomplicated
F11.120	Opioid abuse with intoxication, uncomplicated
F11.121	Opioid abuse with intoxication delirium
F11.122	Opioid abuse with intoxication with perceptual disturbance
F11.14	Opioid abuse with opioid-induced mood disorder
F11.150	Opioid abuse with opioid-induced psychotic disorder with delusions
F11.151	Opioid abuse with opioid-induced psychotic disorder with hallucinations
F11.181	Opioid abuse with opioid-induced sexual dysfunction
F11.182	Opioid abuse with opioid-induced sleep disorder
F11.188	Opioid abuse with other opioid-induced disorder
F11.20	Opioid dependence, uncomplicated
F11.21	Opioid dependence, in remission
F11.220	Opioid dependence with intoxication, uncomplicated
F11.221	Opioid dependence with intoxication delirium
F11.222	Opioid dependence with intoxication with perceptual disturbance
F11.23	Opioid dependence with withdrawal
F11.24	Opioid dependence with opioid-induced mood disorder
F11.250	Opioid dependence with opioid-induced psychotic disorder with delusions
F11.251	Opioid dependence with opioid-induced psychotic disorder with hallucinations
F11.281	Opioid dependence with opioid-induced sexual dysfunction
F11.282	Opioid dependence with opioid-induced sleep disorder
F11.288	Opioid dependence with other opioid-induced disorder
F11.29	Opioid dependence with unspecified opioid-induced disorder
F11.90	Opioid use, unspecified, uncomplicated
F11.920	Opioid use, unspecified with intoxication, uncomplicated
F11.921	Opioid use, unspecified with intoxication delirium
F11.922	Opioid use, unspecified with intoxication with perceptual disturbance
F11.929	Opioid use, unspecified with intoxication, unspecified
T40.2X1A	Poisoning by other opioids, accidental (unintentional), initial encounter
T40.2X2A	Poisoning by other opioids, intentional self-harm, initial encounter
T40.2X3A	Poisoning by other opioids, assault, initial encounter
T40.2X5A	Adverse effect of other opioids, initial encounter
T40.4X1A	Poisoning by other synthetic narcotics, accidental (unintentional), initial encounter
T40.4X2A	Poisoning by other synthetic narcotics, intentional self-harm, initial encounter
T40.4X3A	Poisoning by other synthetic narcotics, assault, initial encounter
T40.4X5A	Adverse effect of other synthetic narcotics, initial encounter
T40.4X6A	Underdosing of other synthetic narcotics, initial encounter
T40.601A	Poisoning by unspecified narcotics, accidental (unintentional), initial encounter
T40.602A	Poisoning by unspecified narcotics, intentional self-harm, initial encounter
T40.603A	Poisoning by unspecified narcotics, assault, initial encounter
T40.605A	Adverse effect of unspecified narcotics, initial encounter
T40.606A	Underdosing of unspecified narcotics, initial encounter
Z02.83	Encounter for blood-alcohol and blood-drug test

Please note that this list of associated ICD-10-CM codes is not all-inclusive. The procedure may be performed for reasons other than those listed that support the medical necessity of the service. Only those conditions supported by the medical record documentation should be reported.

Medicare Edits

	Fac RVU	Non-Fac RVU	FUD	Status	MUE
80367	0.0	0.0	N/A	I	-

	Modifiers				Medicare References
80367	N/A	N/A	N/A	N/A	None

* with documentation

(80368)

80368 Sedative hypnotics (non-benzodiazepines)

Explanation

This test may be requested as a qualitative, quantitative, or combination analysis for sedative hypnotics, specifically non-benzodiazepines. This classification of drugs includes eszopiclone, zaleplon, and zolpidem. These drugs are typically used to treat insomnia. The effect allows the patient to fall asleep faster and promotes continued and/or extended sleep cycles. These drugs have a shorter half-life than other sedatives reducing risk of dependence but suggested use is for one to four weeks only.

Coding Tips

This code is a resequenced code and will not display in numeric order. For presumptive drug testing, see the appropriate code from the 80300–80304 code range.

ICD-10-CM contains combination poisoning codes that include not only the poisoning itself and the type of poison involved, but also the associated intent (i.e., accidental, intentional self-harm, assault, and undetermined).

Documentation Tips

Documentation must include the laboratory results to support reporting this service.

Medical record documentation must, at a minimum, include signs and symptoms supporting the ordering of this service.

Reimbursement Tips

Medicare reimburses this service under the laboratory fee schedule.

Terms To Know

qualitative. To determine the nature of the component of substance.

quantitative. To determine the amount and nature of the components of a substance.

ICD-10-CM Diagnostic Codes

F13.10	Sedative, hypnotic or anxiolytic abuse, uncomplicated
F13.120	Sedative, hypnotic or anxiolytic abuse with intoxication, uncomplicated
F13.121	Sedative, hypnotic or anxiolytic abuse with intoxication delirium
F13.129	Sedative, hypnotic or anxiolytic abuse with intoxication, unspecified
F13.14	Sedative, hypnotic or anxiolytic abuse with sedative, hypnotic or anxiolytic-induced mood disorder
F13.150	Sedative, hypnotic or anxiolytic abuse with sedative, hypnotic or anxiolytic-induced psychotic disorder with delusions
F13.151	Sedative, hypnotic or anxiolytic abuse with sedative, hypnotic or anxiolytic-induced psychotic disorder with hallucinations
F13.159	Sedative, hypnotic or anxiolytic abuse with sedative, hypnotic or anxiolytic-induced psychotic disorder, unspecified
F13.180	Sedative, hypnotic or anxiolytic abuse with sedative, hypnotic or anxiolytic-induced anxiety disorder
F13.181	Sedative, hypnotic or anxiolytic abuse with sedative, hypnotic or anxiolytic-induced sexual dysfunction
F13.182	Sedative, hypnotic or anxiolytic abuse with sedative, hypnotic or anxiolytic-induced sleep disorder

F13.188	Sedative, hypnotic or anxiolytic abuse with other sedative, hypnotic or anxiolytic-induced disorder
F13.19	Sedative, hypnotic or anxiolytic abuse with unspecified sedative, hypnotic or anxiolytic-induced disorder
F13.20	Sedative, hypnotic or anxiolytic dependence, uncomplicated
F13.21	Sedative, hypnotic or anxiolytic dependence, in remission
F13.220	Sedative, hypnotic or anxiolytic dependence with intoxication, uncomplicated
F13.221	Sedative, hypnotic or anxiolytic dependence with intoxication delirium
F13.229	Sedative, hypnotic or anxiolytic dependence with intoxication, unspecified
F13.230	Sedative, hypnotic or anxiolytic dependence with withdrawal, uncomplicated
F13.231	Sedative, hypnotic or anxiolytic dependence with withdrawal delirium
F13.232	Sedative, hypnotic or anxiolytic dependence with withdrawal with perceptual disturbance
F13.239	Sedative, hypnotic or anxiolytic dependence with withdrawal, unspecified
F13.24	Sedative, hypnotic or anxiolytic dependence with sedative, hypnotic or anxiolytic-induced mood disorder
F13.250	Sedative, hypnotic or anxiolytic dependence with sedative, hypnotic or anxiolytic-induced psychotic disorder with delusions
F13.251	Sedative, hypnotic or anxiolytic dependence with sedative, hypnotic or anxiolytic-induced psychotic disorder with hallucinations
F13.259	Sedative, hypnotic or anxiolytic dependence with sedative, hypnotic or anxiolytic-induced psychotic disorder, unspecified
F13.26	Sedative, hypnotic or anxiolytic dependence with sedative, hypnotic or anxiolytic-induced persisting amnestic disorder
F13.27	Sedative, hypnotic or anxiolytic dependence with sedative, hypnotic or anxiolytic-induced persisting dementia
F13.280	Sedative, hypnotic or anxiolytic dependence with sedative, hypnotic or anxiolytic-induced anxiety disorder
F13.281	Sedative, hypnotic or anxiolytic dependence with sedative, hypnotic or anxiolytic-induced sexual dysfunction
F13.282	Sedative, hypnotic or anxiolytic dependence with sedative, hypnotic or anxiolytic-induced sleep disorder
F13.288	Sedative, hypnotic or anxiolytic dependence with other sedative, hypnotic or anxiolytic-induced disorder
F13.29	Sedative, hypnotic or anxiolytic dependence with unspecified sedative, hypnotic or anxiolytic-induced disorder
F13.90	Sedative, hypnotic, or anxiolytic use, unspecified, uncomplicated
F13.920	Sedative, hypnotic or anxiolytic use, unspecified with intoxication, uncomplicated
F13.921	Sedative, hypnotic or anxiolytic use, unspecified with intoxication delirium
F13.929	Sedative, hypnotic or anxiolytic use, unspecified with intoxication, unspecified
F13.930	Sedative, hypnotic or anxiolytic use, unspecified with withdrawal, uncomplicated
F13.931	Sedative, hypnotic or anxiolytic use, unspecified with withdrawal delirium
F13.932	Sedative, hypnotic or anxiolytic use, unspecified with withdrawal with perceptual disturbances

F13.939	Sedative, hypnotic or anxiolytic use, unspecified with withdrawal, unspecified
F13.94	Sedative, hypnotic or anxiolytic use, unspecified with sedative, hypnotic or anxiolytic-induced mood disorder
F13.950	Sedative, hypnotic or anxiolytic use, unspecified with sedative, hypnotic or anxiolytic-induced psychotic disorder with delusions
F13.951	Sedative, hypnotic or anxiolytic use, unspecified with sedative, hypnotic or anxiolytic-induced psychotic disorder with hallucinations
F13.959	Sedative, hypnotic or anxiolytic use, unspecified with sedative, hypnotic or anxiolytic-induced psychotic disorder, unspecified
F13.96	Sedative, hypnotic or anxiolytic use, unspecified with sedative, hypnotic or anxiolytic-induced persisting amnestic disorder
F13.97	Sedative, hypnotic or anxiolytic use, unspecified with sedative, hypnotic or anxiolytic-induced persisting dementia
F13.980	Sedative, hypnotic or anxiolytic use, unspecified with sedative, hypnotic or anxiolytic-induced anxiety disorder
F13.981	Sedative, hypnotic or anxiolytic use, unspecified with sedative, hypnotic or anxiolytic-induced sexual dysfunction
F13.982	Sedative, hypnotic or anxiolytic use, unspecified with sedative, hypnotic or anxiolytic-induced sleep disorder
F13.988	Sedative, hypnotic or anxiolytic use, unspecified with other sedative, hypnotic or anxiolytic-induced disorder
F13.99	Sedative, hypnotic or anxiolytic use, unspecified with unspecified sedative, hypnotic or anxiolytic-induced disorder
T42.6X1A	Poisoning by other antiepileptic and sedative-hypnotic drugs, accidental (unintentional), initial encounter
T42.6X2A	Poisoning by other antiepileptic and sedative-hypnotic drugs, intentional self-harm, initial encounter
T42.6X3A	Poisoning by other antiepileptic and sedative-hypnotic drugs, assault, initial encounter
T42.6X4A	Poisoning by other antiepileptic and sedative-hypnotic drugs, undetermined, initial encounter
T42.6X5A	Adverse effect of other antiepileptic and sedative-hypnotic drugs, initial encounter
Z02.83	Encounter for blood-alcohol and blood-drug test

Please note that this list of associated ICD-10-CM codes is not all-inclusive. The procedure may be performed for reasons other than those listed that support the medical necessity of the service. Only those conditions supported by the medical record documentation should be reported.

Medicare Edits

	Fac RVU	Non-Fac RVU	FUD	Status	MUE
80368	0.0	0.0	N/A	I	-

	Modifiers				Medicare References
80368	N/A	N/A	N/A	N/A	None

* with documentation

(80371)

80371	Stimulants, synthetic

Explanation

There are a number of drugs classified as synthetic stimulants (e.g., methylenedioxypyrovalerone). These stimulants, such as bath salts, may be obtained by prescription or through illicit drug use and many consider these designer drugs. A chemical stimulant affects the central nervous system resulting in increased heart rate and altered realistic thinking. Methods used for analysis include gas-liquid chromatography (GLC) and gas chromatometry/mass spectrometry (GC/MS). This is a definitive drug test, meaning methods of testing would not be performed by enzymatic or immunoassays. Specimen is urine.

Coding Tips

This code is a resequenced code and will not display in numeric order. For presumptive drug testing, see the appropriate code from the 80300–80304 code range.

ICD-10-CM contains combination poisoning codes that include not only the poisoning itself and the type of poison involved, but also the associated intent (i.e., accidental, intentional self-harm, assault, and undetermined).

Documentation Tips

Documentation must include the laboratory results to support reporting this service.

Medical record documentation must, at a minimum, include signs and symptoms supporting the ordering of this service.

Reimbursement Tips

Medicare reimburses this service under the laboratory fee schedule.

Terms To Know

qualitative. To determine the nature of the component of substance.
quantitative. To determine the amount and nature of the components of a substance.

ICD-10-CM Diagnostic Codes

F15.10	Other stimulant abuse, uncomplicated
F15.120	Other stimulant abuse with intoxication, uncomplicated
F15.121	Other stimulant abuse with intoxication delirium
F15.122	Other stimulant abuse with intoxication with perceptual disturbance
F15.129	Other stimulant abuse with intoxication, unspecified
F15.14	Other stimulant abuse with stimulant-induced mood disorder
F15.150	Other stimulant abuse with stimulant-induced psychotic disorder with delusions
F15.151	Other stimulant abuse with stimulant-induced psychotic disorder with hallucinations
F15.159	Other stimulant abuse with stimulant-induced psychotic disorder, unspecified
F15.180	Other stimulant abuse with stimulant-induced anxiety disorder
F15.181	Other stimulant abuse with stimulant-induced sexual dysfunction
F15.182	Other stimulant abuse with stimulant-induced sleep disorder
F15.188	Other stimulant abuse with other stimulant-induced disorder

F15.19	Other stimulant abuse with unspecified stimulant-induced disorder
F15.20	Other stimulant dependence, uncomplicated
F15.220	Other stimulant dependence with intoxication, uncomplicated
F15.221	Other stimulant dependence with intoxication delirium
F15.222	Other stimulant dependence with intoxication with perceptual disturbance
F15.229	Other stimulant dependence with intoxication, unspecified
F15.23	Other stimulant dependence with withdrawal
F15.24	Other stimulant dependence with stimulant-induced mood disorder
F15.250	Other stimulant dependence with stimulant-induced psychotic disorder with delusions
F15.251	Other stimulant dependence with stimulant-induced psychotic disorder with hallucinations
F15.259	Other stimulant dependence with stimulant-induced psychotic disorder, unspecified
F15.280	Other stimulant dependence with stimulant-induced anxiety disorder
F15.281	Other stimulant dependence with stimulant-induced sexual dysfunction
F15.288	Other stimulant dependence with other stimulant-induced disorder
F15.29	Other stimulant dependence with unspecified stimulant-induced disorder
F15.90	Other stimulant use, unspecified, uncomplicated
F15.920	Other stimulant use, unspecified with intoxication, uncomplicated
F15.921	Other stimulant use, unspecified with intoxication delirium
F15.922	Other stimulant use, unspecified with intoxication with perceptual disturbance
F15.929	Other stimulant use, unspecified with intoxication, unspecified
F15.93	Other stimulant use, unspecified with withdrawal
F15.94	Other stimulant use, unspecified with stimulant-induced mood disorder
F15.950	Other stimulant use, unspecified with stimulant-induced psychotic disorder with delusions
F15.951	Other stimulant use, unspecified with stimulant-induced psychotic disorder with hallucinations
F15.959	Other stimulant use, unspecified with stimulant-induced psychotic disorder, unspecified
F15.980	Other stimulant use, unspecified with stimulant-induced anxiety disorder
F15.981	Other stimulant use, unspecified with stimulant-induced sexual dysfunction
F15.982	Other stimulant use, unspecified with stimulant-induced sleep disorder
F15.988	Other stimulant use, unspecified with other stimulant-induced disorder
F15.99	Other stimulant use, unspecified with unspecified stimulant-induced disorder
T43.601A	Poisoning by unspecified psychostimulants, accidental (unintentional), initial encounter
T43.602A	Poisoning by unspecified psychostimulants, intentional self-harm, initial encounter

T43.603A	Poisoning by unspecified psychostimulants, assault, initial encounter
T43.604A	Poisoning by unspecified psychostimulants, undetermined, initial encounter
T43.605A	Adverse effect of unspecified psychostimulants, initial encounter
T43.606A	Underdosing of unspecified psychostimulants, initial encounter
T50.991A	Poisoning by other drugs, medicaments and biological substances, accidental (unintentional), initial encounter
T50.992A	Poisoning by other drugs, medicaments and biological substances, intentional self-harm, initial encounter
T50.993A	Poisoning by other drugs, medicaments and biological substances, assault, initial encounter
T50.994A	Poisoning by other drugs, medicaments and biological substances, undetermined, initial encounter
T50.995A	Adverse effect of other drugs, medicaments and biological substances, initial encounter
Z02.83	Encounter for blood-alcohol and blood-drug test

Please note that this list of associated ICD-10-CM codes is not all-inclusive. The procedure may be performed for reasons other than those listed that support the medical necessity of the service. Only those conditions supported by the medical record documentation should be reported.

Medicare Edits

	Fac RVU	Non-Fac RVU	FUD	Status	MUE
80371	0.0	0.0	N/A	I	-

	Modifiers				Medicare References
80371	N/A	N/A	N/A	N/A	None

* with documentation

(80372)

80372   Tapentadol

Explanation

This test may be requested as a qualitative, quantitative, or combination analysis for tapentadol. This drug is an opioid-based analgesic prescribed for pain, most often for patients experiencing pain due to diabetic peripheral neuropathy. The half-life is about four hours. Similar to other opioid-based analgesics, this drug can be highly addictive. Methods used for analysis include gas-liquid chromatography (GLC) and gas chromatometry/mass spectrometry (GC/MS). This is a definitive drug test, meaning methods of testing would not be performed by enzymatic or immunoassays.

Coding Tips

This code is a resequenced code and will not display in numeric order. For presumptive drug testing, see the appropriate code from the 80300–80304 code range.

ICD-10-CM contains combination poisoning codes that include not only the poisoning itself and the type of poison involved, but also the associated intent (i.e., accidental, intentional self-harm, assault, and undetermined).

Documentation Tips

Documentation must include the laboratory results to support reporting this service.

Medical record documentation must, at a minimum, include signs and symptoms supporting the ordering of this service.

Reimbursement Tips

Medicare reimburses this service under the laboratory fee schedule.

Terms To Know

qualitative. To determine the nature of the component of substance.

quantitative. To determine the amount and nature of the components of a substance.

ICD-10-CM Diagnostic Codes

E09.40	Drug or chemical induced diabetes mellitus with neurological complications with diabetic neuropathy, unspecified
E09.41	Drug or chemical induced diabetes mellitus with neurological complications with diabetic mononeuropathy
E09.42	Drug or chemical induced diabetes mellitus with neurological complications with diabetic polyneuropathy
E09.43	Drug or chemical induced diabetes mellitus with neurological complications with diabetic autonomic (poly)neuropathy
E09.44	Drug or chemical induced diabetes mellitus with neurological complications with diabetic amyotrophy
E09.49	Drug or chemical induced diabetes mellitus with neurological complications with other diabetic neurological complication
E10.40	Type 1 diabetes mellitus with diabetic neuropathy, unspecified
E10.41	Type 1 diabetes mellitus with diabetic mononeuropathy
E10.42	Type 1 diabetes mellitus with diabetic polyneuropathy
E10.43	Type 1 diabetes mellitus with diabetic autonomic (poly)neuropathy
E10.44	Type 1 diabetes mellitus with diabetic amyotrophy
E10.49	Type 1 diabetes mellitus with other diabetic neurological complication
E11.40	Type 2 diabetes mellitus with diabetic neuropathy, unspecified
E11.41	Type 2 diabetes mellitus with diabetic mononeuropathy
E11.42	Type 2 diabetes mellitus with diabetic polyneuropathy
E11.43	Type 2 diabetes mellitus with diabetic autonomic (poly)neuropathy
E11.44	Type 2 diabetes mellitus with diabetic amyotrophy
E11.49	Type 2 diabetes mellitus with other diabetic neurological complication
F11.10	Opioid abuse, uncomplicated
F11.120	Opioid abuse with intoxication, uncomplicated
F11.121	Opioid abuse with intoxication delirium
F11.122	Opioid abuse with intoxication with perceptual disturbance
F11.129	Opioid abuse with intoxication, unspecified
F11.14	Opioid abuse with opioid-induced mood disorder
F11.150	Opioid abuse with opioid-induced psychotic disorder with delusions
F11.151	Opioid abuse with opioid-induced psychotic disorder with hallucinations
F11.159	Opioid abuse with opioid-induced psychotic disorder, unspecified
F11.181	Opioid abuse with opioid-induced sexual dysfunction
F11.182	Opioid abuse with opioid-induced sleep disorder
F11.188	Opioid abuse with other opioid-induced disorder
F11.19	Opioid abuse with unspecified opioid-induced disorder
F11.20	Opioid dependence, uncomplicated
F11.21	Opioid dependence, in remission
F11.220	Opioid dependence with intoxication, uncomplicated
F11.221	Opioid dependence with intoxication delirium
F11.222	Opioid dependence with intoxication with perceptual disturbance
F11.229	Opioid dependence with intoxication, unspecified
F11.23	Opioid dependence with withdrawal
F11.24	Opioid dependence with opioid-induced mood disorder
F11.250	Opioid dependence with opioid-induced psychotic disorder with delusions
F11.251	Opioid dependence with opioid-induced psychotic disorder with hallucinations
F11.259	Opioid dependence with opioid-induced psychotic disorder, unspecified
F11.281	Opioid dependence with opioid-induced sexual dysfunction
F11.282	Opioid dependence with opioid-induced sleep disorder
F11.288	Opioid dependence with other opioid-induced disorder
F11.29	Opioid dependence with unspecified opioid-induced disorder
F11.90	Opioid use, unspecified, uncomplicated
F11.920	Opioid use, unspecified with intoxication, uncomplicated
F11.921	Opioid use, unspecified with intoxication delirium
F11.922	Opioid use, unspecified with intoxication with perceptual disturbance
F11.929	Opioid use, unspecified with intoxication, unspecified
F11.93	Opioid use, unspecified with withdrawal
F11.94	Opioid use, unspecified with opioid-induced mood disorder
F11.950	Opioid use, unspecified with opioid-induced psychotic disorder with delusions
F11.951	Opioid use, unspecified with opioid-induced psychotic disorder with hallucinations

F11.959	Opioid use, unspecified with opioid-induced psychotic disorder, unspecified
F11.981	Opioid use, unspecified with opioid-induced sexual dysfunction
F11.982	Opioid use, unspecified with opioid-induced sleep disorder
F11.988	Opioid use, unspecified with other opioid-induced disorder
F11.99	Opioid use, unspecified with unspecified opioid-induced disorder
T40.2X1A	Poisoning by other opioids, accidental (unintentional), initial encounter
T40.2X2A	Poisoning by other opioids, intentional self-harm, initial encounter
T40.2X3A	Poisoning by other opioids, assault, initial encounter
T40.2X4A	Poisoning by other opioids, undetermined, initial encounter
T40.2X5A	Adverse effect of other opioids, initial encounter
Z02.83	Encounter for blood-alcohol and blood-drug test

Please note that this list of associated ICD-10-CM codes is not all-inclusive. The procedure may be performed for reasons other than those listed that support the medical necessity of the service. Only those conditions supported by the medical record documentation should be reported.

Medicare Edits

	Fac RVU	Non-Fac RVU	FUD	Status	MUE
80372	0.0	0.0	N/A	I	-

	Modifiers				Medicare References
80372	N/A	N/A	N/A	N/A	None

* with documentation

(80373)

80373   Tramadol

Explanation

This test may be requested as a qualitative, quantitative, or combination analysis for tramadol. This drug is an opioid-based analgesic prescribed for pain. The half-life is about seven hours. Similar to other opioid-based analgesics, this drug can be highly addictive. Methods used for analysis include gas-liquid chromatography (GLC) and gas chromatometry/mass spectrometry (GC/MS). This is a definitive drug test, meaning methods of testing would not be performed by enzymatic or immunoassays.

Coding Tips

This code is a resequenced code and will not display in numeric order. For presumptive drug testing, see the appropriate code from the 80300–80304 code range.

ICD-10-CM contains combination poisoning codes that include not only the poisoning itself and the type of poison involved, but also the associated intent (i.e., accidental, intentional self-harm, assault, and undetermined).

Documentation Tips

Documentation must include the laboratory results to support reporting this service.

Medical record documentation must, at a minimum, include signs and symptoms supporting the ordering of this service.

Reimbursement Tips

Medicare reimburses this service under the laboratory fee schedule.

ICD-10-CM Diagnostic Codes

F11.10	Opioid abuse, uncomplicated
F11.120	Opioid abuse with intoxication, uncomplicated
F11.121	Opioid abuse with intoxication delirium
F11.122	Opioid abuse with intoxication with perceptual disturbance
F11.129	Opioid abuse with intoxication, unspecified
F11.14	Opioid abuse with opioid-induced mood disorder
F11.150	Opioid abuse with opioid-induced psychotic disorder with delusions
F11.151	Opioid abuse with opioid-induced psychotic disorder with hallucinations
F11.159	Opioid abuse with opioid-induced psychotic disorder, unspecified
F11.181	Opioid abuse with opioid-induced sexual dysfunction
F11.182	Opioid abuse with opioid-induced sleep disorder
F11.188	Opioid abuse with other opioid-induced disorder
F11.19	Opioid abuse with unspecified opioid-induced disorder
F11.20	Opioid dependence, uncomplicated
F11.21	Opioid dependence, in remission
F11.220	Opioid dependence with intoxication, uncomplicated
F11.221	Opioid dependence with intoxication delirium
F11.222	Opioid dependence with intoxication with perceptual disturbance
F11.229	Opioid dependence with intoxication, unspecified
F11.23	Opioid dependence with withdrawal
F11.24	Opioid dependence with opioid-induced mood disorder

F11.250	Opioid dependence with opioid-induced psychotic disorder with delusions
F11.251	Opioid dependence with opioid-induced psychotic disorder with hallucinations
F11.259	Opioid dependence with opioid-induced psychotic disorder, unspecified
F11.281	Opioid dependence with opioid-induced sexual dysfunction
F11.282	Opioid dependence with opioid-induced sleep disorder
F11.288	Opioid dependence with other opioid-induced disorder
F11.29	Opioid dependence with unspecified opioid-induced disorder
F11.90	Opioid use, unspecified, uncomplicated
F11.920	Opioid use, unspecified with intoxication, uncomplicated
F11.921	Opioid use, unspecified with intoxication delirium
F11.922	Opioid use, unspecified with intoxication with perceptual disturbance
F11.929	Opioid use, unspecified with intoxication, unspecified
F11.93	Opioid use, unspecified with withdrawal
F11.94	Opioid use, unspecified with opioid-induced mood disorder
F11.950	Opioid use, unspecified with opioid-induced psychotic disorder with delusions
F11.951	Opioid use, unspecified with opioid-induced psychotic disorder with hallucinations
F11.959	Opioid use, unspecified with opioid-induced psychotic disorder, unspecified
F11.981	Opioid use, unspecified with opioid-induced sexual dysfunction
F11.982	Opioid use, unspecified with opioid-induced sleep disorder
F11.988	Opioid use, unspecified with other opioid-induced disorder
F11.99	Opioid use, unspecified with unspecified opioid-induced disorder
T40.2X1A	Poisoning by other opioids, accidental (unintentional), initial encounter
T40.2X2A	Poisoning by other opioids, intentional self-harm, initial encounter
T40.2X3A	Poisoning by other opioids, assault, initial encounter
T40.2X4A	Poisoning by other opioids, undetermined, initial encounter
T40.2X5A	Adverse effect of other opioids, initial encounter
Z02.83	Encounter for blood-alcohol and blood-drug test

Please note that this list of associated ICD-10-CM codes is not all-inclusive. The procedure may be performed for reasons other than those listed that support the medical necessity of the service. Only those conditions supported by the medical record documentation should be reported.

Medicare Edits

	Fac RVU	Non-Fac RVU	FUD	Status	MUE
80373	0.0	0.0	N/A	I	-

	Modifiers				Medicare References
80373	N/A	N/A	N/A	N/A	None

* with documentation

(80375, 80376, 80377)

80375	Drug(s) or substance(s), definitive, qualitative or quantitative, not otherwise specified; 1-3
80376	4-6
80377	7 or more

Explanation

These tests may be requested as drug screen confirmation. They are performed when the initial drug screen is positive. Confirmatory tests must be sensitive and specific and involve a different technique than the initial screen. Methods used for analysis include gas-liquid chromatography (GLC) and gas chromatometry/mass spectrometry (GC/MS). This is a definitive drug test, meaning methods of testing would not be performed by enzymatic or immunoassays. Report 80375 for one to three analytes; 80376 for four to six analytes; and 80377 for seven or more analytes.

Coding Tips

These codes are resequenced codes and will not display in numeric order. For presumptive drug testing, see the appropriate code from the 80300–80304 code range.

ICD-10-CM contains combination poisoning codes that include not only the poisoning itself and the type of poison involved, but also the associated intent (i.e., accidental, intentional self-harm, assault, and undetermined).

Documentation Tips

Documentation must include the laboratory results to support reporting this service.

Medical record documentation must, at a minimum, include signs and symptoms supporting the ordering of this service.

Reimbursement Tips

Medicare reimburses this service under the laboratory fee schedule.

ICD-10-CM Diagnostic Codes

The application of this code is too broad to adequately present ICD-10-CM diagnostic code links here. Refer to your ICD-10-CM book.

Medicare Edits

	Fac RVU	Non-Fac RVU	FUD	Status	MUE
80375	0.0	0.0	N/A	I	-
80376	0.0	0.0	N/A	I	-
80377	0.0	0.0	N/A	I	-

	Modifiers				Medicare References
80375	N/A	N/A	N/A	N/A	None
80376	N/A	N/A	N/A	N/A	
80377	N/A	N/A	N/A	N/A	

* with documentation

82075

82075   Alcohol (ethanol), breath

Explanation

This test may be used primarily in screening for ethanol levels above the legal limit for driving. The legal limit varies from state to state with levels above 0.08-0.1 g/dL usually being defined as legally intoxicated.

Coding Tips

If a specimen is transported to an outside laboratory, report code 99000 for handling or conveyance. For an alcohol test, any specimen except breath, see code 80320. To report alcohol biomarkers, see codes 80321–80322.

Personal history of alcohol dependence is reported as alcohol dependence in remission.

ICD-10-CM contains combination poisoning codes that include not only the poisoning itself and the type of poison involved, but also the associated intent (i.e., accidental, intentional self-harm, assault, and undetermined).

Documentation Tips

Documentation must include the laboratory results to support reporting this service.

Medical record documentation must, at a minimum, include signs and symptoms supporting the ordering of this service.

Reimbursement Tips

Medicare reimburses this service under the laboratory fee schedule.

ICD-10-CM Diagnostic Codes

F10.10	Alcohol abuse, uncomplicated
F10.120	Alcohol abuse with intoxication, uncomplicated
F10.121	Alcohol abuse with intoxication delirium
F10.14	Alcohol abuse with alcohol-induced mood disorder
F10.150	Alcohol abuse with alcohol-induced psychotic disorder with delusions
F10.151	Alcohol abuse with alcohol-induced psychotic disorder with hallucinations
F10.180	Alcohol abuse with alcohol-induced anxiety disorder
F10.181	Alcohol abuse with alcohol-induced sexual dysfunction
F10.182	Alcohol abuse with alcohol-induced sleep disorder
F10.188	Alcohol abuse with other alcohol-induced disorder
F10.20	Alcohol dependence, uncomplicated
F10.21	Alcohol dependence, in remission
F10.220	Alcohol dependence with intoxication, uncomplicated
F10.221	Alcohol dependence with intoxication delirium
F10.230	Alcohol dependence with withdrawal, uncomplicated
F10.231	Alcohol dependence with withdrawal delirium
F10.232	Alcohol dependence with withdrawal with perceptual disturbance
F10.24	Alcohol dependence with alcohol-induced mood disorder
F10.250	Alcohol dependence with alcohol-induced psychotic disorder with delusions
F10.251	Alcohol dependence with alcohol-induced psychotic disorder with hallucinations

F10.26	Alcohol dependence with alcohol-induced persisting amnestic disorder
F10.27	Alcohol dependence with alcohol-induced persisting dementia
F10.280	Alcohol dependence with alcohol-induced anxiety disorder
F10.281	Alcohol dependence with alcohol-induced sexual dysfunction
F10.282	Alcohol dependence with alcohol-induced sleep disorder
F10.288	Alcohol dependence with other alcohol-induced disorder
F28	Other psychotic disorder not due to a substance or known physiological condition
F29	Unspecified psychosis not due to a substance or known physiological condition
K70.2	Alcoholic fibrosis and sclerosis of liver
K70.30	Alcoholic cirrhosis of liver without ascites
K70.31	Alcoholic cirrhosis of liver with ascites
T51.0X1A	Toxic effect of ethanol, accidental (unintentional), initial encounter
T51.0X2A	Toxic effect of ethanol, intentional self-harm, initial encounter
T51.0X3A	Toxic effect of ethanol, assault, initial encounter
T51.0X4A	Toxic effect of ethanol, undetermined, initial encounter
Z01.812	Encounter for preprocedural laboratory examination

Please note that this list of associated ICD-10-CM codes is not all-inclusive. The procedure may be performed for reasons other than those listed that support the medical necessity of the service. Only those conditions supported by the medical record documentation should be reported.

Medicare Edits

	Fac RVU	Non-Fac RVU	FUD	Status	MUE
82075	0.0	0.0	N/A	X	2(3)

	Modifiers				Medicare References
82075	N/A	N/A	N/A	N/A	None

* with documentation

(83992)

83992   Phencyclidine (PCP)

Explanation

This test is performed to evaluate the presence of phencyclidine (also known as PCP, or angel dust), an illegal street drug. Methodology may include immunoassay, thin-layer chromatography (TLC), gas chromatography (GC), and gas chromatography/mass spectrometry (GC/TC), which quantifies the amount of drug.

Coding Tips

Code 83992 is a resequenced code and will not display in numeric order. Definitive drug testing may be quantitative, qualitative, or a combination of both.

ICD-10-CM contains combination poisoning codes that include not only the poisoning itself and the type of poison involved, but also the associated intent (i.e., accidental, intentional self-harm, assault, and undetermined).

Documentation Tips

Documentation must include the laboratory results to support reporting this service.

Medical record documentation must, at a minimum, include signs and symptoms supporting the ordering of this service.

Reimbursement Tips

Medicare reimburses this service under the laboratory fee schedule.

Terms To Know

assay. Test of purity.

CLIA. Clinical Laboratory Improvement Amendments. Requirements set in 1988, CLIA imposes varying levels of federal regulations on clinical procedures. Few laboratories, including those in physician offices, are exempt. Adopted by Medicare and Medicaid, CLIA regulations redefine laboratory testing in regard to laboratory certification and accreditation, proficiency testing, quality assurance, personnel standards, and program administration.

qualitative. To determine the nature of the component of substance.

quantitative. To determine the amount and nature of the components of a substance.

ICD-10-CM Diagnostic Codes

F16.10	Hallucinogen abuse, uncomplicated
F16.120	Hallucinogen abuse with intoxication, uncomplicated
F16.121	Hallucinogen abuse with intoxication with delirium
F16.122	Hallucinogen abuse with intoxication with perceptual disturbance
F16.129	Hallucinogen abuse with intoxication, unspecified
F16.14	Hallucinogen abuse with hallucinogen-induced mood disorder
F16.150	Hallucinogen abuse with hallucinogen-induced psychotic disorder with delusions
F16.151	Hallucinogen abuse with hallucinogen-induced psychotic disorder with hallucinations
F16.159	Hallucinogen abuse with hallucinogen-induced psychotic disorder, unspecified
F16.180	Hallucinogen abuse with hallucinogen-induced anxiety disorder
F16.183	Hallucinogen abuse with hallucinogen persisting perception disorder (flashbacks)
F16.188	Hallucinogen abuse with other hallucinogen-induced disorder
F16.19	Hallucinogen abuse with unspecified hallucinogen-induced disorder
T40.991A	Poisoning by other psychodysleptics [hallucinogens], accidental (unintentional), initial encounter
T40.992A	Poisoning by other psychodysleptics [hallucinogens], intentional self-harm, initial encounter
T40.993A	Poisoning by other psychodysleptics [hallucinogens], assault, initial encounter
T40.994A	Poisoning by other psychodysleptics [hallucinogens], undetermined, initial encounter
Z02.83	Encounter for blood-alcohol and blood-drug test

Please note that this list of associated ICD-10-CM codes is not all-inclusive. The procedure may be performed for reasons other than those listed that support the medical necessity of the service. Only those conditions supported by the medical record documentation should be reported.

Medicare Edits

	Fac RVU	Non-Fac RVU	FUD	Status	MUE
83992	0.0	0.0	N/A	X	2(3)

	Modifiers				Medicare References
83992	N/A	N/A	N/A	N/A	None

* with documentation

84260

84260   Serotonin

Explanation

This test may also be called 5-HT or 5-Hydroxytryptamine. The specimen is whole blood or serum or spinal fluid. Methods may include fluorometry, radioimmunoassay (RIA), and gas or liquid chromatography. This test may be performed to diagnose carcinoid syndrome and severe depression.

Coding Tips

A separately reportable lumbar puncture performed to collect cerebrospinal fluid (CSF) specimen is reported separately; see 62270.

When performed during the same encounter, management of the patient's medication(s), including review and provision of prescription, is reported separately with 90863.

Documentation Tips

Documentation must include the laboratory results to support reporting this service.

Medical record documentation must, at a minimum, include signs and symptoms supporting the ordering of this service.

Reimbursement Tips

Medicare reimburses this service under the laboratory fee schedule.

Terms To Know

depression. Disproportionate depressive state with behavior disturbance that is usually the result of a distressing experience and may include preoccupation with the psychic trauma and anxiety.

RIA. Radioimmunoassay.

specimen. Tissue cells or sample of fluid taken for analysis, pathologic examination, and diagnosis.

ICD-10-CM Diagnostic Codes

F31.31	Bipolar disorder, current episode depressed, mild
F31.32	Bipolar disorder, current episode depressed, moderate
F31.5	Bipolar disorder, current episode depressed, severe, with psychotic features
F31.75	Bipolar disorder, in partial remission, most recent episode depressed
F31.76	Bipolar disorder, in full remission, most recent episode depressed
F32.0	Major depressive disorder, single episode, mild
F32.1	Major depressive disorder, single episode, moderate
F32.3	Major depressive disorder, single episode, severe with psychotic features
F32.4	Major depressive disorder, single episode, in partial remission
F33.0	Major depressive disorder, recurrent, mild
F33.1	Major depressive disorder, recurrent, moderate
F33.3	Major depressive disorder, recurrent, severe with psychotic symptoms
F33.40	Major depressive disorder, recurrent, in remission, unspecified
F33.41	Major depressive disorder, recurrent, in partial remission
F33.42	Major depressive disorder, recurrent, in full remission
Z01.812	Encounter for preprocedural laboratory examination

Please note that this list of associated ICD-10-CM codes is not all-inclusive. The procedure may be performed for reasons other than those listed that support the medical necessity of the service. Only those conditions supported by the medical record documentation should be reported.

Medicare Edits

	Fac RVU	Non-Fac RVU	FUD	Status	MUE
84260	0.0	0.0	N/A	X	1(3)

	Modifiers				Medicare References
84260	N/A	N/A	N/A	N/A	None

* with documentation

84600

84600   Volatiles (eg, acetic anhydride, diethylether)

Explanation

This is also known as volatile toxicology, which would include testing for acetone, ethanol, isopropanol, and methanol. The specimen is serum or plasma, random urine, or gastric samples (collected by gastric lavage). Method may be gas-liquid chromatography (GLC). This test is performed to determine systemic alcohol levels and possibly as surveillance for drug abuse and to evaluate methanol and isopropanol toxicity due to ingestion, inhalation, or contact.

Coding Tips

To report isopropyl alcohol and methanol, see 80320. For the determination of a blood alcohol level, see 80320. Alcohol biomarkers are reported using 80321–80322. Report 82075 for an alcohol breath test. To report carbon tetrachloride or dichloromethane, see 82441.

ICD-10-CM contains combination poisoning codes that include not only the poisoning itself and the type of poison involved, but also the associated intent (i.e., accidental, intentional self-harm, assault, and undetermined).

Documentation Tips

Documentation must include the laboratory results to support reporting this service.

Medical record documentation must, at a minimum, include signs and symptoms supporting the ordering of this service.

Reimbursement Tips

Medicare reimburses this service under the laboratory fee schedule.

ICD-10-CM Diagnostic Codes

F10.10	Alcohol abuse, uncomplicated
F10.120	Alcohol abuse with intoxication, uncomplicated
F10.121	Alcohol abuse with intoxication delirium
F10.14	Alcohol abuse with alcohol-induced mood disorder
F10.150	Alcohol abuse with alcohol-induced psychotic disorder with delusions
F10.151	Alcohol abuse with alcohol-induced psychotic disorder with hallucinations
F10.180	Alcohol abuse with alcohol-induced anxiety disorder
F10.181	Alcohol abuse with alcohol-induced sexual dysfunction
F10.182	Alcohol abuse with alcohol-induced sleep disorder
F10.188	Alcohol abuse with other alcohol-induced disorder
F10.20	Alcohol dependence, uncomplicated
F10.21	Alcohol dependence, in remission
F10.220	Alcohol dependence with intoxication, uncomplicated
F10.221	Alcohol dependence with intoxication delirium
F10.230	Alcohol dependence with withdrawal, uncomplicated
F10.231	Alcohol dependence with withdrawal delirium
F10.232	Alcohol dependence with withdrawal with perceptual disturbance
F10.24	Alcohol dependence with alcohol-induced mood disorder
F10.250	Alcohol dependence with alcohol-induced psychotic disorder with delusions

F10.251	Alcohol dependence with alcohol-induced psychotic disorder with hallucinations
F10.26	Alcohol dependence with alcohol-induced persisting amnestic disorder
F10.27	Alcohol dependence with alcohol-induced persisting dementia
F10.280	Alcohol dependence with alcohol-induced anxiety disorder
F10.281	Alcohol dependence with alcohol-induced sexual dysfunction
F10.282	Alcohol dependence with alcohol-induced sleep disorder
F10.288	Alcohol dependence with other alcohol-induced disorder
T41.0X1A	Poisoning by inhaled anesthetics, accidental (unintentional), initial encounter
T41.0X2A	Poisoning by inhaled anesthetics, intentional self-harm, initial encounter
T41.0X3A	Poisoning by inhaled anesthetics, assault, initial encounter
T41.0X5A	Adverse effect of inhaled anesthetics, initial encounter
T51.0X1A	Toxic effect of ethanol, accidental (unintentional), initial encounter
T51.0X2A	Toxic effect of ethanol, intentional self-harm, initial encounter
T51.0X3A	Toxic effect of ethanol, assault, initial encounter
T51.1X1A	Toxic effect of methanol, accidental (unintentional), initial encounter
T51.1X2A	Toxic effect of methanol, intentional self-harm, initial encounter
T51.1X3A	Toxic effect of methanol, assault, initial encounter
T51.2X1A	Toxic effect of 2-Propanol, accidental (unintentional), initial encounter
T51.2X2A	Toxic effect of 2-Propanol, intentional self-harm, initial encounter
T51.2X3A	Toxic effect of 2-Propanol, assault, initial encounter
T51.8X1A	Toxic effect of other alcohols, accidental (unintentional), initial encounter
T51.8X2A	Toxic effect of other alcohols, intentional self-harm, initial encounter
T51.8X3A	Toxic effect of other alcohols, assault, initial encounter
T52.8X1A	Toxic effect of other organic solvents, accidental (unintentional), initial encounter
T52.8X2A	Toxic effect of other organic solvents, intentional self-harm, initial encounter
T52.8X3A	Toxic effect of other organic solvents, assault, initial encounter
T53.2X1A	Toxic effect of trichloroethylene, accidental (unintentional), initial encounter
T53.2X2A	Toxic effect of trichloroethylene, intentional self-harm, initial encounter
T53.2X3A	Toxic effect of trichloroethylene, assault, initial encounter
T53.3X1A	Toxic effect of tetrachloroethylene, accidental (unintentional), initial encounter
T53.3X2A	Toxic effect of tetrachloroethylene, intentional self-harm, initial encounter
T53.3X3A	Toxic effect of tetrachloroethylene, assault, initial encounter
T53.4X1A	Toxic effect of dichloromethane, accidental (unintentional), initial encounter
T53.4X2A	Toxic effect of dichloromethane, intentional self-harm, initial encounter
T53.4X3A	Toxic effect of dichloromethane, assault, initial encounter
T59.811A	Toxic effect of smoke, accidental (unintentional), initial encounter
T59.812A	Toxic effect of smoke, intentional self-harm, initial encounter
T59.813A	Toxic effect of smoke, assault, initial encounter

T59.891A	Toxic effect of other specified gases, fumes and vapors, accidental (unintentional), initial encounter	
T59.892A	Toxic effect of other specified gases, fumes and vapors, intentional self-harm, initial encounter	
T59.893A	Toxic effect of other specified gases, fumes and vapors, assault, initial encounter	
Z02.83	Encounter for blood-alcohol and blood-drug test	
Z77.29	Contact with and (suspected) exposure to other hazardous substances	

Please note that this list of associated ICD-10-CM codes is not all-inclusive. The procedure may be performed for reasons other than those listed that support the medical necessity of the service. Only those conditions supported by the medical record documentation should be reported.

Medicare Edits

	Fac RVU	Non-Fac RVU	FUD	Status	MUE
84600	0.0	0.0	N/A	X	2(3)

	Modifiers				Medicare References
84600	N/A	N/A	N/A	N/A	None

* with documentation

90785

90785	Interactive complexity (List separately in addition to the code for primary procedure)

Explanation

This code is reported in addition to the code for a primary psychiatric service. It is reported when the patient being treated has certain factors that increase the complexity of treatment rendered. These certain factors are limited to the following: the need to manage disruptive communication that complicates the delivery of treatment; complications involving the implementation of a treatment plan due to caregiver behavioral or emotional interference; evidence of a sentinel event with subsequent disclosure to a third party and discussion and/or reporting to the patient(s); or use of play equipment or translator to enable communication when a barrier exists.

Coding Tips

As an add-on code, 90785 is not subject to multiple procedure rules. No reimbursement reduction or modifier 51 is applied. Add-on codes describe additional intraservice work associated with the primary procedure. They are performed by the same physician on the same date of service as the primary service/procedure, and must never be reported as stand-alone codes. Interactive complexity is to be reported in conjunction with psychiatric evaluation services (90791–90792), the appropriate psychotherapy code (90832, 90834, or 90837), psychotherapy with evaluation and management service (90833, 90836, 90838), or group psychotherapy service (90853). Interactive complexity should never be reported with psychotherapy for crisis (90839–90840) or an evaluation and management service that was provided without psychotherapy (90833, 90836, 90838). These services should not be reported with psychotherapy provided at crisis (90839–90840) or adaptive behavior treatments (0364T–0374T).

Documentation Tips

Documentation should clearly state the reasons requiring interactive complexity.

Documentation should clearly indicate the type of interactive methods used such as interpreter, use of play, or physical device used, and that the patient did not have the ability to communicate through normal verbal means. Other catatonic states may be covered if documentation is submitted with the claim. Coverage also includes interactive examinations of patients with primary psychiatric diagnoses (excluding dementias and sleep disorders), and one of the following conditions: developmental speech or language disorders conductive hearing loss (total), mixed conductive and sensorineural hearing loss (total), deaf mutism, aphasia, voice disturbance, aphonia, and other speech disturbance such as dysarthria or dysphasia. The conditions must be clearly and concisely recorded in the medical record.

Reimbursement Tips

According to instructions found in the Correct Coding Initiative, "Interactive services (diagnostic or therapeutic) are distinct services for patients who have "lost, or have not yet developed either the expressive language communication skills to explain his/her symptoms and response to treatment..." Interactive complexity to psychiatric services is reported with add-on CPT code 90785."

Assignment of benefits is required when this service is provided by a clinical social worker.

Medicare payment is at 75 percent of the physician fee schedule when the service is provided by a clinical social worker.

Terms To Know

interactive psychotherapy. Use of physical aids and nonverbal communication to overcome barriers to therapeutic interaction between a clinician and a patient who has not yet developed or has lost either the expressive language communication skills to explain his/her symptoms and response to treatment, or the receptive communication skills to understand the clinician if he or she were to use ordinary adult language for communication.

ICD-10-CM Diagnostic Codes

The application of this code is too broad to adequately present ICD-10-CM diagnostic code links here. Refer to your ICD-10-CM book.

Medicare Edits

	Fac RVU	Non-Fac RVU	FUD	Status	MUE
90785	0.39	0.39	N/A	A	1(1)

	Modifiers				Medicare References
90785	N/A	N/A	N/A	N/A	100-2,15,160; 100-2,15,170; 100-3,10.3; 100-3,10.4; 100-4,12,100; 100-4,12,210.1

* with documentation

90791-90792

90791   Psychiatric diagnostic evaluation

90792   Psychiatric diagnostic evaluation with medical services

Explanation

A psychiatric diagnostic evaluation is the assessment of the patient's psychosocial history, current mental status, review and ordering of diagnostic studies followed by appropriate treatment recommendations. In code 90792, additional medical services such as physical examination and prescription of pharmaceuticals, are provided in addition to the diagnostic evaluation. Interviews and communication with family members or other sources is included in these codes.

Coding Tips

These procedures may be performed by a physician or other qualified health care professional. Psychiatric diagnostic evaluation with or without medical services include a history, mental status, and other physical examination elements, the prescribing of medications and review and ordering of laboratory or other diagnostic testing. Check with the specific payer to determine coverage. In some cases family members, guardians, or others may be consulted instead of the patient. Communication factors that complicate the diagnostic evaluation results in the need for interactive complexity (use of play equipment, involvement of third-parties, etc.); code 90785 may be reported with these procedures. These services should not be reported with psychotherapy provided at crisis (90839–90840) or adaptive behavior treatments (0364T–0374T), or evaluation and management (E/M) services (99201–99337, 99341–99350, 99366–99368, or 99401–99444). Diagnostic evaluations may be reported multiple times when performed during separate encounters. These codes should not be reported on the same date of service as an evaluation and management service or a psychotherapy service (including psychotherapy for crisis). To report evaluation of psychiatric hospital records reports, psychometric and/projective testing, or other data, see code 90885. Interpretation or explanation of psychiatric or other medical examinations and procedures is reported using 90887. Health and behavior assessment/reassessment is reported using 96150–96151.

Documentation Tips

Medical record documentation should indicate the need for the interactive complexity services when used. Documentation should clearly indicate the type of interactive methods used such as interpreter, use of play, or physical device used, and that the patient did not have the ability to communicate through normal verbal means. Other catatonic states may be covered if documentation is submitted with the claim. Coverage also includes interactive examinations of patients with primary psychiatric diagnoses, excluding dementias and sleep disorders), and one of the following conditions: developmental speech or language disorders conductive hearing loss (total), mixed conductive and sensorineural hearing loss (total), deaf mutism, aphasia, voice disturbance, aphonia, and other speech disturbance such as dysarthria or dysphasia. The conditions must be clearly and concisely recorded in the medical record.

Reimbursement Tips

According to the instructions found in the Correct Coding Initiative, "CPT codes for psychiatric services include diagnostic (CPT codes 90791, 90792) and therapeutic (individual, group, other) procedures. Since psychotherapy includes continuing psychiatric evaluation, CPT codes 90791 and 90792 are not separately reportable with individual psychotherapy codes. CPT code 90791 or 90792 is separately reportable with a group psychotherapy code if the diagnostic interview and group psychotherapy service occur during separate time intervals on the same date of service. Diagnostic services performed during the group therapy session are not separately reportable."

Diagnostic psychiatric evaluation is reported with one of two CPT codes. CPT code 90791 is psychiatric evaluation without medical E/M, and CPT code 90792 is psychiatric evaluation with medical E/M. Evaluation and management codes (e.g., 99201–99215) should not be reported with either of these diagnostic psychiatric codes.

Assignment of benefits is required when this service is provided by a clinical social worker.

Medicare payment is at 75 percent of the physician fee schedule when the service is provided by a clinical social worker.

Diagnostic psychological testing services performed by psychologists who meet these requirements are covered as other diagnostic tests. When, however, the psychologist is not practicing independently, but is on the staff of an institution, agency, or clinic, that entity bills for the diagnostic services.

Terms To Know

evaluation. Dynamic process in which the dentist makes clinical judgments based on data gathered during the examination.

psychosocial history. Information obtained about the patient's background regarding history of mental and physical health and social history, as well as the status of current and past employment, finances, education, religion, stress, and support networks including family and friends.

ICD-10-CM Diagnostic Codes

The application of this code is too broad to adequately present ICD-10-CM diagnostic code links here. Refer to your ICD-10-CM book.

Medicare Edits

	Fac RVU	Non-Fac RVU	FUD	Status	MUE
90791	3.58	3.69	N/A	A	1(1)
90792	3.97	4.09	N/A	A	1(1)

	Modifiers				Medicare References
90791	N/A	N/A	N/A	N/A	100-3,10.3; 100-4,12,100
90792	N/A	N/A	N/A	N/A	

* with documentation

90832-90833

90832　Psychotherapy, 30 minutes with patient and/or family member

90833　Psychotherapy, 30 minutes with patient and/or family member when performed with an evaluation and management service (List separately in addition to the code for primary procedure)

Explanation

Psychotherapy is a variety of treatment techniques in which a physician or other qualified health care provider helps a patient with a mental illness or behavioral disturbance identify and alleviate any emotional disruptions, maladaptive behavioral patterns, and contributing/exacerbating factors. This treatment also involves encouraging personality growth and development through coping techniques and problem-solving skills. Report code 90832 for 16 to 37 minutes of face-to-face time spent with the patient without an additional evaluation and management (E/M) service. Report code 90833 if a separate E/M is performed during the same encounter as the 16 to 37 minutes of psychotherapy.

Coding Tips

As an add-on code, 90833 is not subject to multiple procedure rules. No reimbursement reduction or modifier 51 is applied. Add-on codes describe additional intraservice work associated with the primary procedure. They are performed by the same physician on the same date of service as the primary service/procedure, and must never be reported as stand-alone codes.

The appropriate evaluation and management (E/M) service should be reported in addition to code 90833. However, the time involved with performing the E/M service should not be considered when selecting the psychotherapy code.

If 38 to 52 minutes of psychotherapy are provided, see codes 90834 or 90836. If 53 or more minutes of psychotherapy are provided, see codes 90837–90838. Do not report prolonged services (99354–99357) with code 90833. Individual psychotherapy and group psychotherapy may be reported on the same date of service if the two services are performed during separate time intervals. Family psychotherapy (90846, 90847) is not separately reportable with psychotherapy (90832–90838) for the same patient encounter, since the latter codes include psychotherapy with family members.

Psychotherapy provided for an urgent assessment and history of a crisis state, including mental status examination and disposition is reported with 90839–90840. Family psychotherapy is reported using 90846–90847. Multiple family or group psychotherapy is reported using 90849 or 90853, respectively.

When it is necessary to perform interactive complexity, code 90785 may be reported separately.

Pharmacologic management is included in psychotherapy services that are reported with E/M services or that include medical services. However, when performed during the same encounter and an evaluation and management service was not provided, management of the patient's medication(s), including review and provision of prescription is reported separately with 90863.

Documentation Tips

Since the psychotherapy codes include time as a component of the code, the total time or the start and stop times of the psychotherapy should be noted in the medical record.

Each psychotherapy note should include the description of at least one of the techniques used to treat the patient's condition. The CPT book describes the techniques specific to psychotherapy as either insight oriented, behavior modifying, and/or supportive techniques. Providers should also include how the patient benefited by the therapy in reaching his or her goals. For example, a note might state, "Supportive psychotherapy was utilized to help alleviate

the patient's depression." The major theme of the discussion should also be recorded with consideration to the patient's privacy.

Documentation should specify whether this is a single episode or recurrent, the current degree of depression, the presence of psychotic features or symptoms, and remission status (i.e., partial, full) when applicable.

Documentation should clearly state the reasons requiring interactive complexity when separately reported.

Reimbursement Tips

Most payers will not cover psychotherapy services that are palliative or provided only to maintain functioning level.

These procedures may be performed by a physician or other qualified health care professional. Check with the specific payer to determine coverage. Site of service does not affect code assignment. Assignment of benefits is required when these services are provided by a clinical social worker. Medicare payment is at 75 percent of the physician fee schedule when these services are provided by a clinical social worker.

Terms To Know

face to face. Interaction between two parties, usually provider and patient, that occurs in the physical presence of each other.

psychotherapy. Treatment for mental illness and behavioral disturbances in which the clinician establishes a professional contract with the patient and, through definitive therapeutic communication, attempts to alleviate the emotional disturbances, reverse or change maladaptive patterns of behavior, and encourage personality growth and development.

ICD-10-CM Diagnostic Codes

The application of this code is too broad to adequately present ICD-10-CM diagnostic code links here. Refer to your ICD-10-CM book.

Medicare Edits

	Fac RVU	Non-Fac RVU	FUD	Status	MUE
90832	1.77	1.79	N/A	A	1(3)
90833	1.83	1.85	N/A	A	1(1)

	Modifiers				Medicare References
90832	N/A	N/A	N/A	N/A	100-1,3,30; 100-1,3,30.3;
90833	N/A	N/A	N/A	N/A	100-2,15,160; 100-2,15,170;
					100-2,15,270;
					100-2,15,270.2;
					100-2,15,270.4; 100-3,10.3;
					100-3,10.4; 100-3,130.3;
					100-4,12,100;
					100-4,12,190.3;
					100-4,12,190.7;
					100-4,12,210.1

* with documentation

90834-90836

90834	Psychotherapy, 45 minutes with patient and/or family member
90836	Psychotherapy, 45 minutes with patient and/or family member when performed with an evaluation and management service (List separately in addition to the code for primary procedure)

Explanation

Psychotherapy is a variety of treatment techniques in which a physician or other qualified health care provider helps a patient with a mental illness or behavioral disturbance identify and alleviate any emotional disruptions, maladaptive behavioral patterns, and contributing/exacerbating factors. This treatment also involves encouraging personality growth and development through coping techniques and problem-solving skills. Report code 90834 for 38 to 52 minutes of face-to-face time spent with the patient without an additional evaluation and management (E/M) service. Report code 90836 if a separate E/M is performed during the same encounter as the 38 to 52 minutes of psychotherapy.

Coding Tips

As an add-on code, 90836 is not subject to multiple procedure rules. No reimbursement reduction or modifier 51 is applied. Add-on codes describe additional intraservice work associated with the primary procedure. They are performed by the same physician on the same date of service as the primary service/procedure, and must never be reported as stand-alone codes.

The appropriate evaluation and management (E/M) service should be reported in addition to code 90836. However, the time involved with performing the E/M service should not be considered when selecting the psychotherapy code.

If 30 minutes of psychotherapy are provided, see code 90832 or 90833. If 53 or more minutes of psychotherapy are provided, see codes 90837–90838. Do not report prolonged services (99354–99357) with code 90833. Individual psychotherapy and group psychotherapy may be reported on the same date of service if the two services are performed during separate time intervals. Family psychotherapy (90846, 90847) is not separately reportable with psychotherapy (90832–90838) for the same patient encounter, since the latter codes include psychotherapy with family members.

Psychotherapy provided for an urgent assessment and history of a crisis state, including mental status examination and disposition, is reported with 90839–90840. Family psychotherapy is reported using 90846–90847. Multiple family or group psychotherapy is reported using 90849 or 90853, respectively.

When it is necessary to perform interactive complexity, code 90785 may be reported separately.

Pharmacologic management is included in psychotherapy services that are reported with E/M services or that include medical services. However, when performed during the same encounter and an evaluation and management service was not provided, management of the patient's medication(s), including review and provision of prescription is reported separately with 90863.

Documentation Tips

Since the psychotherapy codes include time as a component of the code, the total time or the start and stop times of the psychotherapy should be noted in the medical record.

Each psychotherapy note should include the description of at least one of the techniques used to treat the patient's condition. The CPT book describes the techniques specific to psychotherapy as either insight oriented, behavior modifying, and/or supportive techniques. Providers should also include how the patient benefited by the therapy in reaching his or her goals. For example, a note might state, "Supportive psychotherapy was utilized to help alleviate

the patient's depression." The major theme of the discussion should also be recorded with consideration to the patient's privacy.

Documentation should specify whether this is a single episode or recurrent, the current degree of depression, the presence of psychotic features or symptoms, and remission status (i.e., partial, full) when applicable.

Documentation should clearly state the reasons requiring interactive complexity when separately reported.

Reimbursement Tips

Most payers will not cover psychotherapy services that are palliative or provided only to maintain functioning level.

These procedures may be performed by a physician or other qualified health care professional. Check with the specific payer to determine coverage. Site of service does not affect code assignment. Assignment of benefits is required when these services are provided by a clinical social worker. Medicare payment is at 75 percent of the physician fee schedule when these services are provided by a clinical social worker.

Terms To Know

face to face. Interaction between two parties, usually provider and patient, that occurs in the physical presence of each other.

psychotherapy. Treatment for mental illness and behavioral disturbances in which the clinician establishes a professional contract with the patient and, through definitive therapeutic communication, attempts to alleviate the emotional disturbances, reverse or change maladaptive patterns of behavior, and encourage personality growth and development.

ICD-10-CM Diagnostic Codes

The application of this code is too broad to adequately present ICD-10-CM diagnostic code links here. Refer to your ICD-10-CM book.

Medicare Edits

	Fac RVU	Non-Fac RVU	FUD	Status	MUE
90834	2.36	2.38	N/A	A	1(3)
90836	2.33	2.35	N/A	A	1(1)

	Modifiers				Medicare References
90834	N/A	N/A	N/A	N/A	100-1,3,30; 100-1,3,30.3; 100-2,15,270; 100-2,15,270.2; 100-2,15,270.4; 100-3,10.3; 100-3,10.4
90836	N/A	N/A	N/A	N/A	

* with documentation

90837-90838

90837	Psychotherapy, 60 minutes with patient and/or family member
90838	Psychotherapy, 60 minutes with patient and/or family member when performed with an evaluation and management service (List separately in addition to the code for primary procedure)

Explanation

Psychotherapy is a variety of treatment techniques in which a physician or other qualified health care provider helps a patient with a mental illness or behavioral disturbance identify and alleviate any emotional disruptions, maladaptive behavioral patterns, and contributing/exacerbating factors. This treatment also involves encouraging personality growth and development through coping techniques and problem-solving skills. Report code 90837 for 53 minutes or more of face-to-face time spent with the patient without an additional evaluation and management (E/M) service. Report code 90838 if a separate E/M is performed during the same encounter as the 38 to 53 minutes of psychotherapy.

Coding Tips

As an add-on code, 90838 is not subject to multiple procedure rules. No reimbursement reduction or modifier 51 is applied. Add-on codes describe additional intraservice work associated with the primary procedure. They are performed by the same physician on the same date of service as the primary service/procedure, and must never be reported as stand-alone codes.

The appropriate evaluation and management (E/M) service should be reported in addition to code 90838. However, the time involved with performing the E/M service should not be considered when selecting the psychotherapy code.

If 30 minutes of psychotherapy are provided, see codes 90832 or 90833. If 45 minutes of psychotherapy are provided, see codes 90834–90836. Individual psychotherapy and group psychotherapy may be reported on the same date of service if the two services are performed during separate time intervals. Family psychotherapy (90846, 90847) is not separately reportable with psychotherapy (90832–90838) for the same patient encounter, since the latter codes include psychotherapy with family members.

Psychotherapy provided for an urgent assessment and history of a crisis state, including mental status examination and disposition, is reported with 90839–90840. Family psychotherapy is reported using 90846–90847. Multiple family or group psychotherapy is reported using 90849 or 90853, respectively.

When it is necessary to perform interactive complexity, code 90785 may be reported separately.

Pharmacologic management is included in psychotherapy services that are reported with E/M services or that include medical services. However, when performed during the same encounter and an evaluation and management service was not provided, management of the patient's medication(s), including review and provision of prescription is reported separately with 90863.

Documentation Tips

Since the psychotherapy codes include time as a component of the code, the total time or the start and stop times of the psychotherapy should be noted in the medical record.

Each psychotherapy note should include the description of at least one of the techniques used to treat the patient's condition. The CPT book describes the techniques specific to psychotherapy as either insight oriented, behavior modifying, and/or supportive techniques. Providers should also include how the patient benefited by the therapy in reaching his or her goals. For example, a note might state, "Supportive psychotherapy was utilized to help alleviate

the patient's depression." The major theme of the discussion should also be recorded with consideration to the patient's privacy.

Documentation should specify whether this is a single episode or recurrent, the current degree of depression, the presence of psychotic features or symptoms, and remission status (i.e., partial, full) when applicable.

Documentation should clearly state the reasons requiring interactive complexity when separately reported.

Reimbursement Tips

Most payers will not cover psychotherapy services that are palliative or provided only to maintain functioning level.

These procedures may be performed by a physician or other qualified health care professional. Check with the specific payer to determine coverage. Site of service does not affect code assignment. Assignment of benefits is required when these services are provided by a clinical social worker. Medicare payment is at 75 percent of the physician fee schedule when these services are provided by a clinical social worker.

Terms To Know

face to face. Interaction between two parties, usually provider and patient, that occurs in the physical presence of each other.

psychotherapy. Treatment for mental illness and behavioral disturbances in which the clinician establishes a professional contract with the patient and, through definitive therapeutic communication, attempts to alleviate the emotional disturbances, reverse or change maladaptive patterns of behavior, and encourage personality growth and development.

ICD-10-CM Diagnostic Codes

The application of this code is too broad to adequately present ICD-10-CM diagnostic code links here. Refer to your ICD-10-CM book.

Medicare Edits

	Fac RVU	Non-Fac RVU	FUD	Status	MUE
90837	3.55	3.57	N/A	A	1(3)
90838	3.08	3.1	N/A	A	1(1)

	Modifiers				Medicare References
90837	N/A	N/A	N/A	N/A	100-1,3,30; 100-1,3,30.3
90838	N/A	N/A	N/A	N/A	
* with documentation					

90839-90840

90839   Psychotherapy for crisis; first 60 minutes

90840   each additional 30 minutes (List separately in addition to code for primary service)

Explanation

Psychotherapy is a variety of treatment techniques in which a physician or other qualified health care provider helps a patient with a mental illness or behavioral disturbance identify and alleviate any emotional disruptions, maladaptive behavioral patterns, and contributing/exacerbating factors. Report these codes when the psychotherapy is urgent for a life-threatening or highly complex psychiatric crisis state in a patient in distress. Code 90839 is used for the first 30 to 74 minutes of intervention and 90840 for each additional 30 minutes. These codes include history, mental status examination, mobilization of resources and implementation treatment.

Coding Tips

As an add-on code, 90840 is not subject to multiple procedure rules. No reimbursement reduction or modifier 51 is applied. Add-on codes describe additional intraservice work associated with the primary procedure. They are performed by the same physician on the same date of service as the primary service/procedure, and must never be reported as stand-alone codes.

Do not report psychiatric diagnostic evaluation codes (90791–90792) or other psychotherapy (90832–90838) with psychotherapy for crisis services. To report psychotherapy to patients who are not in a crisis situation, see 90832–90838. Family psychotherapy is reported using 90846–90847. Multiple family or group psychotherapy is reported using 90849 or 90853, respectively.

Documentation Tips

Documentation should indicate that psychotherapy was provided for an urgent assessment and history of a crisis state, including mental status examination, disposition, and that the patient presented in a high level of distress with a complex or life-threatening problem that required immediate attention.

Since the psychotherapy codes include time as a component of the code, the total time or the start and stop times of the psychotherapy should be noted in the medical record. Time does not have to be continuous; however, it does have to be face-to-face with the patient, without distraction and without providing services to another patient during the same time period and when it is not continuous the stop and start times for each session should be documented.

Each psychotherapy note should include the description of at least one of the techniques used to treat the patient's condition. The CPT book describes the techniques specific to psychotherapy as either insight oriented, behavior modifying, and/or supportive techniques. Providers should also include how the patient benefited by the therapy in reaching his or her goals. For example, a note might state, "Supportive psychotherapy was utilized to help alleviate the patient's depression." The major theme of the discussion should also be recorded with consideration to the patient's privacy.

Documentation should specify whether this is a single episode or recurrent, the current degree of depression, the presence of psychotic features or symptoms, and remission status (i.e., partial, full) when applicable.

Documentation should clearly state the reasons requiring interactive complexity when separately reported.

Reimbursement Tips

It is important to note that most payers will not cover psychotherapy services that are palliative or provided only to maintain functioning level.

These procedures may be performed by a physician or other qualified health care professional. Check with the specific payer to determine coverage. Site of service does not affect code assignment. Assignment of benefits is required when this service is provided by a clinical social worker. Medicare payment is at 75 percent of the physician fee schedule when the service is provided by a clinical social worker.

Terms To Know

face to face. Interaction between two parties, usually provider and patient, that occurs in the physical presence of each other.

psychotherapy. Treatment for mental illness and behavioral disturbances in which the clinician establishes a professional contract with the patient and, through definitive therapeutic communication, attempts to alleviate the emotional disturbances, reverse or change maladaptive patterns of behavior, and encourage personality growth and development.

ICD-10-CM Diagnostic Codes

The application of this code is too broad to adequately present ICD-10-CM diagnostic code links here. Refer to your ICD-10-CM book.

Medicare Edits

	Fac RVU	Non-Fac RVU	FUD	Status	MUE
90839	3.7	3.73	N/A	A	1(1)
90840	1.77	1.78	N/A	A	-

	Modifiers				Medicare References
90839	N/A	N/A	N/A	80*	100-4,12,100
90840	N/A	N/A	N/A	80*	

* with documentation

90845

90845   Psychoanalysis

Explanation

The therapist performs psychoanalysis by utilizing methods of intense observation and analytical skills to investigate the patient's past experiences, unconscious motivations, and internal conflicts, as well as contributing medical conditions, to discover how these pilot the patient's current behavior and emotions. The psychiatrist seeks to produce change in maladapted behavior. Psychoanalysis includes reviewing medical notes and making clinical setting arrangements, assisting the patient in further self-awareness, working through barriers, understanding self-observations, and modifying mental behavior and status while continuing to elicit more information and personal exploration. This code also includes follow-up work of documentation, content review, and peer consultation.

Coding Tips

Psychoanalysis is reported per day. Psychoanalysis should be differentiated from psychotherapy. Reporting this code for psychoanalysis indicates that treatment is being provided by a physician with the credentials to practice analytic therapy. For Medicare patients, psychotherapy services, including psychoanalysis, are not covered if the medical record indicates that dementia has produced a cognitive defect severe enough to prevent establishment of a relationship allowing therapy to be effective. Likewise, profound mental retardation never supports the medical necessity of psychotherapy services.

Documentation Tips

Documentation should include a list of the patient's complaints and conditions present, the current focus of treatment, the treatment framework, the modality of treatment, the frequency and estimated length of the treatment, a list of family and/or friends who could offer support, status of community resources needed when applicable and an alternative care plan if the patient does not show sufficient improvements.

Reimbursement Tips

For practitioner services, evaluation and management (E/M) codes are not separately reportable on the same date of service as psychoanalysis (90845), narcosynthesis (90865), or hypnotherapy (90880). These psychiatric services include E/M services provided on the same date of service. Facilities may separately report E/M codes and psychoanalysis, narcosynthesis, or hypnotherapy if the services are performed at separate patient encounters on the same date of service.

Terms To Know

cognitive. Being aware by drawing from knowledge, such as judgment, reason, perception, and memory.

consultation. Advice or opinion regarding diagnosis and treatment or determination to accept transfer of care of a patient rendered by a medical professional at the request of the primary care provider.

observation. Perception of events.

psychoanalysis. Specific type of psychotherapy using conscious and unconscious processes to diagnose and help patients with mild to moderate chronic psychiatric or character problems control their life. Psychoanalysis must be performed for appropriate patients in a one-on-one setting by a qualified psychotherapist (MD/DO).

therapeutic. Act meant to alleviate a medical or mental condition.

ICD-10-CM Diagnostic Codes

The application of this code is too broad to adequately present ICD-10-CM diagnostic code links here. Refer to your ICD-10-CM book.

Medicare Edits

	Fac RVU	Non-Fac RVU	FUD	Status	MUE
90845	2.56	2.57	N/A	A	1(2)

	Modifiers				Medicare References
90845	N/A	N/A	N/A	80*	100-2,15,160; 100-2,15,170; 100-3,10.3; 100-3,10.4; 100-3,130.1; 100-3,130.3; 100-4,12,160; 100-4,12,160.1; 100-4,12,170

* with documentation

90846-90849

90846	Family psychotherapy (without the patient present)
90847	Family psychotherapy (conjoint psychotherapy) (with patient present)
90849	Multiple-family group psychotherapy

Explanation

The therapist provides family psychotherapy in a setting where the care provider meets with the patient's family. The family is part of the patient evaluation and treatment process. Family dynamics as they relate to the patient's mental status and behavior are a main focus of the sessions. Attention is also given to the impact the patient's condition has on the family, with therapy aimed at improving the interaction between the patient and family members. Report 90846 when the patient is not present. Report 90847 when the patient is present with the family; 90849 when the patient is present with his or her family as well a other patients and families. When the patient is present, continuing evaluation and drug management may be indicated.

Coding Tips

Code assignment is based on whether the patient is present during the session or not. See code 90853 for group psychotherapy that does not consist of multiple families. Do not report codes 90846–90847 with adaptive behavior treatment protocol modification, family adaptive behavior treatment guidance, or multiple-family adaptive behavior treatment guidance (0368T–0371T).

Documentation Tips

Each patient record must have patient specific documentation. Documentation should include specific participation, contributions, and reactions of each family member.

Reimbursement Tips

Family psychotherapy is covered by Medicare when the primary purpose of such counseling is the treatment of the patient. It may be necessary to submit the medical record documentation to substantiate the need for family psychotherapy. Some payers require prior authorization before covering family or group therapy services.

For Medicare patients, psychotherapy services are not covered if the medical record indicates that dementia has produced a cognitive defect severe enough to prevent establishment of a relationship allowing therapy to be effective. Likewise, profound mental retardation never supports the medical necessity of psychotherapy services.

Individual psychotherapy and group psychotherapy may be reported on the same date of service if the two services are performed during separate time intervals. Family psychotherapy (90846, 90847) is not separately reportable with psychotherapy (90832–90838) for the same patient encounter since the latter codes include psychotherapy with family members.

Terms To Know

psychotherapy. Treatment for mental illness and behavioral disturbances in which the clinician establishes a professional contract with the patient and, through definitive therapeutic communication, attempts to alleviate the emotional disturbances, reverse or change maladaptive patterns of behavior, and encourage personality growth and development.

ICD-10-CM Diagnostic Codes

The application of this code is too broad to adequately present ICD-10-CM diagnostic code links here. Refer to your ICD-10-CM book.

Medicare Edits

	Fac RVU	Non-Fac RVU	FUD	Status	MUE
90846	2.87	2.89	N/A	R	1(3)
90847	2.97	2.99	N/A	R	1(3)
90849	0.86	0.96	N/A	R	1(3)

	Modifiers				Medicare References
90846	N/A	N/A	N/A	80*	100-1,3,30; 100-1,3,30.3;
90847	N/A	N/A	N/A	80*	100-3,130.1; 100-3,130.3;
90849	N/A	N/A	N/A	80*	100-4,12,160;
					100-4,12,160.1

* with documentation

90853

90853   Group psychotherapy (other than of a multiple-family group)

Explanation

The psychiatric treatment provider conducts psychotherapy for a group of several patients in one session. Group dynamics are explored. Emotional and rational cognitive interactions between individual persons in the group are facilitated and observed. Personal dynamics of any individual patient may be discussed within the group setting. Processes that help patients move toward emotional healing and modification of thought and behavior are used, such as facilitating improved interpersonal exchanges, group support, and reminiscing. The group may be composed of patients with separate and distinct maladaptive disorders or persons sharing some facet of a disorder. This code should be used for group psychotherapy with other patients, and not members of the patients' families.

Coding Tips

Report interactive complexity (90785) in addition to this service when provided during the group psychotherapy session. Some payers require prior authorization before covering family or group therapy services. If multiple family group psychotherapy is performed, see 90849. Do not report this service with adaptive behavior treatments social skills group (0372T).

Documentation Tips

Each patient record must have patient specific documentation. Documentation should include specific participation, contributions, and reactions of each member.

Reimbursement Tips

Family psychotherapy is covered by Medicare when the primary purpose of such counseling is the treatment of the patient. It may be necessary to submit the medical record documentation to substantiate the need for family psychotherapy. Some payers require prior authorization before covering family or group therapy services.

For Medicare patients, psychotherapy services are not covered if the medical record indicates that dementia has produced a cognitive defect severe enough to prevent establishment of a relationship allowing therapy to be effective. Likewise, profound mental retardation never supports the medical necessity of psychotherapy services.

Individual psychotherapy and group psychotherapy may be reported on the same date of service if the two services are performed during separate time intervals. Family psychotherapy (90846, 90847) is not separately reportable with psychotherapy (90832–90838) for the same patient encounter since the latter codes include psychotherapy with family members.

Terms To Know

cognitive. Being aware by drawing from knowledge, such as judgment, reason, perception, and memory.

preauthorization. Requirement that approval for requested services be obtained before providing those services.

psychotherapy. Treatment for mental illness and behavioral disturbances in which the clinician establishes a professional contract with the patient and, through definitive therapeutic communication, attempts to alleviate the emotional disturbances, reverse or change maladaptive patterns of behavior, and encourage personality growth and development.

ICD-10-CM Diagnostic Codes

The application of this code is too broad to adequately present ICD-10-CM diagnostic code links here. Refer to your ICD-10-CM book.

Medicare Edits

	Fac RVU	Non-Fac RVU	FUD	Status	MUE
90853	0.71	0.72	N/A	A	1(3)

		Modifiers			Medicare References
90853	N/A	N/A	N/A	80*	100-1,3,30; 100-1,3,30.3; 100-3,130.1; 100-3,130.3; 100-4,12,160; 100-4,12,160.1

* with documentation

90863

90863   Pharmacologic management, including prescription and review of medication, when performed with psychotherapy services (List separately in addition to the code for primary procedure)

Explanation

This code describes the psychiatric services of managing the patient's medications, including the patient's current use of the medicines, a medical review of the benefits and treatment progression, management of side effects, and review or change of prescription. This is a pharmacologically related service and is reported in addition to non-crisis related psychotherapy when there is no other evaluation and management performed during the encounter.

Coding Tips

This procedure may be performed by a physician or other qualified health care professional. As an add-on code, 90863 is not subject to multiple procedure rules. No reimbursement reduction or modifier 51 is applied. Add-on codes describe additional intraservice work associated with the primary procedure. They are performed by the same physician on the same date of service as the primary service/procedure, and must never be reported as stand-alone codes. The appropriate psychotherapy code without evaluation and management (E/M) service (90832, 90834, or 90837) should be reported in addition to code 90838. When determining the appropriate psychotherapy code to be reported with this procedure, any time spent providing the medication management should be excluded. For example, if the patient is seen for 45 minutes, and 15 minutes is spent performing medication management, code 90832 Psychotherapy, 30 minutes with patient and/or family, and code 90863 are reported. This code should not be reported with an evaluation and management code as the service is included as part of the E/M code.

Documentation Tips

The written plan for care should include treatments and medications—specifying frequency and dosage, any referrals and consultations, patient and family education, and specific instructions for follow-up.

Reimbursement Tips

Third-party payers may not reimburse separately for this service. Check with the payer for specific guidelines.

Terms To Know

encounter. 1) Direct personal contact between a registered hospital outpatient (in a medical clinic or emergency department, for example) and a physician (or other person authorized by state law and hospital bylaws to order or furnish services) for the diagnosis and treatment of an illness or injury. Visits with more than one health professional that take place during the same session and at a single location within the hospital are considered a single visit. 2) Physician Quality Reporting System (PQRS) term for meetings with patients during a reporting period represented by the following: CPT Category I E/M service or procedure codes or HCPCS codes located in a PQRS measure's denominator. Reporting of these codes counts as eligibility to meet a measure's inclusion requirements when the service occurs during the specified reporting period.

evaluation and management. Assessment, counseling, and other services provided to a patient reported through CPT codes.

psychotherapy. Treatment for mental illness and behavioral disturbances in which the clinician establishes a professional contract with the patient and, through definitive therapeutic communication, attempts to alleviate the emotional disturbances, reverse or change maladaptive patterns of behavior, and encourage personality growth and development.

ICD-10-CM Diagnostic Codes

The application of this code is too broad to adequately present ICD-10-CM diagnostic code links here. Refer to your ICD-10-CM book.

Medicare Edits

	Fac RVU	Non-Fac RVU	FUD	Status	MUE
90863	0.0	0.0	N/A	I	1(1)

	Modifiers				Medicare References
90863	N/A	N/A	N/A	N/A	None

* with documentation

90865

| 90865 | Narcosynthesis for psychiatric diagnostic and therapeutic purposes (eg, sodium amobarbital (Amytal) interview) |

Explanation

A hypnotic drug known as Amytal or sodium amobarbital is infused into the patient via an intravenous drip for psychiatric diagnostic or psychotherapeutic treatment purposes. Amytal is a hypnotic sedative used for diagnosing dissociative disorders and to treat trauma victims by accessing repressed memories, emotions, or events to facilitate healing. This is often used after other measures have failed and/or when gaining a definitive diagnosis is medically essential. A sodium Amytal interview is often conducted in an inpatient setting, to monitor the effects of the drug. The patient is in a hypnotic state, where memories, as the patient perceives them, are more confidently reviewed. These interviews are often videotaped for later discussion.

Coding Tips

This code is only to be used by physicians (MD/DO).

Documentation Tips

Medical record documentation should indicate the type of medications used and the dosage administered, in addition to the findings during the examination.

Reimbursement Tips

Third-party payers may have special coverage guidelines for this service. Check with the payer for guidelines before providing the service.

Terms To Know

amobarbital. Barbiturate causing central nervous system depression with sedative hypnotic and anticonvulsant properties as well. Amytal is the trade name. May be sold under the brand name Amytal.

therapeutic. Act meant to alleviate a medical or mental condition.

ICD-10-CM Diagnostic Codes

F05	Delirium due to known physiological condition
F06.0	Psychotic disorder with hallucinations due to known physiological condition
F06.1	Catatonic disorder due to known physiological condition
F06.2	Psychotic disorder with delusions due to known physiological condition
F06.30	Mood disorder due to known physiological condition, unspecified
F06.31	Mood disorder due to known physiological condition with depressive features
F06.32	Mood disorder due to known physiological condition with major depressive-like episode
F06.33	Mood disorder due to known physiological condition with manic features
F06.34	Mood disorder due to known physiological condition with mixed features
F06.8	Other specified mental disorders due to known physiological condition
F07.0	Personality change due to known physiological condition
F07.81	Postconcussional syndrome
F20.0	Paranoid schizophrenia
F20.1	Disorganized schizophrenia

F20.2	Catatonic schizophrenia	F31.77	Bipolar disorder, in partial remission, most recent episode mixed
F20.3	Undifferentiated schizophrenia	F31.78	Bipolar disorder, in full remission, most recent episode mixed
F20.5	Residual schizophrenia	F31.81	Bipolar II disorder
F20.81	Schizophreniform disorder	F32.0	Major depressive disorder, single episode, mild
F20.89	Other schizophrenia	F32.1	Major depressive disorder, single episode, moderate
F21	Schizotypal disorder	F32.2	Major depressive disorder, single episode, severe without psychotic features
F22	Delusional disorders		
F23	Brief psychotic disorder	F32.3	Major depressive disorder, single episode, severe with psychotic features
F24	Shared psychotic disorder		
F25.0	Schizoaffective disorder, bipolar type	F32.4	Major depressive disorder, single episode, in partial remission
F25.1	Schizoaffective disorder, depressive type	F32.5	Major depressive disorder, single episode, in full remission
F25.8	Other schizoaffective disorders	F32.8	Other depressive episodes
F28	Other psychotic disorder not due to a substance or known physiological condition	F32.9	Major depressive disorder, single episode, unspecified
		F33.0	Major depressive disorder, recurrent, mild
F30.10	Manic episode without psychotic symptoms, unspecified	F33.1	Major depressive disorder, recurrent, moderate
F30.11	Manic episode without psychotic symptoms, mild	F33.2	Major depressive disorder, recurrent severe without psychotic features
F30.12	Manic episode without psychotic symptoms, moderate		
F30.13	Manic episode, severe, without psychotic symptoms	F33.3	Major depressive disorder, recurrent, severe with psychotic symptoms
F30.2	Manic episode, severe with psychotic symptoms		
F30.3	Manic episode in partial remission	F33.41	Major depressive disorder, recurrent, in partial remission
F30.4	Manic episode in full remission	F33.42	Major depressive disorder, recurrent, in full remission
F30.8	Other manic episodes	F33.8	Other recurrent depressive disorders
F31.0	Bipolar disorder, current episode hypomanic	F34.0	Cyclothymic disorder
F31.10	Bipolar disorder, current episode manic without psychotic features, unspecified	F34.1	Dysthymic disorder
		F34.8	Other persistent mood [affective] disorders
F31.11	Bipolar disorder, current episode manic without psychotic features, mild	F34.9	Persistent mood [affective] disorder, unspecified
		F40.01	Agoraphobia with panic disorder
F31.12	Bipolar disorder, current episode manic without psychotic features, moderate	F40.02	Agoraphobia without panic disorder
		F40.10	Social phobia, unspecified
F31.13	Bipolar disorder, current episode manic without psychotic features, severe	F40.11	Social phobia, generalized
		F40.210	Arachnophobia
F31.2	Bipolar disorder, current episode manic severe with psychotic features	F40.218	Other animal type phobia
		F40.220	Fear of thunderstorms
F31.31	Bipolar disorder, current episode depressed, mild	F40.228	Other natural environment type phobia
F31.32	Bipolar disorder, current episode depressed, moderate	F40.230	Fear of blood
F31.4	Bipolar disorder, current episode depressed, severe, without psychotic features	F40.231	Fear of injections and transfusions
		F40.232	Fear of other medical care
F31.5	Bipolar disorder, current episode depressed, severe, with psychotic features	F40.233	Fear of injury
		F40.240	Claustrophobia
F31.61	Bipolar disorder, current episode mixed, mild	F40.241	Acrophobia
F31.62	Bipolar disorder, current episode mixed, moderate	F40.242	Fear of bridges
F31.63	Bipolar disorder, current episode mixed, severe, without psychotic features	F40.243	Fear of flying
		F40.290	Androphobia
F31.64	Bipolar disorder, current episode mixed, severe, with psychotic features	F40.291	Gynephobia
		F40.298	Other specified phobia
F31.71	Bipolar disorder, in partial remission, most recent episode hypomanic	F40.8	Other phobic anxiety disorders
		F40.9	Phobic anxiety disorder, unspecified
F31.72	Bipolar disorder, in full remission, most recent episode hypomanic	F41.0	Panic disorder [episodic paroxysmal anxiety] without agoraphobia
F31.73	Bipolar disorder, in partial remission, most recent episode manic		
F31.74	Bipolar disorder, in full remission, most recent episode manic	F41.1	Generalized anxiety disorder
		F41.3	Other mixed anxiety disorders
F31.75	Bipolar disorder, in partial remission, most recent episode depressed	F41.8	Other specified anxiety disorders
F31.76	Bipolar disorder, in full remission, most recent episode depressed	F41.9	Anxiety disorder, unspecified

F42	Obsessive-compulsive disorder
F43.0	Acute stress reaction
F43.11	Post-traumatic stress disorder, acute
F43.12	Post-traumatic stress disorder, chronic
F43.20	Adjustment disorder, unspecified
F43.21	Adjustment disorder with depressed mood
F43.22	Adjustment disorder with anxiety
F43.23	Adjustment disorder with mixed anxiety and depressed mood
F43.24	Adjustment disorder with disturbance of conduct
F43.25	Adjustment disorder with mixed disturbance of emotions and conduct
F43.8	Other reactions to severe stress
F44.0	Dissociative amnesia
F44.1	Dissociative fugue
F44.2	Dissociative stupor
F44.4	Conversion disorder with motor symptom or deficit
F44.5	Conversion disorder with seizures or convulsions
F44.6	Conversion disorder with sensory symptom or deficit
F44.7	Conversion disorder with mixed symptom presentation
F44.81	Dissociative identity disorder
F45.0	Somatization disorder
F45.1	Undifferentiated somatoform disorder
F45.20	Hypochondriacal disorder, unspecified
F45.21	Hypochondriasis
F45.22	Body dysmorphic disorder
F45.29	Other hypochondriacal disorders
F45.41	Pain disorder exclusively related to psychological factors
F45.8	Other somatoform disorders
F48.1	Depersonalization-derealization syndrome
F48.2	Pseudobulbar affect
F51.01	Primary insomnia
F51.02	Adjustment insomnia
F51.03	Paradoxical insomnia
F51.09	Other insomnia not due to a substance or known physiological condition
F51.11	Primary hypersomnia
F51.12	Insufficient sleep syndrome
F51.19	Other hypersomnia not due to a substance or known physiological condition
F51.3	Sleepwalking [somnambulism]
F51.4	Sleep terrors [night terrors]
F51.5	Nightmare disorder
F51.8	Other sleep disorders not due to a substance or known physiological condition
F60.0	Paranoid personality disorder
F60.1	Schizoid personality disorder
F60.2	Antisocial personality disorder
F60.3	Borderline personality disorder
F60.4	Histrionic personality disorder
F60.5	Obsessive-compulsive personality disorder
F60.6	Avoidant personality disorder
F60.7	Dependent personality disorder
F60.81	Narcissistic personality disorder

F60.89	Other specific personality disorders
F63.0	Pathological gambling
F63.1	Pyromania
F63.2	Kleptomania
F63.3	Trichotillomania
F63.81	Intermittent explosive disorder
F63.89	Other impulse disorders
F64.1	Gender identity disorder in adolescence and adulthood
F64.2	Gender identity disorder of childhood
F93.0	Separation anxiety disorder of childhood
F93.8	Other childhood emotional disorders
F94.0	Selective mutism
F94.1	Reactive attachment disorder of childhood
F94.2	Disinhibited attachment disorder of childhood
F94.8	Other childhood disorders of social functioning
F94.9	Childhood disorder of social functioning, unspecified
F95.0	Transient tic disorder
F98.5	Adult onset fluency disorder
F99	Mental disorder, not otherwise specified
G44.209	Tension-type headache, unspecified, not intractable
G47.29	Other circadian rhythm sleep disorder
H93.25	Central auditory processing disorder
R41.841	Cognitive communication deficit
R41.843	Psychomotor deficit
R41.89	Other symptoms and signs involving cognitive functions and awareness
R45.6	Violent behavior
R45.7	State of emotional shock and stress, unspecified
R45.850	Homicidal ideations
R48.0	Dyslexia and alexia
Z86.51	Personal history of combat and operational stress reaction
Z87.890	Personal history of sex reassignment

Please note that this list of associated ICD-10-CM codes is not all-inclusive. The procedure may be performed for reasons other than those listed that support the medical necessity of the service. Only those conditions supported by the medical record documentation should be reported.

Medicare Edits

	Fac RVU	Non-Fac RVU	FUD	Status	MUE
90865	3.63	4.69	N/A	A	1(3)

	Modifiers				Medicare References
90865	N/A	N/A	N/A	80*	100-1,3,30.1; 100-2,15,170

* with documentation

90867-90869

90867 Therapeutic repetitive transcranial magnetic stimulation (TMS) treatment; initial, including cortical mapping, motor threshold determination, delivery and management

90868 subsequent delivery and management, per session

90869 subsequent motor threshold re-determination with delivery and management

Explanation

Transcranial magnetic stimulation (TMS) is a technique to stimulate the brain by electromagnetic induction with a coil placed on the scalp. For direct stimulation to cortical neurons, a strong magnetic field pulse is generated over the patient's scalp to activate cortical neurons in the brain and to disturb the normal operation of the brain. Report 90867 for the initial treatment session, including cortical mapping, motor threshold determination, delivery, and management. Report 90868 for each subsequent session, including delivery and management only. Report 90869 for a subsequent session in which the motor threshold is re-determined and delivery and management are performed.

Coding Tips

Report 90867 for the initial session and 90868 for any subsequent sessions. When subsequent redetermination is performed, only 90869 should be reported. Do not report 90867 in conjunction with needle electromyography procedures (95860–95870) or transcranial motor stimulation of upper or lower limbs (95928, 95829, or 95839). The delivery of TMS may be reported once per session with code 90867, 90868, or 90869. Medication management (90863) or psychotherapy (90832–90840) may also be coded separately when supported by documentation.

Documentation Tips

Medical record documentation should indicate the nature and extent of the TMS planning.

When documentation supports that a significant, separately identifiable evaluation and management (E/M) service was rendered, the appropriate code for the E/M service may be reported additionally.

Reimbursement Tips

Third-party payers may have special coverage guidelines for these services. Check with the payer for guidelines before providing these services.

Terms To Know

depression. Disproportionate depressive state with behavior disturbance that is usually the result of a distressing experience and may include preoccupation with the psychic trauma and anxiety.

schizophrenia. Fundamental disturbance of personality and characteristic distortion of thinking, often a sense of being controlled by alien forces, delusions, disturbed perception, abnormal affect out of keeping with the real situation, and auditory or visual hallucinations with fear that intimate thoughts, feelings, and acts are known by others although clear consciousness and intellectual capacity are usually maintained.

ICD-10-CM Diagnostic Codes

F20.0	Paranoid schizophrenia
F20.1	Disorganized schizophrenia
F20.2	Catatonic schizophrenia
F20.3	Undifferentiated schizophrenia
F20.5	Residual schizophrenia
F20.81	Schizophreniform disorder
F20.89	Other schizophrenia
F20.9	Schizophrenia, unspecified
F21	Schizotypal disorder
F25.0	Schizoaffective disorder, bipolar type
F25.1	Schizoaffective disorder, depressive type
F25.8	Other schizoaffective disorders
F25.9	Schizoaffective disorder, unspecified
F30.10	Manic episode without psychotic symptoms, unspecified
F30.12	Manic episode without psychotic symptoms, moderate
F30.13	Manic episode, severe, without psychotic symptoms
F30.2	Manic episode, severe with psychotic symptoms
F30.8	Other manic episodes
F30.9	Manic episode, unspecified
F31.0	Bipolar disorder, current episode hypomanic
F31.10	Bipolar disorder, current episode manic without psychotic features, unspecified
F31.12	Bipolar disorder, current episode manic without psychotic features, moderate
F31.13	Bipolar disorder, current episode manic without psychotic features, severe
F31.2	Bipolar disorder, current episode manic severe with psychotic features
F31.30	Bipolar disorder, current episode depressed, mild or moderate severity, unspecified
F31.32	Bipolar disorder, current episode depressed, moderate
F31.4	Bipolar disorder, current episode depressed, severe, without psychotic features
F31.5	Bipolar disorder, current episode depressed, severe, with psychotic features
F31.60	Bipolar disorder, current episode mixed, unspecified
F31.62	Bipolar disorder, current episode mixed, moderate
F31.63	Bipolar disorder, current episode mixed, severe, without psychotic features
F31.64	Bipolar disorder, current episode mixed, severe, with psychotic features
F31.70	Bipolar disorder, currently in remission, most recent episode unspecified
F31.71	Bipolar disorder, in partial remission, most recent episode hypomanic
F31.72	Bipolar disorder, in full remission, most recent episode hypomanic
F31.81	Bipolar II disorder
F31.89	Other bipolar disorder
F31.9	Bipolar disorder, unspecified
F32.1	Major depressive disorder, single episode, moderate
F32.2	Major depressive disorder, single episode, severe without psychotic features
F32.3	Major depressive disorder, single episode, severe with psychotic features
F32.8	Other depressive episodes
F32.9	Major depressive disorder, single episode, unspecified
F33.1	Major depressive disorder, recurrent, moderate
F33.2	Major depressive disorder, recurrent severe without psychotic features

F33.3	Major depressive disorder, recurrent, severe with psychotic symptoms
F33.40	Major depressive disorder, recurrent, in remission, unspecified
F33.8	Other recurrent depressive disorders
F33.9	Major depressive disorder, recurrent, unspecified
F34.8	Other persistent mood [affective] disorders
F34.9	Persistent mood [affective] disorder, unspecified
F39	Unspecified mood [affective] disorder

Please note that this list of associated ICD-10-CM codes is not all-inclusive. The procedure may be performed for reasons other than those listed that support the medical necessity of the service. Only those conditions supported by the medical record documentation should be reported.

Medicare Edits

	Fac RVU	Non-Fac RVU	FUD	Status	MUE
90867	0.0	0.0	0	C	1(2)
90868	0.0	0.0	0	C	1(3)
90869	0.0	0.0	0	C	1(3)

	Modifiers				Medicare References
90867	N/A	N/A	N/A	N/A	None
90868	N/A	N/A	N/A	N/A	
90869	N/A	N/A	N/A	N/A	

* with documentation

90870

| 90870 | Electroconvulsive therapy (includes necessary monitoring) |

Explanation

The treating clinician initiates a seizure using electroconvulsive therapy (ECT), most often to combat chronic or profound depression, especially psychotic or intractable manic forms and used for people who cannot take antidepressants. The clinician anesthetizes the patient with a barbiturate and a muscle relaxant. Electrodes are placed on the patient's temples and/or forehead and a measured electrical dose is applied for about a second to commence the seizure, typically lasting 30 seconds to a minute. EEG and EKG monitors follow the seizure activity and heart rhythm while the patient sleeps through the therapy. The patient awakens a few minutes later.

Coding Tips

According to the American Medical Association (AMA), this code includes the management of the seizures by EEG, observation of the patient, and decision making regarding further treatment. The AMA goes further, stating that if the psychiatrist also administers the anesthesia for the therapy, the appropriate anesthesia code (00104) should be coded in addition. However, most third-party payers, including Medicare, will not reimburse the physician performing the procedure separately for anesthesia services.

Documentation Tips

Documentation should include a history and physical examination; an established psychiatric diagnosis; evaluation and management findings and treatments including clinical signs, symptoms, and abnormal diagnostic tests; changes or alterations, as well as the response or nonresponse to medical management and the need and appropriateness for initial or continued ECT therapy based on the ongoing assessment and mental status; and the procedure report.

Reimbursement Tips

Third-party payers may have special coverage guidelines for this service. Check with the payer for guidelines before providing the service.

Terms To Know

chronic. Persistent, continuing, or recurring.

depression. Disproportionate depressive state with behavior disturbance that is usually the result of a distressing experience and may include preoccupation with the psychic trauma and anxiety.

electrode. Electric terminal specialized for a particular electrochemical reaction that acts as a medium between a body surface and another instrument, commonly termed a lead.

ICD-10-CM Diagnostic Codes

F05	Delirium due to known physiological condition
F06.0	Psychotic disorder with hallucinations due to known physiological condition
F06.1	Catatonic disorder due to known physiological condition
F06.2	Psychotic disorder with delusions due to known physiological condition
F06.30	Mood disorder due to known physiological condition, unspecified
F06.31	Mood disorder due to known physiological condition with depressive features
F06.32	Mood disorder due to known physiological condition with major depressive-like episode

F06.33	Mood disorder due to known physiological condition with manic features	F31.71	Bipolar disorder, in partial remission, most recent episode hypomanic
F06.34	Mood disorder due to known physiological condition with mixed features	F31.72	Bipolar disorder, in full remission, most recent episode hypomanic
F06.8	Other specified mental disorders due to known physiological condition	F31.73	Bipolar disorder, in partial remission, most recent episode manic
F07.0	Personality change due to known physiological condition	F31.75	Bipolar disorder, in partial remission, most recent episode depressed
F20.0	Paranoid schizophrenia	F31.77	Bipolar disorder, in partial remission, most recent episode mixed
F20.1	Disorganized schizophrenia	F31.81	Bipolar II disorder
F20.2	Catatonic schizophrenia	F31.89	Other bipolar disorder
F20.3	Undifferentiated schizophrenia	F32.0	Major depressive disorder, single episode, mild
F20.5	Residual schizophrenia	F32.1	Major depressive disorder, single episode, moderate
F20.81	Schizophreniform disorder	F32.2	Major depressive disorder, single episode, severe without psychotic features
F20.89	Other schizophrenia	F32.3	Major depressive disorder, single episode, severe with psychotic features
F21	Schizotypal disorder		
F22	Delusional disorders	F32.4	Major depressive disorder, single episode, in partial remission
F23	Brief psychotic disorder	F32.8	Other depressive episodes
F24	Shared psychotic disorder	F32.9	Major depressive disorder, single episode, unspecified
F25.0	Schizoaffective disorder, bipolar type	F33.0	Major depressive disorder, recurrent, mild
F25.1	Schizoaffective disorder, depressive type	F33.1	Major depressive disorder, recurrent, moderate
F25.8	Other schizoaffective disorders	F33.2	Major depressive disorder, recurrent severe without psychotic features
F28	Other psychotic disorder not due to a substance or known physiological condition	F33.3	Major depressive disorder, recurrent, severe with psychotic symptoms
F30.10	Manic episode without psychotic symptoms, unspecified	F33.40	Major depressive disorder, recurrent, in remission, unspecified
F30.11	Manic episode without psychotic symptoms, mild	F33.41	Major depressive disorder, recurrent, in partial remission
F30.12	Manic episode without psychotic symptoms, moderate	F33.8	Other recurrent depressive disorders
F30.13	Manic episode, severe, without psychotic symptoms	F33.9	Major depressive disorder, recurrent, unspecified
F30.2	Manic episode, severe with psychotic symptoms	F34.0	Cyclothymic disorder
F30.3	Manic episode in partial remission	F34.1	Dysthymic disorder
F30.8	Other manic episodes	F34.8	Other persistent mood [affective] disorders
F31.0	Bipolar disorder, current episode hypomanic	F34.9	Persistent mood [affective] disorder, unspecified
F31.11	Bipolar disorder, current episode manic without psychotic features, mild	F39	Unspecified mood [affective] disorder
F31.12	Bipolar disorder, current episode manic without psychotic features, moderate	F43.0	Acute stress reaction
		F43.10	Post-traumatic stress disorder, unspecified
F31.13	Bipolar disorder, current episode manic without psychotic features, severe	F43.11	Post-traumatic stress disorder, acute
		F43.12	Post-traumatic stress disorder, chronic
F31.2	Bipolar disorder, current episode manic severe with psychotic features	F43.21	Adjustment disorder with depressed mood
		F43.22	Adjustment disorder with anxiety
F31.31	Bipolar disorder, current episode depressed, mild	F43.23	Adjustment disorder with mixed anxiety and depressed mood
F31.32	Bipolar disorder, current episode depressed, moderate	F43.24	Adjustment disorder with disturbance of conduct
F31.4	Bipolar disorder, current episode depressed, severe, without psychotic features	F43.25	Adjustment disorder with mixed disturbance of emotions and conduct
F31.5	Bipolar disorder, current episode depressed, severe, with psychotic features	F43.29	Adjustment disorder with other symptoms
		F44.4	Conversion disorder with motor symptom or deficit
F31.61	Bipolar disorder, current episode mixed, mild	F44.5	Conversion disorder with seizures or convulsions
F31.62	Bipolar disorder, current episode mixed, moderate	F44.6	Conversion disorder with sensory symptom or deficit
F31.63	Bipolar disorder, current episode mixed, severe, without psychotic features	F44.7	Conversion disorder with mixed symptom presentation
F31.64	Bipolar disorder, current episode mixed, severe, with psychotic features	F44.81	Dissociative identity disorder
		F44.89	Other dissociative and conversion disorders
F31.70	Bipolar disorder, currently in remission, most recent episode unspecified	F44.9	Dissociative and conversion disorder, unspecified
		F48.1	Depersonalization-derealization syndrome
		F51.01	Primary insomnia

F51.03	Paradoxical insomnia
F51.09	Other insomnia not due to a substance or known physiological condition
F51.11	Primary hypersomnia
F51.12	Insufficient sleep syndrome
F51.19	Other hypersomnia not due to a substance or known physiological condition
F51.9	Sleep disorder not due to a substance or known physiological condition, unspecified
F53	Puerperal psychosis
F60.0	Paranoid personality disorder
F60.1	Schizoid personality disorder
F60.2	Antisocial personality disorder
F60.3	Borderline personality disorder
F60.4	Histrionic personality disorder
F60.5	Obsessive-compulsive personality disorder
F60.6	Avoidant personality disorder
F60.7	Dependent personality disorder
F60.81	Narcissistic personality disorder
F60.89	Other specific personality disorders
F60.9	Personality disorder, unspecified
F63.0	Pathological gambling
F63.1	Pyromania
F63.2	Kleptomania
F63.3	Trichotillomania
F63.81	Intermittent explosive disorder
F63.89	Other impulse disorders
F63.9	Impulse disorder, unspecified
F69	Unspecified disorder of adult personality and behavior
F80.4	Speech and language development delay due to hearing loss
F84.3	Other childhood disintegrative disorder
F91.1	Conduct disorder, childhood-onset type
F91.2	Conduct disorder, adolescent-onset type
F94.8	Other childhood disorders of social functioning
F95.1	Chronic motor or vocal tic disorder
F95.2	Tourette's disorder
F95.8	Other tic disorders
F95.9	Tic disorder, unspecified
F98.4	Stereotyped movement disorders
G44.209	Tension-type headache, unspecified, not intractable

Please note that this list of associated ICD-10-CM codes is not all-inclusive. The procedure may be performed for reasons other than those listed that support the medical necessity of the service. Only those conditions supported by the medical record documentation should be reported.

Medicare Edits

	Fac RVU	Non-Fac RVU	FUD	Status	MUE
90870	3.12	4.99	0	A	2(3)

	Modifiers				Medicare References
90870	N/A	N/A	N/A	80*	100-1,3,30.1; 100-2,15,170

* with documentation

90875-90876

90875 Individual psychophysiological therapy incorporating biofeedback training by any modality (face-to-face with the patient), with psychotherapy (eg, insight oriented, behavior modifying or supportive psychotherapy); 30 minutes

90876 45 minutes

Explanation

The treating clinician gives individual psychophysiological therapy by utilizing biofeedback training together with psychotherapy to modify behavior. The clinician prepares the patient with sensors that read and display skin temperature, blood pressure, muscle tension, or brain wave activity. The patient is taught how certain thought processes, stimuli, and actions affect these physiological responses. The treating clinician works with the patient to learn to recognize and manipulate these responses, to control maladapted physiological functions, through relaxation and awareness techniques. Psychotherapy is also rendered using supportive interactions, suggestion, persuasion, reality discussions, re-education, behavior modification techniques, reassurance, and the occasional aid of medication. Individual psychophysiological therapy is performed face to face with the patient. Report 90875 for sessions of 30 minutes and 90876 for sessions of 45 minutes.

Coding Tips

These procedures may be performed by a physician or other qualified health care professional.

Documentation Tips

Documentation should specify whether this is a single episode or recurrent, the current degree of depression, the presence of psychotic features or symptoms, and remission status (i.e., partial, full) when applicable.

Documentation should reflect any treatment failure or a change in diagnosis and/or a change in treatment plan. There should also be evidence of any initiation or reinstitution of a drug regime, which requires close and continuous skilled medical observation. Treatment plan goals and objectives must be well defined and signed by the attending physician, and progress notes must clearly demonstrate that the patient displays evidence of improvement or regression.

Reimbursement Tips

Check with the specific payer to determine coverage. Most third-party payers, including Medicare, do not provide coverage of biofeedback therapy when used to treat psychiatric conditions.

Terms To Know

psychophysiological disorders. Various physical symptoms or types of physiological malfunctions of mental origin, usually manifested in the autonomic nervous system.

psychotherapy. Treatment for mental illness and behavioral disturbances in which the clinician establishes a professional contract with the patient and, through definitive therapeutic communication, attempts to alleviate the emotional disturbances, reverse or change maladaptive patterns of behavior, and encourage personality growth and development.

ICD-10-CM Diagnostic Codes

The application of this code is too broad to adequately present ICD-10-CM diagnostic code links here. Refer to your ICD-10-CM book.

Medicare Edits

	Fac RVU	Non-Fac RVU	FUD	Status	MUE
90875	1.73	1.73	N/A	N	-
90876	2.74	3.05	N/A	N	-

	Modifiers				Medicare References
90875	N/A	N/A	N/A	N/A	100-1,3,30.1; 100-2,15,160;
90876	N/A	N/A	N/A	N/A	100-3,10.4; 100-4,12,160;
					100-4,12,160.1;
					100-4,12,170

* with documentation

90880

90880   Hypnotherapy

Explanation

Hypnosis is used as a modality for psychotherapy. The therapist induces an altered state of consciousness, or focused attention, in the patient. While patients are in this relaxed state of heightened awareness and suggestibility, they can experience changes in the way they feel, think, and behave in response to suggestions directed to them by the hypnotherapist. This modality for psychiatric services helps the therapist to achieve an alteration in the patient's thought and behavior patterns.

Coding Tips

This procedure may be performed by a physician or other qualified health care professional.

Documentation Tips

Documentation should reflect any treatment failure or a change in diagnosis and/or a change in treatment plan. There should also be evidence of any initiation or reinstitution of a drug regime, which requires close and continuous skilled medical observation. Treatment plan goals and objectives must be well defined and signed by the attending physician, and progress notes must clearly demonstrate that the patient displays evidence of improvement or regression.

Reimbursement Tips

Many payers have guidelines that indicate that when hypnotherapy is used in conjunction with psychotherapy (during the same session), only the hypnotherapy (90880) should be reported.

Third-party payers may have special coverage guidelines for this service. Check with the payer for guidelines before providing the service.

Terms To Know

psychogenic fugue. Rapid onset form of dissociative hysteria characterized by an episode of wandering with the inability to recall one's prior identity, followed by a quick recovery and no recollection of events that took place during the fugue state.

ICD-10-CM Diagnostic Codes

The application of this code is too broad to adequately present ICD-10-CM diagnostic code links here. Refer to your ICD-10-CM book.

Medicare Edits

	Fac RVU	Non-Fac RVU	FUD	Status	MUE
90880	2.64	2.85	N/A	A	1(3)

	Modifiers				Medicare References
90880	N/A	N/A	N/A	80*	100-1,3,30.1

* with documentation

90882

90882 Environmental intervention for medical management purposes on a psychiatric patient's behalf with agencies, employers, or institutions

Explanation

The clinician uses this code to report work done with agencies, employers, or institutions on a psychiatric patient's behalf in order to achieve environmental changes and interventions for managing the patient's medical condition.

Coding Tips

This procedure may be performed by a physician or other qualified health care professional.

Documentation Tips

Documentation should reflect any treatment failure or a change in diagnosis and/or a change in treatment plan. There should also be evidence of any initiation or reinstitution of a drug regime, which requires close and continuous skilled medical observation. Treatment plan goals and objectives must be well defined and signed by the attending physician, and progress notes must clearly demonstrate that the patient displays evidence of improvement or regression.

Reimbursement Tips

Check with the specific payer to determine coverage. Medicare and most third-party payers do not reimburse for this service.

Terms To Know

intervention. Purposeful interaction of the physical therapist with the patient and, when appropriate, with other individuals involved in patient care, using various physical therapy procedures and techniques to produce changes in the condition.

noncovered procedure. Health care treatment not reimbursable according to provisions of a given insurance policy, or in the case of Medicare, in accordance with Medicare laws and regulations.

ICD-10-CM Diagnostic Codes

The application of this code is too broad to adequately present ICD-10-CM diagnostic code links here. Refer to your ICD-10-CM book.

Medicare Edits

	Fac RVU	Non-Fac RVU	FUD	Status	MUE
90882	0.0	0.0	N/A	N	-

	Modifiers				Medicare References
90882	N/A	N/A	N/A	N/A	100-4,12,170

* with documentation

90885

90885 Psychiatric evaluation of hospital records, other psychiatric reports, psychometric and/or projective tests, and other accumulated data for medical diagnostic purposes

Explanation

The clinician reviews and evaluates the patient's hospital records, other psychiatric reports such as psychometric and projective tests, and other pertinent data for the purpose of gaining a medical diagnosis and insight into the patient's present condition.

Coding Tips

This procedure may be performed by a physician or other qualified health care professional. This service indicates the evaluation of hospital records, other psychiatric reports, diagnostic tests, or other data to diagnosis the patient's condition. If this interpretation is provided on the day that the physician is providing other services, an evaluation and management (E/M) code may be more appropriate. In the case of an encounter where evaluation and psychotherapy were performed, the appropriate psychotherapy code that includes the E/M service should be used.

Documentation Tips

Documentation should clearly identify all evaluated data, as well as the provider's interpretation of the data evaluation. All entries to the medical record should be dated and authenticated.

Reimbursement Tips

Check with the specific payer to determine coverage. Very few third-party payers provide coverage of this service. In the case of reports provided at an agency's or employer's request, a fee should be discussed and payment arrangement made prior to the rendering of the service.

Terms To Know

diagnosis. Determination or confirmation of a condition, disease, or syndrome and its implications.

evaluation and management. Assessment, counseling, and other services provided to a patient reported through CPT codes.

noncovered procedure. Health care treatment not reimbursable according to provisions of a given insurance policy, or in the case of Medicare, in accordance with Medicare laws and regulations.

ICD-10-CM Diagnostic Codes

The application of this code is too broad to adequately present ICD-10-CM diagnostic code links here. Refer to your ICD-10-CM book.

Medicare Edits

	Fac RVU	Non-Fac RVU	FUD	Status	MUE
90885	1.4	1.4	N/A	B	0(3)

	Modifiers				Medicare References
90885	N/A	N/A	N/A	N/A	100-1,3,30.1; 100-2,15,160

* with documentation

90887

90887   Interpretation or explanation of results of psychiatric, other medical examinations and procedures, or other accumulated data to family or other responsible persons, or advising them how to assist patient

Explanation

The clinician interprets the results of a patient's psychiatric and medical examinations and procedures, as well as any other pertinent recorded data, and spends time explaining the patient's condition to family members and other responsible parties involved with the patient's care and well-being. Advice is also given as to how family members can best assist the patient.

Coding Tips

This procedure may be performed by a physician or other qualified health care professional. This service indicates that the physician has explained to the patient's family, care taker, or to the patient's employer, the medical examinations, procedures, and other accumulated data performed on that patient in order to obtain the responsible parties' participation and/or support in that patient's treatment. If this interpretation is provided on the day that the physician is providing other services, an evaluation and management (E/M) code may be more appropriate. In the case of an encounter where evaluation and psychotherapy were performed, the appropriate psychotherapy code that includes the E/M service should be used. Do not report this service with adaptive behavior treatment with protocol modification, family adaptive behavior treatment guidance, or multiple-family group adaptive behavior treatment guidance.

Documentation Tips

Documentation should clearly identify all evaluated data, as well as the provider's interpretation of the data evaluation. All entries to the medical record should be dated and authenticated.

Reimbursement Tips

Check with the specific payer to determine coverage. Very few third-party payers provide coverage of this service. In the case of reports provided at an agency's or employer's request, a fee should be discussed and payment arrangement made prior to the rendering of the service.

Terms To Know

noncovered procedure. Health care treatment not reimbursable according to provisions of a given insurance policy, or in the case of Medicare, in accordance with Medicare laws and regulations.

ICD-10-CM Diagnostic Codes

The application of this code is too broad to adequately present ICD-10-CM diagnostic code links here. Refer to your ICD-10-CM book.

Medicare Edits

	Fac RVU	Non-Fac RVU	FUD	Status	MUE
90887	2.14	2.49	N/A	B	0(3)

	Modifiers				Medicare References
90887	N/A	N/A	N/A	N/A	100-1,3,30.1; 100-4,12,210.1

* with documentation

90889

90889   Preparation of report of patient's psychiatric status, history, treatment, or progress (other than for legal or consultative purposes) for other individuals, agencies, or insurance carriers

Explanation

The clinician prepares a report on a patient's mental condition, current psychiatric status, history, treatment regimen, and progress for other physicians, agencies, or insurance carriers involved with the patient's care, except for legal or consultative purposes.

Coding Tips

If this service is provided on the day the physician is provides other services, an evaluation and management (E/M) code may be more appropriate. In the case of an encounter where evaluation and psychotherapy were performed, the appropriate psychotherapy code that includes the E/M service should be used. The preparation of a report describing the patient's psychiatric condition and status provided to agencies, insurance carriers, and other physicians (not including consultations) would be reported using 90889. However, it is not to be used when providing information for legal purposes. It should be noted that very few third-party payers provide coverage of this service. In the case of reports provided at an agency's or employer's request, a fee should be discussed and payment arrangement made prior to the rendering of the service.

Documentation Tips

Documentation should clearly identify all evaluated data, as well as the provider's interpretation of the data evaluation. All entries to the medical record should be dated and authenticated.

Reimbursement Tips

Check with the specific payer to determine coverage. Very few third-party payers provide coverage of this service. In the case of reports provided at an agency's or employer's request, a fee should be discussed and payment arrangement made prior to the rendering of the service.

Terms To Know

encounter. Direct personal contact between a patient and a physician, or other person who is authorized by state licensure law and, if applicable, by hospital staff bylaws, to order or furnish hospital services for diagnosis or treatment of the patient.

ICD-10-CM Diagnostic Codes

The application of this code is too broad to adequately present ICD-10-CM diagnostic code links here. Refer to your ICD-10-CM book.

Medicare Edits

	Fac RVU	Non-Fac RVU	FUD	Status	MUE
90889	0.0	0.0	N/A	B	0(3)

	Modifiers				Medicare References
90889	N/A	N/A	N/A	N/A	100-1,3,30.1

* with documentation

90901-90911

90901	Biofeedback training by any modality
90911	Biofeedback training, perineal muscles, anorectal or urethral sphincter, including EMG and/or manometry

Explanation

Biofeedback trains patients to control their autonomic or involuntary nervous system responses to regulate vital signs such as heart rate, blood pressure, temperature, and muscle tension. Monitors of various types are used to indicate body responses, which the patient learns to associate with related stimuli and also control in serial sessions. This code applies to any of several modalities of biofeedback training. Biofeedback is used for treatment of conditions including high blood pressure, incontinence, Raynaud's syndrome, and anticipatory nausea due to chemotherapy. For biofeedback using any modality, see code 90901. When biofeedback is performed to help the incontinent patient gain control of the related muscles, see code 90911.

Coding Tips

If biofeedback is used to facilitate psychotherapy, see codes 90875 and 90876.

Documentation Tips

The anatomical location, as well as the condition necessitating the treatment, should be clearly identified in the medical record.

Reimbursement Tips

Medicare provides benefits for these procedures only when medically necessary for the re-education of specific muscle groups or for the treatment of pathological muscle conditions not able to be treated using conventional methods. Biofeedback is not covered for muscle tension and for psychosomatic conditions. Be sure to check coverage guidelines with each individual payer.

Terms To Know

autonomic nervous system. Portion of the nervous system that controls involuntary body functions. The fibers of the autonomic nervous system regulate the iris of the eye and the smooth-muscle action of the heart, blood vessels, lungs, glands, stomach, colon, bladder, and other visceral organs that are not under conscious control by the individual. The autonomic nerve fibers exit from the central nervous system and branch out into the sympathetic and parasympathetic nervous systems.

ICD-10-CM Diagnostic Codes

The application of this code is too broad to adequately present ICD-10-CM diagnostic code links here. Refer to your ICD-10-CM book.

Medicare Edits

	Fac RVU	Non-Fac RVU	FUD	Status	MUE
90901	0.56	1.08	0	A	1(3)
90911	1.26	2.37	0	A	1(3)

	Modifiers				Medicare References
90901	N/A	N/A	N/A	80*	None
90911	N/A	N/A	N/A	80*	

* with documentation

96020

96020	Neurofunctional testing selection and administration during noninvasive imaging functional brain mapping, with test administered entirely by a physician or other qualified health care professional (ie, psychologist), with review of test results and report

Explanation

During a separately reported functional MRI (fMRI), the physician or psychologist administers a series of tests involving language, memory, cognition, movement, and sensation, and reviews the results and reports upon them in a process called functional brain mapping. These reports identify the expected versus observed locations of brain activity documented by the fMRI as the patient performs specific tasks.

Coding Tips

Code 96020 should not be reported with psychological testing (96101–96103) or neurobehavioral status examination services (96116–96120). Evaluation and management services would not be reported for the same date of service. When a functional MRI is performed and the neurofunctional tests are provided by a technician or other nonphysician, nonpsychologist provider, see 70554. See 70555 when neurofunctional testing is provided by the physician or psychologist and his or her presence is required during the entire MRI. Code 70555 should not be reported except when 96020 is performed. Do not report 96020 with 70554. Neurofunctional testing should not be reported in addition to psychological testing (96101–96103) or neurobehavioral status examinations or testing (96116–96120).

Documentation Tips

All entries to the medical record should be dated and authenticated.

Reimbursement Tips

Special coverage instructions may apply. Check with the third-party payer before providing the service. Note that for Medicare purposes, this service is carrier priced.

Terms To Know

evaluation and management. Assessment, counseling, and other services provided to a patient reported through CPT codes.

fMRI. Functional magnetic resonance imaging. Technique to identify which part of the brain is activated by stimulus or activity; a type of brain mapping useful prior to brain surgery and in cases of epilepsy and mental disorders.

ICD-10-CM Diagnostic Codes

The application of this code is too broad to adequately present ICD-10-CM diagnostic code links here. Refer to your ICD-10-CM book.

Medicare Edits

	Fac RVU	Non-Fac RVU	FUD	Status	MUE
96020	0.0	0.0	N/A	C	1(2)

	Modifiers				Medicare References
96020	N/A	N/A	N/A	80*	None

* with documentation

96101-96103

96101 Psychological testing (includes psychodiagnostic assessment of emotionality, intellectual abilities, personality and psychopathology, eg, MMPI, Rorschach, WAIS), per hour of the psychologist's or physician's time, both face-to-face time administering tests to the patient and time interpreting these test results and preparing the report

96102 Psychological testing (includes psychodiagnostic assessment of emotionality, intellectual abilities, personality and psychopathology, eg, MMPI and WAIS), with qualified health care professional interpretation and report, administered by technician, per hour of technician time, face-to-face

96103 Psychological testing (includes psychodiagnostic assessment of emotionality, intellectual abilities, personality and psychopathology, eg, MMPI), administered by a computer, with qualified health care professional interpretation and report

Explanation

The physician or psychologist administers and interprets the results of psychological testing. The testing in written, oral, computer, or combined formats measures personality, emotions, intellectual functioning, and psychopathology. Code 96101 applies to each hour of testing and includes both face-to-face time administering tests to the patient, as well as interpretation and preparation of the report; however, it is not used to report the interpretation of technician- or computer-administered tests. In 96102, a technician administers the test, which is interpreted and reported by a qualified health care professional. In 96103, the test is administered by computer, which is interpreted and reported by a qualified health care professional.

Coding Tips

These codes are used to report services provided during testing of the cognitive function of the central nervous system. Report these codes once for each hour of testing, which includes interpretation and preparation of the report. A written report must be generated. A minimum of 31 minutes must be provided before assigning one of these codes. Codes 96102 and 96103 are used when the testing is performed by a qualified technician or computer, respectively. It is appropriate, however, to assign code 96101 when reporting the additional time necessary for the health care provider to incorporate clinical data including data previously completed and reported by a technician (or computer-administered testing data). To report a minimental health status, see the appropriate level of evaluation and management service. Do not report this service with adaptive behavior treatment by protocol (0364T–0365T), group adaptive behavior treatment by protocol (0366T–0367T), or exposure adaptive behavior treatment (0373T–0374T).

Documentation Tips

Because these are time-based codes, the medical record documentation should contain the total time spent rendering and interpreting the service, including the stop and start times of testing.

Reimbursement Tips

The diagnosis code must support the medical necessity of the service; otherwise, it will likely be denied.

Terms To Know

assessment. Process of collecting and studying information and data, such as test values, signs, and symptoms.

cognitive. Being aware by drawing from knowledge, such as judgment, reason, perception, and memory.

interpretation. Professional health care provider's review of data with a written or verbal opinion.

ICD-10-CM Diagnostic Codes

The application of this code is too broad to adequately present ICD-10-CM diagnostic code links here. Refer to your ICD-10-CM book.

Medicare Edits

	Fac RVU	Non-Fac RVU	FUD	Status	MUE
96101	2.23	2.25	N/A	A	-
96102	0.66	1.79	N/A	A	-
96103	0.76	0.79	N/A	A	1(2)

	Modifiers				Medicare References
96101	N/A	N/A	N/A	80*	100-1,3,30; 100-1,3,30.3;
96102	N/A	N/A	N/A	80*	100-2,15,80.2; 100-2,15,160;
96103	N/A	N/A	N/A	80*	100-4,12,210.1

* with documentation

96110-96111

96110 Developmental screening (eg, developmental milestone survey, speech and language delay screen), with scoring and documentation, per standardized instrument

96111 Developmental testing, (includes assessment of motor, language, social, adaptive, and/or cognitive functioning by standardized developmental instruments) with interpretation and report

Explanation

The physician or other health care professional performs a developmental screening on a provider standardized form (meeting industry standards). The screening is to determine whether the patient needs additional work up for a developmental disorder or at periodic intervals throughout infancy and adolescent years. This code includes interpretation and report of the findings.

Coding Tips

Note that these codes are not time-based codes. Information obtained through the assessment testing is interpreted and a written report is generated. The interpretation and preparation of the report are included in the service. Developmental screening includes screening for conditions such as autism and behavioral and emotional disorders. Developmental testing includes the assessment of motor, language, social, adaptive, and/or cognitive function. For neuropsychological testing, see codes from range 96118–96120. For psychological testing, see codes from range 96101–96103. To report an emotional/behavioral assessment, see 96127. Do not report this service with adaptive behavior treatment by protocol (0364T–0365T), group adaptive behavior treatment by protocol (0366T–0367T), or exposure adaptive behavior treatment (0373T–0374T).

Documentation Tips

All entries to the medical record should be dated and authenticated.

Reimbursement Tips

Coverage guidelines may vary. Check with the third-party payer before providing the service.

Terms To Know

cognitive. Being aware by drawing from knowledge, such as judgment, reason, perception, and memory.

developmental delay disorders. Various disorders manifested by a delay in development based on that anticipated for a certain age level or period of development. Both biological and nonbiological factors may be involved. Originating before age 18, these impairments may continue indefinitely.

motor function. Ability to learn or demonstrate skillful and efficient assumption, maintenance, modification, and control of voluntary postures and movement patterns.

ICD-10-CM Diagnostic Codes

The application of this code is too broad to adequately present ICD-10-CM diagnostic code links here. Refer to your ICD-10-CM book.

Medicare Edits

	Fac RVU	Non-Fac RVU	FUD	Status	MUE
96110	0.25	0.25	N/A	N	-
96111	3.47	3.65	N/A	A	-

	Modifiers				Medicare References
96110	N/A	N/A	N/A	N/A	100-1,3,30; 100-1,3,30.1;
96111	N/A	N/A	N/A	80*	100-1,3,30.3; 100-4,12,160

* with documentation

96116

96116   Neurobehavioral status exam (clinical assessment of thinking, reasoning and judgment, eg, acquired knowledge, attention, language, memory, planning and problem solving, and visual spatial abilities), per hour of the psychologist's or physician's time, both face-to-face time with the patient and time interpreting test results and preparing the report

Explanation

The physician or psychologist evaluates aspects of thinking, reasoning, and judgment to evaluate a patient's neurocognitive abilities. This code applies to each hour of examination time and includes both face-to-face time with the patient and time spent interpreting test results and preparing a report.

Coding Tips

Report this code once for each hour of testing, which includes interpretation and preparation of the report. A written report must be generated. A minimum of 31 minutes of testing must be provided before assigning one of these codes. For psychological testing, see codes from range 96101–96103. For neuropsychological testing, see codes from range 96118–96120. Developmental screening or testing is reported using 96110 or 96111, respectively. Do not report this service with adaptive behavior treatment by protocol (0364T–0365T), group adaptive behavior treatment by protocol (0366T–0367T), or exposure adaptive behavior treatment (0373T–0374T).

Documentation Tips

Because these are time-based codes, the medical record documentation should contain the total time spent rendering and interpreting the service, including the stop and start times of testing.

Reimbursement Tips

Coverage guidelines may vary. Check with the third-party payer before providing the service.

Terms To Know

assessment. Process of collecting and studying information and data, such as test values, signs, and symptoms.

cognitive. Being aware by drawing from knowledge, such as judgment, reason, perception, and memory.

face to face. Interaction between two parties, usually provider and patient, that occurs in the physical presence of each other.

interpretation. Professional health care provider's review of data with a written or verbal opinion.

ICD-10-CM Diagnostic Codes

The application of this code is too broad to adequately present ICD-10-CM diagnostic code links here. Refer to your ICD-10-CM book.

Medicare Edits

	Fac RVU	Non-Fac RVU	FUD	Status	MUE
96116	2.46	2.62	N/A	A	-

	Modifiers				Medicare References
96116	N/A	N/A	N/A	80*	100-1,3,30; 100-1,3,30.3; 100-2,15,270; 100-2,15,270.2; 100-2,15,270.4; 100-4,12,190.3; 100-4,12,190.7

* with documentation

96118-96120

96118   Neuropsychological testing (eg, Halstead-Reitan Neuropsychological Battery, Wechsler Memory Scales and Wisconsin Card Sorting Test), per hour of the psychologist's or physician's time, both face-to-face time administering tests to the patient and time interpreting these test results and preparing the report

96119   Neuropsychological testing (eg, Halstead-Reitan Neuropsychological Battery, Wechsler Memory Scales and Wisconsin Card Sorting Test), with qualified health care professional interpretation and report, administered by technician, per hour of technician time, face-to-face

96120   Neuropsychological testing (eg, Wisconsin Card Sorting Test), administered by a computer, with qualified health care professional interpretation and report

Explanation

The physician or psychologist administers a series of tests in thinking, reasoning, judgment, and memory to evaluate the patient's neurocognitive abilities. Code 96118 applies to each hour of testing and includes face-to-face time administering tests to the patient, as well as interpretation and preparation of the report; however, it is not used to report the interpretation of technician- or computer-administered tests. In 96119, a technician administers the test, which is interpreted and reported by a qualified health care professional. In 96120, the test is administered by computer, which is interpreted and reported by a qualified health care professional.

Coding Tips

Codes 96118 and 96119 are reported per hour of service. Information obtained through the assessment testing is interpreted and a written report is generated. The interpretation and preparation of the report are included in the service. For psychological testing, see codes from range 96101–96103; for neurobehavioral testing, see code 96116; for standardized cognitive performance testing, see code 96125; for developmental screening or testing, see codes from range 96110–96111. Code 96118 is not to be reported for the interpretation and reporting; neither is 96119 or 96120. Code 96118 may also be reported when additional time is needed to integrate other clinical data including technician and computer-administered test results. Do not report this service with adaptive behavior treatment by protocol (0364T–0365T), group adaptive behavior treatment by protocol (0366T–0367T), or exposure adaptive behavior treatment (0373T–0374T).

Documentation Tips

Because these are time-based codes, the medical record documentation should contain the total time spent rendering and interpreting the service, including the stop and start times of testing.

Reimbursement Tips

Coverage guidelines may vary. Check with the third-party payer before providing the service.

Terms To Know

assessment. Process of collecting and studying information and data, such as test values, signs, and symptoms.

cognitive. Being aware by drawing from knowledge, such as judgment, reason, perception, and memory.

interpretation. Professional health care provider's review of data with a written or verbal opinion.

ICD-10-CM Diagnostic Codes

The application of this code is too broad to adequately present ICD-10-CM diagnostic code links here. Refer to your ICD-10-CM book.

Medicare Edits

	Fac RVU	Non-Fac RVU	FUD	Status	MUE
96118	2.22	2.76	N/A	A	-
96119	0.67	2.26	N/A	A	-
96120	0.74	1.36	N/A	A	1(2)

	Modifiers				Medicare References
96118	N/A	N/A	N/A	80*	100-1,3,30; 100-1,3,30.3
96119	N/A	N/A	N/A	80*	
96120	N/A	N/A	N/A	80*	

* with documentation

96125

96125   Standardized cognitive performance testing (eg, Ross Information Processing Assessment) per hour of a qualified health care professional's time, both face-to-face time administering tests to the patient and time interpreting these test results and preparing the report

Explanation

A qualified health care professional administers standardized cognitive performance testing to evaluate such factors as the patient's immediate, recent, and remote memory; temporal and spatial orientation; general information recall; problem-solving and abstract reasoning abilities; organizational skills; and auditory processing and retention. This code applies to each hour of testing and includes face-to-face time administering tests to the patient, as well as interpretation and preparation of the report.

Coding Tips

Report this code once for each hour of testing, which includes interpretation and preparation of the report. For psychological testing, see codes from range 96101–96103; for neurobehavioral testing, see code 96116; for neuropsychological testing, see codes 96118–96120; for developmental screening or testing, see codes from range 96110–96111. Do not report this service with adaptive behavior treatment by protocol (0364T–0365T), group adaptive behavior treatment by protocol (0366T–0367T), or exposure adaptive behavior treatment (0373T–0374T).

Documentation Tips

A written report must be generated.

Reimbursement Tips

A minimum of 31 minutes of testing must be provided before assigning this code.

Terms To Know

cognitive. Being aware by drawing from knowledge, such as judgment, reason, perception, and memory.

interpretation. Professional health care provider's review of data with a written or verbal opinion.

ICD-10-CM Diagnostic Codes

The application of this code is too broad to adequately present ICD-10-CM diagnostic code links here. Refer to your ICD-10-CM book.

Medicare Edits

	Fac RVU	Non-Fac RVU	FUD	Status	MUE
96125	3.31	3.31	N/A	A	2(1)

	Modifiers				Medicare References
96125	N/A	N/A	N/A	80*	100-2,15,160; 100-2,15,230.4; 100-4,5,10.2; 100-4,5,10.6

* with documentation

96127

96127   Brief emotional/behavioral assessment (eg, depression inventory, attention-deficit/hyperactivity disorder [ADHD] scale), with scoring and documentation, per standardized instrument

Explanation

The physician or other health care professional performs a brief assessment of the patient's emotions and behaviors associated with conditions such as depression or attention-deficit/hyperactivity disorder (ADHD) using an inventory or scale method. The screening is used to determine whether the patient requires additional work up or treatment. This code includes scoring and documentation by standardized instrument.

Coding Tips

To report a minimental status examination, see the appropriate level of evaluation and management service. To report developmental screening, see 96110.

Documentation Tips

Documentation may include the completion of standardized tools that include scoring.

Reimbursement Tips

Coverage may vary. Check with third-party payers before providing this service.

Terms To Know

attention deficit disorder. Syndrome characterized by short attention span, distractibility, and overactivity without significant disturbance of conduct or delay in specific skills.

depression. Disproportionate depressive state with behavior disturbance that is usually the result of a distressing experience and may include preoccupation with the psychic trauma and anxiety.

ICD-10-CM Diagnostic Codes

F06.31	Mood disorder due to known physiological condition with depressive features
F06.32	Mood disorder due to known physiological condition with major depressive-like episode
F32.0	Major depressive disorder, single episode, mild
F32.1	Major depressive disorder, single episode, moderate
F32.2	Major depressive disorder, single episode, severe without psychotic features
F32.3	Major depressive disorder, single episode, severe with psychotic features
F32.4	Major depressive disorder, single episode, in partial remission
F32.5	Major depressive disorder, single episode, in full remission
F32.8	Other depressive episodes
F32.9	Major depressive disorder, single episode, unspecified
F33.0	Major depressive disorder, recurrent, mild
F33.1	Major depressive disorder, recurrent, moderate
F33.2	Major depressive disorder, recurrent severe without psychotic features
F33.3	Major depressive disorder, recurrent, severe with psychotic symptoms
F33.40	Major depressive disorder, recurrent, in remission, unspecified
F33.41	Major depressive disorder, recurrent, in partial remission

F33.42	Major depressive disorder, recurrent, in full remission
F33.8	Other recurrent depressive disorders
F33.9	Major depressive disorder, recurrent, unspecified
F90.0	Attention-deficit hyperactivity disorder, predominantly inattentive type
F90.1	Attention-deficit hyperactivity disorder, predominantly hyperactive type
F90.2	Attention-deficit hyperactivity disorder, combined type
F90.8	Attention-deficit hyperactivity disorder, other type
F90.9	Attention-deficit hyperactivity disorder, unspecified type
F98.8	Other specified behavioral and emotional disorders with onset usually occurring in childhood and adolescence
F98.9	Unspecified behavioral and emotional disorders with onset usually occurring in childhood and adolescence
Z13.89	Encounter for screening for other disorder

Please note that this list of associated ICD-10-CM codes is not all-inclusive. The procedure may be performed for reasons other than those listed that support the medical necessity of the service. Only those conditions supported by the medical record documentation should be reported.

Medicare Edits

	Fac RVU	Non-Fac RVU	FUD	Status	MUE
96127	0.15	0.15	N/A	A	2(1)

	Modifiers				Medicare References
96127	N/A	N/A	N/A	80*	None

* with documentation

96150-96151

96150 Health and behavior assessment (eg, health-focused clinical interview, behavioral observations, psychophysiological monitoring, health-oriented questionnaires), each 15 minutes face-to-face with the patient; initial assessment

96151 re-assessment

Explanation

These codes report assessment of psychological, behavioral, emotional, cognitive, and relevant social factors that can prevent, treat, or manage physical health problems. The assessment must be associated with an acute or chronic illness, the prevention of a physical illness or disability, and the maintenance of health. The initial assessment (96150) and re-assessment (96151) apply to each 15-minute direct, face-to-face session with the patient. A reassessment (96151) is reported to obtain objective measures of goals formulated in the initial assessment and to modify plans as is indicated to support the goals.

Coding Tips

These services are used to identify the assessment of a patient's psychological, behavioral, emotional, cognitive, and social factors as they relate to the prevention, treatment, or management of conditions affecting the patient's physical health. These codes do not identify a service that focuses on the mental health of the patient, but rather on the biopsychosocial factors that are, or could affect the treatment of or severity of, the patient's physical condition. These services are, however, used to modify the psychological, behavioral, emotional, cognitive, and social factors that are identified directly affecting the patient's physiological functioning, disease status, health, and general well-being. They are offered to those patients that have established illnesses or symptoms, but who are not diagnosed with mental illness. They do not, however, represent preventive medical counseling or risk factor reduction interventions. For patients that require psychiatric services as well as health and behavior assessment/intervention, report those services using the appropriate code from the 90785–90899 or 96150–96155 range, respectively. However, do not report codes 90785–90899 and 96150–96155 on the same date of service. Report code 96150 or 96151 for a health and behavior assessment; codes 96152–96155 for interventional services. Do not report this service with adaptive behavior treatment by protocol (0364T–0365T), group adaptive behavior treatment by protocol (0366T–0367T), or exposure adaptive behavior treatment (0373T–0374T).

Documentation Tips

All entries to the medical record should be dated and authenticated.

Reimbursement Tips

Coverage may vary. Check with third-party payers before providing this service.

Terms To Know

assessment. Process of collecting and studying information and data, such as test values, signs, and symptoms.

cognitive. Being aware by drawing from knowledge, such as judgment, reason, perception, and memory.

face to face. Interaction between two parties, usually provider and patient, that occurs in the physical presence of each other.

intervention. Purposeful interaction of the physical therapist with the patient and, when appropriate, with other individuals involved in patient care, using various physical therapy procedures and techniques to produce changes in the condition.

ICD-10-CM Diagnostic Codes

The application of this code is too broad to adequately present ICD-10-CM diagnostic code links here. Refer to your ICD-10-CM book.

Medicare Edits

	Fac RVU	Non-Fac RVU	FUD	Status	MUE
96150	0.6	0.61	N/A	A	-
96151	0.57	0.58	N/A	A	-

	Modifiers				Medicare References
96150	N/A	N/A	N/A	80*	None
96151	N/A	N/A	N/A	80*	

* with documentation

96152-96155

96152	Health and behavior intervention, each 15 minutes, face-to-face; individual
96153	group (2 or more patients)
96154	family (with the patient present)
96155	family (without the patient present)

Explanation

These are interventional services prescribed to modify the psychological, behavioral, emotional, cognitive, and social factors relevant to and affecting the patient's physical health problems. Each code applies to a 15-minute session of direct face-to-face intervention. Report 96152 for the initial assessment with the individual/patient only. Report 96153 for intervention attended by a group (two or more patients). Report 96154 for intervention that includes the family with the patient present. Report 96155 for intervention with the family without the patient's presence.

Coding Tips

These services are used to identify the assessment of a patient's psychological, behavioral, emotional, cognitive, and social factors as they relate to the prevention, treatment, or management of conditions affecting the patient's physical health. These codes do not identify a service that focuses on the mental health of the patient but rather on the biopsychosocial factors that are, or could affect the treatment of or severity of, the patient's physical condition. These services are, however, used to modify the psychological, behavioral, emotional, cognitive, and social factors that are identified directly affecting the patient's physiological functioning, disease status, health, and general well-being. They are offered to those patients that have established illnesses or symptoms, but who are not diagnosed with mental illness. They do not, however, represent preventive medical counseling or risk factor reduction interventions. For patients that require psychiatric services as well as health and behavior assessment/intervention, report those services using the appropriate code from the 90785–90899 or 96150–96155 range respectively. However, do not report codes 90785–90899 and 96150–96155 on the same date of service. Report code 96150 or 96151 for a health and behavior assessment; codes 96152–96155 for interventional services. Do not report this service with adaptive behavior treatment by protocol (0364T–0365T), group adaptive behavior treatment by protocol (0366T–0367T), or exposure adaptive behavior treatment (0373T–0374T).

Documentation Tips

All entries to the medical record should be dated and authenticated.

Reimbursement Tips

Coverage may vary. Check with third-party payers before providing this service.

Terms To Know

assessment. Process of collecting and studying information and data, such as test values, signs, and symptoms.

cognitive. Being aware by drawing from knowledge, such as judgment, reason, perception, and memory.

intervention. Purposeful interaction of the physical therapist with the patient and, when appropriate, with other individuals involved in patient care, using various physical therapy procedures and techniques to produce changes in the condition.

ICD-10-CM Diagnostic Codes

The application of this code is too broad to adequately present ICD-10-CM diagnostic code links here. Refer to your ICD-10-CM book.

Medicare Edits

	Fac RVU	Non-Fac RVU	FUD	Status	MUE
96152	0.55	0.56	N/A	A	-
96153	0.13	0.13	N/A	A	-
96154	0.54	0.55	N/A	A	-
96155	0.64	0.64	N/A	N	-

	Modifiers				Medicare References
96152	N/A	N/A	N/A	80*	None
96153	N/A	N/A	N/A	80*	
96154	N/A	N/A	N/A	80*	
96155	N/A	N/A	N/A	N/A	

* with documentation

97532

| 97532 | Development of cognitive skills to improve attention, memory, problem solving (includes compensatory training), direct (one-on-one) patient contact, each 15 minutes |

Explanation

A patient with inherited learning disabilities or in individuals who have lost these skills as a result of illness or brain injury is worked with on a direct, one-on-one basis to assist in the development of cognitive skills. The individual often needs to develop compensatory methods of processing and retrieving information when disability, illness, or injury has affected these cognitive processes. Cognitive skill development includes mental exercises that assist the patient in areas such as attention, memory, perception, language, reasoning, planning, problem-solving, and related skills.

Coding Tips

This procedure may be performed by a physician or other qualified health care professional. Do not report this service with adaptive behavior treatment by protocol (0364T–0365T) or adaptive behavior treatment with protocol modification (0368T–0369T).

Documentation Tips

The following is a sample of a clinical vignette for this code. A 74-year-old male presents with a combination of depression and organic brain syndrome. The patient lives with his wife but has difficulty remembering to take his medications and, according to his wife, remembering to eat. The clinician develops a structured system by which the patient incorporates taking his medication and eating meals at a set time each day as part of his daily living activities after a thorough discussion of the home environment and the couple's daily routine.

Reimbursement Tips

Check with the specific payer to determine coverage.

ICD-10-CM Diagnostic Codes

The application of this code is too broad to adequately present ICD-10-CM diagnostic code links here. Refer to your ICD-10-CM book.

Medicare Edits

	Fac RVU	Non-Fac RVU	FUD	Status	MUE
97532	0.75	0.75	N/A	A	-

	Modifiers				Medicare References
97532	N/A	N/A	N/A	80*	100-4,5,10

* with documentation

97533

97533	Sensory integrative techniques to enhance sensory processing and promote adaptive responses to environmental demands, direct (one-on-one) patient contact, each 15 minutes

Explanation

Individuals with sensory integration disorders are worked with to teach techniques for enhancing sensory processing and adapting to environmental demands. Sensory experiences include touch, movement, body awareness, sight, sound, and the pull of gravity. The process of the brain organizing and interpreting this information is called sensory integration. Sensory integration provides a crucial foundation for later, more complex learning and behavior. Sensory integration disorders may be the result of a learning disability, illness, or brain injury.

Coding Tips

This procedure may be performed by a physician or other qualified health care professional.

Documentation Tips

The following is a sample clinical vignette for sensory integrative techniques used for this code. A child is fearful of walking down stairs, has poor balance, and difficulty focusing on the task. Evaluation revealed the patient to exhibit difficulty in processing vestibular, proprioceptive, and tactile input. The child is engaged in activities that provide the appropriate sensory input including heavy touch or pressure with graded movement in order to improve the patient's ability to make adaptive motor and behavioral responses. This also helps the child cope with environmental demands. With the improvement in sensorimotor and perceptual skills, the patient is able to walk down stairs with less fear and better balance. The child also appears to be able to sit longer to attend to an assigned task.

Reimbursement Tips

Check with the specific payer to determine coverage.

Terms To Know

sensory integration. Ability to integrate information that is derived from the environment and that relates to movement.

tactile. Having or related to touch.

ICD-10-CM Diagnostic Codes

The application of this code is too broad to adequately present ICD-10-CM diagnostic code links here. Refer to your ICD-10-CM book.

Medicare Edits

	Fac RVU	Non-Fac RVU	FUD	Status	MUE
97533	0.82	0.82	N/A	A	-

	Modifiers				Medicare References
97533	N/A	N/A	N/A	80*	None

* with documentation

98960-98962

98960	Education and training for patient self-management by a qualified, nonphysician health care professional using a standardized curriculum, face-to-face with the patient (could include caregiver/family) each 30 minutes; individual patient
98961	2-4 patients
98962	5-8 patients

Explanation

The qualified, nonphysician health care professional provides education and training using a standard curriculum. This training is prescribed by a physician to enable the patient to concurrently self-manage established illnesses or diseases with health care providers. Report 98960 for education and training provided for an individual patient for each 30 minutes of service. Report 98961 for a group of two to four patients and 98962 for a group of five to eight patients.

Coding Tips

The focus of the training should be to teach patients how to effectively manage their clinical condition. The training may also include a patient's caregiver. The service can be provided to either a single patient (98960) or a group of patients (98961–98962). For individual counseling and education provided by a physician, see the evaluation and management codes; for group education and counseling, see code 99078. See 96150–96155 when a health and behavior assessment or intervention is provided that is not part of a standard curriculum.

Documentation Tips

Documentation should include a description of the type of education and training provided, the materials used, and the reason the education was medically necessary.

Reimbursement Tips

Check with third-party payers to determine coverage guidelines.

ICD-10-CM Diagnostic Codes

The application of this code is too broad to adequately present ICD-10-CM diagnostic code links here. Refer to your ICD-10-CM book.

Medicare Edits

	Fac RVU	Non-Fac RVU	FUD	Status	MUE
98960	0.79	0.79	N/A	B	-
98961	0.38	0.38	N/A	B	-
98962	0.28	0.28	N/A	B	-

	Modifiers				Medicare References
98960	N/A	N/A	N/A	N/A	None
98961	N/A	N/A	N/A	N/A	
98962	N/A	N/A	N/A	N/A	

* with documentation

98966-98968

98966   Telephone assessment and management service provided by a qualified nonphysician health care professional to an established patient, parent, or guardian not originating from a related assessment and management service provided within the previous 7 days nor leading to an assessment and management service or procedure within the next 24 hours or soonest available appointment; 5-10 minutes of medical discussion

98967   11-20 minutes of medical discussion

98968   21-30 minutes of medical discussion

Explanation

A qualified health care professional (nonphysician) provides telephone assessment and management services to a patient in a non-face-to-face encounter. These episodes of care may be initiated by an established patient or by the patient's guardian. These codes are not reported if the telephone service results in a decision to see the patient within 24 hours or at the next available urgent visit appointment; instead, the phone encounter is regarded as part of the pre-service work of the subsequent face-to-face encounter. These codes are also not reported if the telephone call is in reference to a service performed and reported by the qualified health care professional that occurred within the past seven days or within the postoperative period of a previously completed procedure. This applies both to unsolicited patient follow-up or that requested by the health care professional. Report 98966 for telephone services requiring five to 10 minutes of medical discussion, 98967 for telephone services requiring 11 to 20 minutes of medical discussion, and 98968 for telephone services requiring 21 to 30 minutes of medical discussion. Do not report 98966-98968 if these codes have been reported within the previous seven days.

Coding Tips

Telephone services report the evaluation and management (E/M) provided by the nonphysician provider to an established patient or the guardian of the established patient and must be initiated by the patient. These codes are only reported if there is no decision to see the patient within 24 hours or the next available urgent appointment, or if it does not refer to an E/M service performed and reported by the physician within seven days or within the postoperative period of the previously completed procedure. Appropriate code selection is dependent upon the time spent in discussion with the patient. Time documenting the discussion is excluded. This procedure may be performed by a physician or other qualified health care professional.

Documentation Tips

Documentation should include the amount of time, the issues discussed, and any recommendations that were made.

Terms To Know

assessment. Process of collecting and studying information and data, such as test values, signs, and symptoms.

evaluation and management. Assessment, counseling, and other services provided to a patient reported through CPT codes.

ICD-10-CM Diagnostic Codes

The application of this code is too broad to adequately present ICD-10-CM diagnostic code links here. Refer to your ICD-10-CM book.

Medicare Edits

	Fac RVU	Non-Fac RVU	FUD	Status	MUE
98966	0.36	0.39	N/A	N	-
98967	0.72	0.76	N/A	N	-
98968	1.08	1.12	N/A	N	-

	Modifiers				Medicare References
98966	N/A	N/A	N/A	N/A	None
98967	N/A	N/A	N/A	N/A	
98968	N/A	N/A	N/A	N/A	

* with documentation

98969

98969   Online assessment and management service provided by a qualified nonphysician health care professional to an established patient or guardian, not originating from a related assessment and management service provided within the previous 7 days, using the Internet or similar electronic communications network

Explanation

On-line medical assessment and management services are provided to an established patient or guardian in response to a patient's on-line inquiry utilizing Internet resources in a non-face-to-face encounter. Services must be provided by a qualified health care professional (nonphysician). In order for these services to be reportable, the health care professional must provide a personal, timely response to the inquiry and the encounter must be permanently stored via electronic means or hard copy. A reportable service includes all communication related to the on-line encounter, such as phone calls, provision of prescriptions, and orders for laboratory services. This code is not reported if the on-line evaluation is in reference to a service performed and reported by the same health care professional within the past seven days or within the postoperative period of a previously completed procedure. Rather, the on-line service is considered to be part of the previous service or procedure. This applies both to unsolicited patient follow-up or that requested by the health care professional. Report 98969 only once for the same episode of care during a seven-day period.

Coding Tips

This procedure may be performed by a physician or other qualified health care professional. This code is not reported if the online evaluation is in reference to a service performed and reported by the same health care professional within the past seven days or within the postoperative period of a previously completed procedure. Rather, the online service is considered to be part of the previous service or procedure. This applies both to unsolicited patient follow-up or that requested by the health care professional. Report 98969 only once for the same episode of care during a seven-day period. Do not report online assessment and management services during the same month that complex chronic care coordination (99487–99489) or transitional care management services (99495–99496) are reported.

Documentation Tips

Medical record documentation should indicate the information reviewed.

Reimbursement Tips

Medicare and other third-party payers may not provide coverage for this service. Check with the payer to determine coverage requirements.

ICD-10-CM Diagnostic Codes

The application of this code is too broad to adequately present ICD-10-CM diagnostic code links here. Refer to your ICD-10-CM book.

Medicare Edits

	Fac RVU	Non-Fac RVU	FUD	Status	MUE
98969	0.0	0.0	N/A	N	-

	Modifiers				Medicare References
98969	N/A	N/A	N/A	N/A	None

* with documentation

99510

99510   Home visit for individual, family, or marriage counseling

Explanation

A nonphysician home health professional makes an initial visit to the home to evaluate specific needs. If home health care would be of benefit, a plan of care is developed based on medical orders from the patient's provider. For example, a plan might specify one or more visits from a therapist. The provider regularly reviews progress reports.

Coding Tips

This code is for use by the nonphysician provider. For physician services, see the evaluation and management (E/M) home visits (99341–99350), individual psychotherapy (90832–90840), family psychotherapy (90846–90847), and group psychotherapy (90849–90853) codes. Those nonphysician providers who may report E/M codes may report an E/M service with this code when the E/M service is significant and separately identifiable. Medical record documentation must support the use of both codes.

Documentation Tips

All entries to the medical record should be dated and authenticated.

Reimbursement Tips

Medicare and other third-party payers may not provide coverage for this service. Check with the payer to determine coverage requirements.

Terms To Know

counseling. Discussion with a patient and/or family concerning one or more of the following areas: diagnostic results, impressions, and/or recommended diagnostic studies; prognosis; risks and benefits of management (treatment) options; instructions for management (treatment) and/or follow-up; importance of compliance with chosen management (treatment) options; risk factor reduction; and patient and family education.

ICD-10-CM Diagnostic Codes

R41.83	Borderline intellectual functioning
Z32.2	Encounter for childbirth instruction
Z32.3	Encounter for childcare instruction
Z60.0	Problems of adjustment to life-cycle transitions
Z60.8	Other problems related to social environment
Z60.9	Problem related to social environment, unspecified
Z63.4	Disappearance and death of family member
Z63.9	Problem related to primary support group, unspecified
Z64.4	Discord with counselors
Z65.4	Victim of crime and terrorism
Z65.8	Other specified problems related to psychosocial circumstances
Z65.9	Problem related to unspecified psychosocial circumstances
Z69.81	Encounter for mental health services for victim of other abuse
Z70.0	Counseling related to sexual attitude
Z70.1	Counseling related to patient's sexual behavior and orientation
Z70.2	Counseling related to sexual behavior and orientation of third party
Z70.3	Counseling related to combined concerns regarding sexual attitude, behavior and orientation
Z70.8	Other sex counseling

Z70.9	Sex counseling, unspecified
Z71.41	Alcohol abuse counseling and surveillance of alcoholic
Z71.42	Counseling for family member of alcoholic
Z71.51	Drug abuse counseling and surveillance of drug abuser
Z71.52	Counseling for family member of drug abuser
Z71.6	Tobacco abuse counseling
Z71.7	Human immunodeficiency virus [HIV] counseling
Z71.81	Spiritual or religious counseling
Z71.89	Other specified counseling
Z71.9	Counseling, unspecified
Z73.3	Stress, not elsewhere classified
Z73.6	Limitation of activities due to disability

Please note that this list of associated ICD-10-CM codes is not all-inclusive. The procedure may be performed for reasons other than those listed that support the medical necessity of the service. Only those conditions supported by the medical record documentation should be reported.

Medicare Edits

	Fac RVU	Non-Fac RVU	FUD	Status	MUE
99510	0.0	0.0	N/A	I	-

	Modifiers				Medicare References
99510	N/A	N/A	N/A	N/A	None

* with documentation

G0175

G0175   Scheduled interdisciplinary team conference (minimum of 3 exclusive of patient care nursing staff) with patient present

Explanation

Use this code to report an interdisciplinary team conference with a minimum of three care-giving professionals present, not counting the patient care nursing staff. The patient is also present. An interdisciplinary team is composed of professionals who are specialists in different areas and who work together to coordinate the care of patients whose medical condition has multiple diagnoses that require more than one focus of care from different or related fields.

Coding Tips

Some payers may require that this service be reported using the appropriate CPT code (99367–99368). Other payers may require that this service be reported using the appropriate code from the S0220–S0221 range. Check with third-party payers for their requirements.

Documentation Tips

All entries to the medical record should be dated and authenticated.

Reimbursement Tips

This service is for outpatient reporting and is not paid under the Medicare physician fee schedule. This service is paid at the carrier discretion for Medicare.

Terms To Know

interdisciplinary care. Two or more health care professions working in a collaborative manner for the benefit of the patient.

ICD-10-CM Diagnostic Codes

The application of this code is too broad to adequately present ICD-10-CM diagnostic code links here. Refer to your ICD-10-CM book.

Associated CPT Codes

99367	Medical team conference with interdisciplinary team of health care professionals, patient and/or family not present, 30 minutes or more; participation by physician
99368	Medical team conference with interdisciplinary team of health care professionals, patient and/or family not present, 30 minutes or more; participation by nonphysician qualified health care professional

Medicare Edits

	Fac RVU	Non-Fac RVU	FUD	Status	MUE
G0175	0.0	0.0	N/A	X	1(3)

	Modifiers				Medicare References
G0175	N/A	N/A	N/A	N/A	None

* with documentation

G0176

G0176   Activity therapy, such as music, dance, art or play therapies not for recreation, related to the care and treatment of patient's disabling mental health problems, per session (45 minutes or more)

Explanation

Activities engaging a patient in music, dance, art creations, or any type of play, not as recreation but as therapeutic processes for the care and treatment of a patient with disabling mental health problems, are reported using these codes. Every session should last 45 minutes or more.

Coding Tips

See also 90785 to report the use of play equipment, other physical devices, or a translator to communicate with a patient as a means to overcome communication barriers.

Documentation Tips

Documentation should clearly indicate the type of interactive methods used, such as the use of play, or physical device used, and that the patient did not have the ability to communicate through normal verbal means.

Reimbursement Tips

This service is for outpatient reporting and is not paid under the Medicare physician fee schedule. Special coverage instructions apply to this service. Check with third-party payers to determine their specific requirements.

Terms To Know

interactive psychotherapy. Use of physical aids and nonverbal communication to overcome barriers to therapeutic interaction between a clinician and a patient who has not yet developed or has lost either the expressive language communication skills to explain his/her symptoms and response to treatment, or the receptive communication skills to understand the clinician if he or she were to use ordinary adult language for communication.

ICD-10-CM Diagnostic Codes

The application of this code is too broad to adequately present ICD-10-CM diagnostic code links here. Refer to your ICD-10-CM book.

Medicare Edits

	Fac RVU	Non-Fac RVU	FUD	Status	MUE
G0176	0.0	0.0	N/A	X	-

	Modifiers				Medicare References
G0176	N/A	N/A	N/A	N/A	None

* with documentation

G0177

G0177   Training and educational services related to the care and treatment of patient's disabling mental health problems per session (45 minutes or more)

Explanation

Training and educational services are therapeutic procedures related to the care and treatment of patient's disabling mental health problems. The goal is to alleviate patient discomfort and allow the patient to cope or control mental health issues. Each session should be 45 minutes or more.

Coding Tips

To report training of activities of daily living, see 97535 and 99509. To report cognitive skills training, see 97532. Community or work reintegration is reported using 97537.

Documentation Tips

All entries to the medical record should be dated and authenticated.

Reimbursement Tips

This service is for outpatient reporting and is not paid under the Medicare physician fee schedule. Special coverage instructions apply to this service. Check with third-party payers to determine their specific requirements.

ICD-10-CM Diagnostic Codes

The application of this code is too broad to adequately present ICD-10-CM diagnostic code links here. Refer to your ICD-10-CM book.

Medicare Edits

	Fac RVU	Non-Fac RVU	FUD	Status	MUE
G0177	0.0	0.0	N/A	X	0(3)

	Modifiers				Medicare References
G0177	N/A	N/A	N/A	N/A	None

* with documentation

G0436-G0437

G0436 Smoking and tobacco cessation counseling visit for the asymptomatic patient; intermediate, greater than 3 minutes, up to 10 minutes

G0437 Smoking and tobacco cessation counseling visit for the asymptomatic patient; intensive, greater than 10 minutes

Explanation

Tobacco cessation counseling services provide instruction, assistance, and guidance in the discontinuance of smoking. Nonsymptomatic patients are those who do not have signs or symptoms of tobacco-related disease. Smoking usually refers to tobacco smoking, but may also apply to other substances. The counseling may include educating the patient about tobacco, providing strategies for handling situations that may be difficult for the patient, and relaxation and stress management techniques. Medication may or may not be used. Code G0436 represents intermediate counseling of greater than 3 minutes up to 10 minutes. Code G0437 represents intensive counseling of greater than 10 minutes.

Coding Tips

Payers may require that CPT codes 99406–99407 be reported. See also HCPCS Level II code S9453 to report smoking cessation classes provided by a nonphysician provider.

Documentation Tips

All entries to the medical record should be dated and authenticated.

Reimbursement Tips

For Medicare purposes, this is a covered service for those patients who use tobacco, regardless of whether they exhibit signs or symptoms of tobacco-related disease, are competent and alert at the time of counseling, and who get counseling furnished by a qualified physician or other Medicare-recognized practitioner. Medicare provides coverage for two cessation counseling attempts (up to eight counseling sessions) per year. Check with third-party payers for their specific reporting guidelines.

Terms To Know

counseling. Discussion with a patient and/or family concerning one or more of the following areas: diagnostic results, impressions, and/or recommended diagnostic studies; prognosis; risks and benefits of management (treatment) options; instructions for management (treatment) and/or follow-up; importance of compliance with chosen management (treatment) options; risk factor reduction; and patient and family education.

ICD-10-CM Diagnostic Codes

F17.200	Nicotine dependence, unspecified, uncomplicated
F17.201	Nicotine dependence, unspecified, in remission
F17.203	Nicotine dependence unspecified, with withdrawal
F17.208	Nicotine dependence, unspecified, with other nicotine-induced disorders
F17.209	Nicotine dependence, unspecified, with unspecified nicotine-induced disorders
F17.210	Nicotine dependence, cigarettes, uncomplicated
F17.211	Nicotine dependence, cigarettes, in remission
F17.213	Nicotine dependence, cigarettes, with withdrawal
F17.218	Nicotine dependence, cigarettes, with other nicotine-induced disorders

F17.219	Nicotine dependence, cigarettes, with unspecified nicotine-induced disorders
F17.220	Nicotine dependence, chewing tobacco, uncomplicated
F17.221	Nicotine dependence, chewing tobacco, in remission
F17.223	Nicotine dependence, chewing tobacco, with withdrawal
F17.228	Nicotine dependence, chewing tobacco, with other nicotine-induced disorders
F17.229	Nicotine dependence, chewing tobacco, with unspecified nicotine-induced disorders
F17.290	Nicotine dependence, other tobacco product, uncomplicated
F17.291	Nicotine dependence, other tobacco product, in remission
F17.293	Nicotine dependence, other tobacco product, with withdrawal
F17.298	Nicotine dependence, other tobacco product, with other nicotine-induced disorders
F17.299	Nicotine dependence, other tobacco product, with unspecified nicotine-induced disorders

Please note that this list of associated ICD-10-CM codes is not all-inclusive. The procedure may be performed for reasons other than those listed that support the medical necessity of the service. Only those conditions supported by the medical record documentation should be reported.

Associated CPT Codes

99406	Smoking and tobacco use cessation counseling visit; intermediate, greater than 3 minutes up to 10 minutes
99407	Smoking and tobacco use cessation counseling visit; intensive, greater than 10 minutes

Medicare Edits

	Fac RVU	Non-Fac RVU	FUD	Status	MUE
G0436	0.35	0.41	N/A	A	1(2)
G0437	0.73	0.78	N/A	A	1(2)

	Modifiers				Medicare References
G0436	N/A	N/A	N/A	80*	None
G0437	N/A	N/A	N/A	80*	
* with documentation					

G0442-G0443

G0442 Annual alcohol misuse screening, 15 minutes

G0443 Brief face-to-face behavioral counseling for alcohol misuse, 15 minutes

Explanation

Screening and behavioral counseling interventions are used to identify and reduce alcohol misuse

Coding Tips

To report alcohol abuse structured assessment, see HCPCS Level II codes G0396–G0397 or 99408–99409. To report alcohol assessment, see H0001. Note that code H0001 is not valid for payment under the Medicare physician fee schedule.

Documentation Tips

Alcohol dependence (i.e., alcoholism) is a chronic disorder characterized by large or frequent consumption of ethanol in which the individual becomes physically and mentally dependent upon to function. Long-term consequences are physical, psychological, and behavioral, some of which are liver disease, undernutrition with electrolyte disorders and vitamin deficiencies, coagulopathy, depression, dementia, psychosis, heart disease, and violent behavior. Criterion denoting dependence is increased tolerance and continued use despite impairment of health, social life, and job performance. Cessation results in withdrawal symptoms, including early seizures.

The provider must state the pattern of harmful usage (i.e., dependence, abuse, or use) and its current clinical state (e.g., uncomplicated, intoxication, remission, etc.) and indicate the relationship to any identified mental, behavioral, or physical disorder, or its relevance to the patient's status or encounter including its clinical significance.

Reimbursement Tips

Check with third-party payers to determine their reporting requirements.

ICD-10-CM Diagnostic Codes

F10.10	Alcohol abuse, uncomplicated
F10.120	Alcohol abuse with intoxication, uncomplicated
F10.121	Alcohol abuse with intoxication delirium
F10.129	Alcohol abuse with intoxication, unspecified
F10.14	Alcohol abuse with alcohol-induced mood disorder
F10.150	Alcohol abuse with alcohol-induced psychotic disorder with delusions
F10.151	Alcohol abuse with alcohol-induced psychotic disorder with hallucinations
F10.159	Alcohol abuse with alcohol-induced psychotic disorder, unspecified
F10.180	Alcohol abuse with alcohol-induced anxiety disorder
F10.181	Alcohol abuse with alcohol-induced sexual dysfunction
F10.182	Alcohol abuse with alcohol-induced sleep disorder
F10.188	Alcohol abuse with other alcohol-induced disorder
F10.19	Alcohol abuse with unspecified alcohol-induced disorder
F10.20	Alcohol dependence, uncomplicated
F10.21	Alcohol dependence, in remission
F10.220	Alcohol dependence with intoxication, uncomplicated
F10.221	Alcohol dependence with intoxication delirium

F10.229	Alcohol dependence with intoxication, unspecified
F10.230	Alcohol dependence with withdrawal, uncomplicated
F10.231	Alcohol dependence with withdrawal delirium
F10.232	Alcohol dependence with withdrawal with perceptual disturbance
F10.239	Alcohol dependence with withdrawal, unspecified
F10.24	Alcohol dependence with alcohol-induced mood disorder
F10.250	Alcohol dependence with alcohol-induced psychotic disorder with delusions
F10.251	Alcohol dependence with alcohol-induced psychotic disorder with hallucinations
F10.259	Alcohol dependence with alcohol-induced psychotic disorder, unspecified
F10.26	Alcohol dependence with alcohol-induced persisting amnestic disorder
F10.27	Alcohol dependence with alcohol-induced persisting dementia
F10.280	Alcohol dependence with alcohol-induced anxiety disorder
F10.281	Alcohol dependence with alcohol-induced sexual dysfunction
F10.282	Alcohol dependence with alcohol-induced sleep disorder
F10.288	Alcohol dependence with other alcohol-induced disorder
F10.29	Alcohol dependence with unspecified alcohol-induced disorder
F10.920	Alcohol use, unspecified with intoxication, uncomplicated
F10.921	Alcohol use, unspecified with intoxication delirium
F10.929	Alcohol use, unspecified with intoxication, unspecified
F10.94	Alcohol use, unspecified with alcohol-induced mood disorder
F10.950	Alcohol use, unspecified with alcohol-induced psychotic disorder with delusions
F10.951	Alcohol use, unspecified with alcohol-induced psychotic disorder with hallucinations
F10.959	Alcohol use, unspecified with alcohol-induced psychotic disorder, unspecified
F10.96	Alcohol use, unspecified with alcohol-induced persisting amnestic disorder
F10.97	Alcohol use, unspecified with alcohol-induced persisting dementia
F10.980	Alcohol use, unspecified with alcohol-induced anxiety disorder
F10.981	Alcohol use, unspecified with alcohol-induced sexual dysfunction
F10.982	Alcohol use, unspecified with alcohol-induced sleep disorder
F10.988	Alcohol use, unspecified with other alcohol-induced disorder
F10.99	Alcohol use, unspecified with unspecified alcohol-induced disorder

Please note that this list of associated ICD-10-CM codes is not all-inclusive. The procedure may be performed for reasons other than those listed that support the medical necessity of the service. Only those conditions supported by the medical record documentation should be reported.

Associated CPT Codes

99408	Alcohol and/or substance (other than tobacco) abuse structured screening (eg, AUDIT, DAST), and brief intervention (SBI) services; 15 to 30 minutes
99409	Alcohol and/or substance (other than tobacco) abuse structured screening (eg, AUDIT, DAST), and brief intervention (SBI) services; greater than 30 minutes

Medicare Edits

	Fac RVU	Non-Fac RVU	FUD	Status	MUE
G0442	0.26	0.51	N/A	A	1(2)
G0443	0.67	0.73	N/A	A	1(2)

	Modifiers				Medicare References
G0442	N/A	N/A	N/A	80*	None
G0443	N/A	N/A	N/A	80*	

* with documentation

G0451

G0451	Development testing, with interpretation and report, per standardized instrument form

Explanation

Developmental testing is an assessment of the patient's mastery of developmental milestones. The assessment usually includes observation, interviews, and actual tests. The aim is to assess the person's current skills based on standardized criteria for each age group. This code represents testing using a standardized test form and includes the interpretation and a report prepared by a professional practitioner.

Coding Tips

Most payers require that this service be reported using CPT codes 96110–96111. Developmental screening includes screening for conditions such as autism and behavioral and emotional disorders. Developmental testing includes the assessment of motor, language, social, adaptive, and/or cognitive function. For neuropsychological testing, see codes from range 96118–96120. For psychological testing, see codes from range 96101–96103.

Documentation Tips

Note that this code is not a time-based code and, therefore, time does not have to be a component of the documentation. Information obtained through the assessment testing is interpreted and a written report is generated. The interpretation of the results and preparation of the report are included in the service.

Reimbursement Tips

Check with third-party payers to determine their specific reporting requirements.

Terms To Know

cognitive. Being aware by drawing from knowledge, such as judgment, reason, perception, and memory.

interpretation. Professional health care provider's review of data with a written or verbal opinion.

motor function. Ability to learn or demonstrate skillful and efficient assumption, maintenance, modification, and control of voluntary postures and movement patterns.

ICD-10-CM Diagnostic Codes

Z00.121	Encounter for routine child health examination with abnormal findings
Z00.129	Encounter for routine child health examination without abnormal findings

Please note that this list of associated ICD-10-CM codes is not all-inclusive. The procedure may be performed for reasons other than those listed that support the medical necessity of the service. Only those conditions supported by the medical record documentation should be reported.

Associated CPT Codes

96110	Developmental screening (eg, developmental milestone survey, speech and language delay screen), with scoring and documentation, per standardized instrument
96111	Developmental testing, (includes assessment of motor, language, social, adaptive, and/or cognitive functioning by standardized developmental instruments) with interpretation and report

Medicare Edits

	Fac RVU	Non-Fac RVU	FUD	Status	MUE
G0451	0.25	0.25	N/A	A	-

	Modifiers				Medicare References
G0451	N/A	N/A	N/A	80*	None

* with documentation

G0469-G0470

G0469 Federally qualified health center (FQHC) visit, mental health, new patient

G0470 Federally qualified health center (FQHC) visit, mental health, established patient

Explanation

Federally qualified health center (FQHC) visit, mental health is a visit code payable under the FQHC PPS. Code G0469 is for a new patient and G0470 for an established patient. Codes G0469 and G0470 must be accompanied by a qualifying visit code of: 90791, 90792, 90832–90839, 90845. Mental health visit codes G0469 and G0470 must be reported with revenue code 0900 or 0519.

Coding Tips

Correct code assignment is determined by whether or not the patient is new or established.

Documentation Tips

All entries to the medical record should be dated and authenticated.

Reimbursement Tips

This code is reported on the UB-04 by the federally qualified health center (FQHC). Providers should report the appropriate CPT code for the service rendered using the CMS-1500 claim form.

Terms To Know

established patient. 1) Patient who has received professional services in a face-to-face setting within the last three years from the same physician/qualified health care professional or another physician/qualified health care professional of the exact same specialty and subspecialty who belongs to the same group practice. 2) For OPPS hospitals, patient who has been registered as an inpatient or outpatient in a hospital's provider-based clinic or emergency department within the past three years.

FQHC. Federally qualified health center, as designated by CMS.

new patient. Patient who is receiving face-to-face care from a provider/qualified health care professional or another physician/qualified health care professional of the exact same specialty and subspecialty who belongs to the same group practice for the first time in three years. For OPPS hospitals, a patient who has not been registered as an inpatient or outpatient, including off-campus provider based clinic or emergency department, within the past three years.

ICD-10-CM Diagnostic Codes

The application of this code is too broad to adequately present ICD-10-CM diagnostic code links here. Refer to your ICD-10-CM book.

Medicare Edits

	Fac RVU	Non-Fac RVU	FUD	Status	MUE
G0469	0.0	0.0	N/A	X	-
G0470	0.0	0.0	N/A	X	-

	Modifiers				Medicare References
G0469	N/A	N/A	N/A	N/A	None
G0470	N/A	N/A	N/A	N/A	

* with documentation

S0220-S0221

S0220 Medical conference by a physician with interdisciplinary team of health professionals or representatives of community agencies to coordinate activities of patient care (patient is present); approximately 30 minutes

S0221 Medical conference by a physician with interdisciplinary team of health professionals or representatives of community agencies to coordinate activities of patient care (patient is present); approximately 60 minutes

Explanation

A medical conference is a meeting for review, discussion, and/or care planning related to a medical illness or condition. This meeting includes the patient, the physician, and an interdisciplinary team of health professionals, and may include representatives of community agencies. The purpose of the meeting is to plan and coordinate activities of patient care.

Coding Tips

Some payers may require that these services be reported using the appropriate CPT code (99367–99368). Other payers may require that these services be reported using the appropriate HCPCS Level II code (G0175). Check with third-party payers for their requirements.

Documentation Tips

All entries to the medical record should be dated and authenticated.

Reimbursement Tips

These services are not paid under the Medicare physician fee schedule. These services are paid at the carrier discretion for Medicare.

Terms To Know

interdisciplinary care. Two or more health care professions working in a collaborative manner for the benefit of the patient.

ICD-10-CM Diagnostic Codes

The application of this code is too broad to adequately present ICD-10-CM diagnostic code links here. Refer to your ICD-10-CM book.

Associated CPT Codes

99367 Medical team conference with interdisciplinary team of health care professionals, patient and/or family not present, 30 minutes or more; participation by physician

99368 Medical team conference with interdisciplinary team of health care professionals, patient and/or family not present, 30 minutes or more; participation by nonphysician qualified health care professional

Medicare Edits

	Fac RVU	Non-Fac RVU	FUD	Status	MUE
S0220	0.0	0.0	N/A	I	-
S0221	0.0	0.0	N/A	I	-

	Modifiers				Medicare References
S0220	N/A	N/A	N/A	N/A	None
S0221	N/A	N/A	N/A	N/A	

* with documentation

S9453

S9453 Smoking cessation classes, nonphysician provider, per session

Explanation

Smoking cessation classes are organized sessions that provide instruction, assistance, and guidance in the discontinuance of smoking. Smoking usually refers to tobacco smoking, but may also apply to other substances. Smoking cessation can be achieved with or without the assistance of health care professionals and with or without the use of medications. Groups of people who are trying to quit smoking can also provide support to each other.

Coding Tips

See also HCPCS Level II code G0436–G0437 to report smoking cessation counseling. Some payers may require CPT codes 99406–99407 be reported.

Documentation Tips

All entries to the medical record should be dated and authenticated.

Reimbursement Tips

This is not a Medicare-covered service. Check with third-party payers for their specific reporting guidelines.

Terms To Know

counseling. Discussion with a patient and/or family concerning one or more of the following areas: diagnostic results, impressions, and/or recommended diagnostic studies; prognosis; risks and benefits of management (treatment) options; instructions for management (treatment) and/or follow-up; importance of compliance with chosen management (treatment) options; risk factor reduction; and patient and family education.

ICD-10-CM Diagnostic Codes

F17.200	Nicotine dependence, unspecified, uncomplicated
F17.201	Nicotine dependence, unspecified, in remission
F17.203	Nicotine dependence unspecified, with withdrawal
F17.208	Nicotine dependence, unspecified, with other nicotine-induced disorders
F17.209	Nicotine dependence, unspecified, with unspecified nicotine-induced disorders
F17.210	Nicotine dependence, cigarettes, uncomplicated
F17.211	Nicotine dependence, cigarettes, in remission
F17.213	Nicotine dependence, cigarettes, with withdrawal
F17.218	Nicotine dependence, cigarettes, with other nicotine-induced disorders
F17.219	Nicotine dependence, cigarettes, with unspecified nicotine-induced disorders
F17.220	Nicotine dependence, chewing tobacco, uncomplicated
F17.221	Nicotine dependence, chewing tobacco, in remission
F17.223	Nicotine dependence, chewing tobacco, with withdrawal
F17.228	Nicotine dependence, chewing tobacco, with other nicotine-induced disorders
F17.229	Nicotine dependence, chewing tobacco, with unspecified nicotine-induced disorders
F17.290	Nicotine dependence, other tobacco product, uncomplicated
F17.291	Nicotine dependence, other tobacco product, in remission
F17.293	Nicotine dependence, other tobacco product, with withdrawal

| F17.298 | Nicotine dependence, other tobacco product, with other nicotine-induced disorders |
| F17.299 | Nicotine dependence, other tobacco product, with unspecified nicotine-induced disorders |

Please note that this list of associated ICD-10-CM codes is not all-inclusive. The procedure may be performed for reasons other than those listed that support the medical necessity of the service. Only those conditions supported by the medical record documentation should be reported.

Associated CPT Codes

| 99406 | Smoking and tobacco use cessation counseling visit; intermediate, greater than 3 minutes up to 10 minutes |
| 99407 | Smoking and tobacco use cessation counseling visit; intensive, greater than 10 minutes |

Medicare Edits

	Fac RVU	Non-Fac RVU	FUD	Status	MUE
S9453	0.0	0.0	N/A	I	-

	Modifiers				Medicare References
S9453	N/A	N/A	N/A	N/A	None

* with documentation

S9454

| S9454 | Stress management classes, nonphysician provider, per session |

Explanation

Stress management classes are organized education and training on the techniques and methods of controlling levels of stress, particularly chronic stress, to improve life functioning. Medication can be used to decrease feelings of anxiety and stress. Among the other techniques available are yoga, exercise, meditation, deep breathing, progressive relaxation, time management, planning and decision making, and pet therapy.

Coding Tips

When individual psychotherapy is performed, see codes 90832–90838. Multiple-family and group psychotherapy are reported using 90849–90853.

Documentation Tips

All entries to the medical record should be dated and authenticated.

Reimbursement Tips

This service is not covered by Medicare.

Terms To Know

psychotherapy. Treatment for mental illness and behavioral disturbances in which the clinician establishes a professional contract with the patient and, through definitive therapeutic communication, attempts to alleviate the emotional disturbances, reverse or change maladaptive patterns of behavior, and encourage personality growth and development.

ICD-10-CM Diagnostic Codes

The application of this code is too broad to adequately present ICD-10-CM diagnostic code links here. Refer to your ICD-10-CM book.

Medicare Edits

	Fac RVU	Non-Fac RVU	FUD	Status	MUE
S9454	0.0	0.0	N/A	I	-

	Modifiers				Medicare References
S9454	N/A	N/A	N/A	N/A	None

* with documentation

0364T-0365T

0364T

0365T   Adaptive behavior treatment by protocol, administered by technician, face-to-face with one patient; each additional 30 minutes of technician time (List separately in addition to code for primary procedure)

Explanation

A trained technician or assistant behavior analyst conducts a face-to-face behavior therapy session to a single patient with destructive behavioral concerns, such as harming oneself, damaging property, and aggression or behaviors resulting from recurring actions or issues related to communication or social interactions. A physician or other qualified health care professional, who may or may not be present during the course of the treatment encounter, devises the treatment plan for the technician prior to the patient encounter. Report 0364T for the first 30 minutes of face-to-face technician time and 0365T for each additional 30 minutes.

Coding Tips

As an add-on code, 0365T is not subject to multiple procedure rules. No reimbursement reduction or modifier 51 is applied. Add-on codes describe additional intraservice work associated with the primary procedure. They are performed by the same physician on the same date of service as the primary service/procedure, and must never be reported as stand-alone codes. These codes are time-based codes. Code 0364T is reported for the first 30 minutes of time. Code 0365T is reported once for each additional 30 minutes. According to CPT guidelines, an additional unit may be reported once the mid-point (i.e., 16 minutes) has passed. Note that when determining time, these codes are based on the face-to-face time of a single technician. However, when the physician or qualified health care professional personally performs some of the technician activities, this time may be included. Do not report these services with interactive complexity services (90785), psychiatric diagnostic procedures (90791–90792), psychotherapy services (90832–90853), or other psychiatric services or procedures (90863–90899). These services should also not be reported in conjunction with treatment of speech, language, voice, or other communication disorder (92507); central nervous system assessments/testing (96101–96125); or health and behavior assessments/intervention services (96120–96155). When performed in the group setting, report 0366T–0367T.

Documentation Tips

Medical record documentation must, at a minimum, include signs and symptoms supporting the ordering of this service.

Reimbursement Tips

Third-party payers may not reimburse separately for this service. Check with the payer for specific guidelines.

Terms To Know

adaptation reaction. Abnormal or maladaptive reaction with emotional or behavioral characteristics as a result of a life event or stressor that is usually temporary.
behavior management. Education and modification techniques or methodologies aimed at helping a patient change undesirable habits or behaviors.

encounter. 1) Direct personal contact between a registered hospital outpatient (in a medical clinic or emergency department, for example) and a physician (or other person authorized by state law and hospital bylaws to order or furnish services) for the diagnosis and treatment of an illness or injury. Visits with more than one health professional that take place during the same session and at a single location within the hospital are considered a single visit. 2) Physician Quality Reporting System (PQRS) term for meetings with patients during a reporting period represented by the following: CPT Category I E/M service or procedure codes or HCPCS codes located in a PQRS measure's denominator. Reporting of these codes counts as eligibility to meet a measure's inclusion requirements when the service occurs during the specified reporting period.

ICD-10-CM Diagnostic Codes

The application of this code is too broad to adequately present ICD-10-CM diagnostic code links here. Refer to your ICD-10-CM book.

Medicare Edits

	Fac RVU	Non-Fac RVU	FUD	Status	MUE
0364T	0.0	0.0	N/A	C	1(2)
0365T	0.0	0.0	N/A	C	-

	Modifiers				Medicare References
0364T	N/A	N/A	N/A	N/A	None
0365T	N/A	N/A	N/A	N/A	

* with documentation

0366T-0367T

0366T	Group adaptive behavior treatment by protocol, administered by technician, face-to-face with two or more patients; first 30 minutes of technician time
0367T	each additional 30 minutes of technician time (List separately in addition to code for primary procedure)

Explanation

A trained technician or assistant behavior analyst conducts a face-to-face behavior therapy session with at least two but no more than eight patients with destructive behavioral concerns, such as harming oneself, damaging property, and aggression or behaviors resulting from recurring actions or issues related to communication or social interactions. A physician or other qualified health care professional, who may or may not be present during the course of the treatment encounter, devises the treatment plan for the technician prior to the patient encounter. Report 0366T for the first 30 minutes of face-to-face technician time and 0367T for each additional 30 minutes.

Coding Tips

As an add-on code, 0367T is not subject to multiple procedure rules. No reimbursement reduction or modifier 51 is applied. Add-on codes describe additional intraservice work associated with the primary procedure. They are performed by the same physician on the same date of service as the primary service/procedure, and must never be reported as stand-alone codes. These codes are time-based codes. These services should not be reported if the group is larger than eight patients. Code 0366T is reported for the first 30 minutes of time. Code 0367T is reported once for each additional 30 minutes. According to CPT guidelines, an additional unit may be reported once the mid-point (i.e., 16 minutes) has passed. Note that when determining time, these codes are based on the face-to-face time of a single technician. However, when the physician or qualified health care professional personally performs some of the technician activities, this time may be included. Do not report these services with interactive complexity services (90785), psychiatric diagnostic procedures (90791–90792), psychotherapy services (90832–90853), or other psychiatric services or procedures (90863–90899). These services should also not be reported in conjunction with treatment of speech, language, voice, or other communication disorder (92507); central nervous system assessments/testing (96101–96125); or health and behavior assessments/intervention services (96120–96155). When performed with a single patient, see 0364T–0365T.

Documentation Tips

Medical record documentation must, at a minimum, include signs and symptoms supporting the ordering of this service.

Reimbursement Tips

Third-party payers may not reimburse separately for this service. Check with the payer for specific guidelines.

Terms To Know

adaptation reaction. Abnormal or maladaptive reaction with emotional or behavioral characteristics as a result of a life event or stressor that is usually temporary.

behavior management. Education and modification techniques or methodologies aimed at helping a patient change undesirable habits or behaviors.

encounter. 1) Direct personal contact between a registered hospital outpatient (in a medical clinic or emergency department, for example) and a physician (or other person authorized by state law and hospital bylaws to order or furnish services) for the diagnosis and treatment of an illness or injury. Visits with more than one health professional that take place during the same session and at a single location within the hospital are considered a single visit. 2) Physician Quality Reporting System (PQRS) term for meetings with patients during a reporting period represented by the following: CPT Category I E/M service or procedure codes or HCPCS codes located in a PQRS measure's denominator. Reporting of these codes counts as eligibility to meet a measure's inclusion requirements when the service occurs during the specified reporting period.

ICD-10-CM Diagnostic Codes

The application of this code is too broad to adequately present ICD-10-CM diagnostic code links here. Refer to your ICD-10-CM book.

Medicare Edits

	Fac RVU	Non-Fac RVU	FUD	Status	MUE
0366T	0.0	0.0	N/A	C	1(2)
0367T	0.0	0.0	N/A	C	-

	Modifiers				Medicare References
0366T	N/A	N/A	N/A	N/A	None
0367T	N/A	N/A	N/A	N/A	

* with documentation

0368T-0369T

0368T

0369T   Adaptive behavior treatment with protocol modification administered by physician or other qualified health care professional with one patient; each additional 30 minutes of patient face-to-face time (List separately in addition to code for primary procedure)

Explanation

The physician or other qualified health care provider conducts a face-to-face behavior therapy session to a single patient with destructive behavioral concerns, such as harming oneself, damaging property, and aggression or behaviors resulting from recurring actions or issues related to communication or social interactions. During the encounter, the provider solves at least one problem and may, at the same time, coach a technician or assistant behavior analyst, guardian, and/or caregiver in how to oversee the treatment procedures. The patient must be present during the session, including instructions provided to the technician and/or caregiver. Report 0368T for the first 30 minutes of face-to-face time and 0369T for each additional 30 minutes.

Coding Tips

As an add-on code, 0369T is not subject to multiple procedure rules. No reimbursement reduction or modifier 51 is applied. Add-on codes describe additional intraservice work associated with the primary procedure. They are performed by the same physician on the same date of service as the primary service/procedure, and must never be reported as stand-alone codes. These codes are time-based codes. Code 0368T is reported for the first 30 minutes of time. Code 0369T is reported once for each additional 30 minutes. According to CPT guidelines, an additional unit may be reported once the mid-point (i.e., 16 minutes) has passed. These services should not be reported in addition to psychiatric diagnostic procedures (90791–90792); family psychotherapy (90846–90847); interpretation or explanation of psychiatric and/or medical examinations or procedures (90887); treatment of speech, language, voice, or communication disorders (92507); or development of cognitive skills (97532).

Terms To Know

adaptation reaction. Abnormal or maladaptive reaction with emotional or behavioral characteristics as a result of a life event or stressor that is usually temporary.

behavior management. Education and modification techniques or methodologies aimed at helping a patient change undesirable habits or behaviors.

ICD-10-CM Diagnostic Codes

Medicare Edits

	Fac RVU	Non-Fac RVU	FUD	Status	MUE
0368T	0.0	0.0	N/A	C	1(2)
0369T	0.0	0.0	N/A	C	-

	Modifiers				Medicare References
0368T	N/A	N/A	N/A	N/A	None
0369T	N/A	N/A	N/A	N/A	

* with documentation

0370T-0371T

0370T   Family adaptive behavior treatment guidance, administered by physician or other qualified health care professional (without the patient present)

0371T   Multiple-family group adaptive behavior treatment guidance, administered by physician or other qualified health care professional (without the patient present)

Explanation

The physician or other qualified health care provider conducts a face-to-face family behavior therapy session to a single patient's guardian and/or caregiver without the patient present. During the encounter, the provider helps the guardian and/or caregiver learn how to identify behavioral problems, as well as teaches them how to implement treatment strategies to minimize destructive behavioral concerns. Report 0371T when the session involves multiple patients.

Coding Tips

Report 0370T for a single family, 0371T for multiple families. Do not report 0371T when eight or more families participate. These services should not be reported in addition to psychiatric diagnostic procedures (90791–90792), family psychotherapy (90846–90847), or the interpretation or explanation of psychiatric and/or medical examinations or procedures (90887).

Documentation Tips

Medical record documentation must, at a minimum, include signs and symptoms supporting the ordering of this service.

Reimbursement Tips

Third-party payers may not reimburse separately for this service. Check with the payer for specific guidelines.

Terms To Know

adaptation reaction. Abnormal or maladaptive reaction with emotional or behavioral characteristics as a result of a life event or stressor that is usually temporary.

behavior management. Education and modification techniques or methodologies aimed at helping a patient change undesirable habits or behaviors.

ICD-10-CM Diagnostic Codes

Medicare Edits

	Fac RVU	Non-Fac RVU	FUD	Status	MUE
0370T	0.0	0.0	N/A	C	1(3)
0371T	0.0	0.0	N/A	C	1(3)

	Modifiers				Medicare References
0370T	N/A	N/A	N/A	N/A	None
0371T	N/A	N/A	N/A	N/A	

* with documentation

0372T

| 0372T | Adaptive behavior treatment social skills group, administered by physician or other qualified health care professional face-to-face with multiple patients |

Explanation

The physician or other qualified health care provider conducts a face-to-face group session to assist patients in improving social skills through practice, corrective feedback, and homework assignments and honing in on individual social or behavioral issues. The provider oversees individual needs and makes appropriate adjustments for the group as necessary in real time. This code is reported for groups consisting of no more than eight patients.

Coding Tips

This service is reported once regardless of the amount of time spent rendering the service. Do not report this code if the service is provided to a group that is larger than eight patients. Do not report this service in addition to group psychotherapy (90853); treatment of speech, language, voice, or communication disorders (92508); or physical therapy therapeutic procedures (97150).

Documentation Tips

Medical record documentation must, at a minimum, include signs and symptoms supporting the ordering of this service.

Reimbursement Tips

Third-party payers may not reimburse separately for this service. Check with the payer for specific guidelines.

Terms To Know

socialized conduct disorder. Acquired values or behavior of a peer group that the individual is loyal to and with whom the individual characteristically steals, is truant, stays out late at night, and is sexually promiscuous or engages in other socially delinquent practices.

ICD-10-CM Diagnostic Codes

The application of this code is too broad to adequately present ICD-10-CM diagnostic code links here. Refer to your ICD-10-CM book.

Medicare Edits

	Fac RVU	Non-Fac RVU	FUD	Status	MUE
0372T	0.0	0.0	N/A	C	1(3)

	Modifiers				Medicare References
0372T	N/A	N/A	N/A	N/A	None

* with documentation

0373T-0374T

| 0373T | Exposure adaptive behavior treatment with protocol modification requiring two or more technicians for severe maladaptive behavior(s); first 60 minutes of technicians' time, face-to-face with patient |
| 0374T | each additional 30 minutes of technicians' time face-to-face with patient (List separately in addition to code for primary procedure) |

Explanation

The physician or other qualified health care provider conducts a face-to-face behavior therapy session for a single patient with serious destructive behavioral concerns, such as harming oneself, damaging property, and aggression or behaviors. During the encounter, the provider has a minimum of two technicians or assistant behavioral analysts present to assist in provoking responses from various but specific environmental circumstances the patient may experience or has experienced. The technicians or assistant behavioral analysts record the responses while the provider studies the data and makes appropriate adjustments until specific discharge goals have been met. These services are conducted in controlled and safe settings and may involve the use of protective equipment to ensure the safety of the patient and clinical personnel. Report 0373T for the first 60 minutes of face-to-face technician time and 0374T for each additional 30 minutes.

Coding Tips

As an add-on code, 0374T is not subject to multiple procedure rules. No reimbursement reduction or modifier 51 is applied. Add-on codes describe additional intraservice work associated with the primary procedure. They are performed by the same physician on the same date of service as the primary service/procedure, and must never be reported as stand-alone codes. These codes are time-based codes. Code 0373T is reported for the first 30 minutes of time. Code 0374T is reported once for each additional 30 minutes. According to CPT guidelines, an additional unit may be reported once the mid-point (i.e., 16 minutes) has passed. Note that when determining time, these codes are based on the face-to-face time of a single technician. Do not report these codes in addition to interactive complexity services (90785), psychiatric diagnostic procedures (90791–90792), psychotherapy services (90832–90853), or other psychiatric services or procedures (90863–90899). These services should also not be reported in conjunction with central nervous system assessments/testing 996101–96125) or health and behavior assessments/intervention services (96120–96155).

Documentation Tips

Medical record documentation must, at a minimum, include signs and symptoms supporting the ordering of this service.

Reimbursement Tips

Third-party payers may not reimburse separately for this service. Check with the payer for specific guidelines.

Terms To Know

adaptation reaction. Abnormal or maladaptive reaction with emotional or behavioral characteristics as a result of a life event or stressor that is usually temporary.
behavior management. Education and modification techniques or methodologies aimed at helping a patient change undesirable habits or behaviors.

ICD-10-CM Diagnostic Codes

The application of this code is too broad to adequately present ICD-10-CM diagnostic code links here. Refer to your ICD-10-CM book.

Medicare Edits

	Fac RVU	Non-Fac RVU	FUD	Status	MUE
0373T	0.0	0.0	N/A	C	1(2)
0374T	0.0	0.0	N/A	C	-

	Modifiers				Medicare References
0373T	N/A	N/A	N/A	N/A	None
0374T	N/A	N/A	N/A	N/A	

* with documentation

0359T

0359T   Behavior identification assessment, by the physician or other qualified health care professional, face-to-face with patient and caregiver(s), includes administration of standardized and non-standardized tests, detailed behavioral history, patient observation and caregiver interview, interpretation of test results, discussion of findings and recommendations with the primary guardian(s)/caregiver(s), and preparation of report

Explanation

The physician or other qualified health care professional performs an assessment of the patient to identify any impaired social skills, communication deficits, destructive behaviors, and any additional functional limitations resulting from noted maladaptive behaviors. This service includes obtaining a detailed history relative to the patient's behavior, observation of behaviors, administration of standardized and non-standardized testing, focused interviews with the primary guardian or caregiver, interpretation of test results, and the creation of a care plan that may include recommendations for further observational or exposure behavioral follow-up assessments, discussions, including recommendations, with the primary guardian or caregiver, and preparation of reports.

Coding Tips

Typically, this service requires approximately 90 minutes to provide. This code is reported once, regardless of the amount of time involved in providing the service. Do not report this service with interactive complexity services (90785), psychiatric diagnostic procedures (90791–90792), psychotherapy services (90832–90853), or other psychiatric services or procedures (90863–90899). This service should also not be reported in conjunction with central nervous system assessments/testing (96101–96125) or health and behavior assessments/intervention services (96120–96155).

Documentation Tips

Documentation should contain the interpretation of results as well as the development of a treatment plan. The treatment plan should outline the provider's plan of care. Successive progress review treatment plan gains should be noted and modifications to the treatment plan should be recorded as necessary.

Reimbursement Tips

This service may not be covered. Check with third-party payers to determine coverage. Medicare contractors price this service individually.

ICD-10-CM Diagnostic Codes

The application of this code is too broad to adequately present ICD-10-CM diagnostic code links here. Refer to your ICD-10-CM book.

Medicare Edits

	Fac RVU	Non-Fac RVU	FUD	Status	MUE
0359T	0.0	0.0	N/A	C	1(2)

	Modifiers				Medicare References
0359T	N/A	N/A	N/A	N/A	None

* with documentation

0360T-0361T

0360T   Observational behavioral follow-up assessment, includes physician or other qualified health care professional direction with interpretation and report, administered by one technician; first 30 minutes of technician time, face-to-face with the patient

0361T   each additional 30 minutes of technician time, face-to-face with the patient (List separately in addition to code for primary service)

Explanation

The physician or other qualified health care professional performs a face-to-face subsequent assessment of the patient with destructive behavioral concerns, such as harming oneself, damaging property, and aggression or behaviors resulting from recurring actions or issues related to communication or social interactions. The physician or other qualified health care professional may or may not be on site during the test. This service includes focused observation and administration of standardized and non-standardized testing. Areas of evaluation include patient's cooperation, motivation, visual understanding, receptive and expressive language, imitation, requests, playing and relaxing, and social interactions. Evaluation targeting certain destructive behaviors includes monitoring events, cues, responses, and consequences associated with the destructive behavior(s). Report 0360T for the first 30 minutes of face-to-face technician time and 0361T for each additional 30 minutes.

Coding Tips

As an add-on code, 0361T is not subject to multiple procedure rules. No reimbursement reduction or modifier 51 is applied. Add-on codes describe additional intraservice work associated with the primary procedure. They are performed by the same physician on the same date of service as the primary service/procedure, and must never be reported as stand-alone codes. These services are designed to enable the face-to-face time of the technician to serve as a proxy for capturing the work of the qualified health care provider and include the direction of technician, analysis of results of testing, and necessary data collection. These codes are time-based codes. Code 0360T is reported for the first 30 minutes of time. Code 0361T is reported once for each additional 30 minutes. According to CPT guidelines, an additional unit may be reported once the mid-point (i.e., 16 minutes) has passed. Do not report these services with interactive complexity services (90785), psychiatric diagnostic procedures (90791–90792), psychotherapy services (90832–90853), or other psychiatric services or procedures (90863–90899). These services should also not be reported in conjunction with central nervous system assessments/testing (96101–96125) or health and behavior assessments/intervention services (96120–96155).

Documentation Tips

Documentation should contain the interpretation of results as well as the development of a treatment plan. The treatment plan should outline the provider's plan of care. Successive progress review treatment plan gains should be noted and modifications to the treatment plan should be recorded as necessary. Because time is a component of the code, the total time or the start and stop times of the assessment should be noted in the medical record.

Reimbursement Tips

This service may not be covered. Check with third-party payers to determine coverage. Medicare contractors price this service individually.

Terms To Know

adaptation reaction. Abnormal or maladaptive reaction with emotional or behavioral characteristics as a result of a life event or stressor that is usually temporary.

behavior management. Education and modification techniques or methodologies aimed at helping a patient change undesirable habits or behaviors.

ICD-10-CM Diagnostic Codes

The application of this code is too broad to adequately present ICD-10-CM diagnostic code links here. Refer to your ICD-10-CM book.

Medicare Edits

	Fac RVU	Non-Fac RVU	FUD	Status	MUE
0360T	0.0	0.0	N/A	C	1(2)
0361T	0.0	0.0	N/A	C	3(3)

	Modifiers				Medicare References
0360T	N/A	N/A	N/A	N/A	None
0361T	N/A	N/A	N/A	N/A	

* with documentation

0362T-0363T

0362T Exposure behavioral follow-up assessment, includes physician or other qualified health care professional direction with interpretation and report, administered by physician or other qualified health care professional with the assistance of one or more technicians; first 30 minutes of technician(s) time, face-to-face with the patient

0363T each additional 30 minutes of technician(s) time, face-to-face with the patient (List separately in addition to code for primary procedure)

Explanation

The physician or other qualified health care professional, with assistance from one or more technicians, performs a face-to-face subsequent assessment of a patient with serious destructive behavioral concerns, such as harming oneself, damaging property, and aggression or behaviors resulting from recurring actions or issues related to communication or social interactions. This service includes exposure of the patient to a number of social and environmental elements associated with the maladaptive behaviors conducted in a structured and safe environment. Evaluation targeting certain destructive behaviors includes assessing triggers, events, cues, responses, and consequences associated with the destructive behavior(s). Report 0362T for the first 30 minutes of face-to-face technician time and 0363T for each additional 30 minutes.

Coding Tips

As an add-on code, 0363T is not subject to multiple procedure rules. No reimbursement reduction or modifier 51 is applied. Add-on codes describe additional intraservice work associated with the primary procedure. They are performed by the same physician on the same date of service as the primary service/procedure, and must never be reported as stand-alone codes. These services are designed to enable the face-to-face time of the technician to serve as a proxy for capturing the work of the qualified health care provider and include the direction of technician, analysis of results of testing, and necessary data collection. These services include the interpretation of results and preparation of the report. These codes are time-based codes. Code 0362T is reported for the first 30 minutes of time. Code 0363T is reported once for each additional 30 minutes. According to CPT guidelines, an additional unit may be reported once the mid-point (i.e., 16 minutes) has passed. When determining time, it should be noted that these codes are based on the face-to-face time of a single technician. However, when the physician or qualified health care professional personally performs some of the technician activities, this time may be included. Do not report these services with interactive complexity services (90785), psychiatric diagnostic procedures (90791–90792), psychotherapy services (90832–90853), or other psychiatric services or procedures (90863–90899). These services should also not be reported in conjunction with central nervous system assessments/testing (96101–96125) or health and behavior assessments/intervention services (96120–96155).

Documentation Tips

Documentation should contain the interpretation of results as well as the development of a treatment plan. The treatment plan should outline the provider's plan of care. Successive progress review treatment plan gains should be noted and modifications to the treatment plan should be recorded as necessary. Because time is a component of the code, the total time or the start and stop times of the assessment should be noted in the medical record.

Reimbursement Tips

This service may not be covered. Check with third-party payers to determine coverage. Medicare contractors price this service individually.

Terms To Know

adaptation reaction. Abnormal or maladaptive reaction with emotional or behavioral characteristics as a result of a life event or stressor that is usually temporary.

behavior management. Education and modification techniques or methodologies aimed at helping a patient change undesirable habits or behaviors.

ICD-10-CM Diagnostic Codes

The application of this code is too broad to adequately present ICD-10-CM diagnostic code links here. Refer to your ICD-10-CM book.

Medicare Edits

	Fac RVU	Non-Fac RVU	FUD	Status	MUE
0362T	0.0	0.0	N/A	C	1(2)
0363T	0.0	0.0	N/A	C	3(3)

	Modifiers				Medicare References
0362T	N/A	N/A	N/A	N/A	None
0363T	N/A	N/A	N/A	N/A	

* with documentation

0403T

0403T

Explanation

A provider conducts a face-to-face intensive behavior change therapy session in a group setting, aimed at diabetes prevention using standard program parameters. Recent studies have shown several behavioral adjustments can be made in order to help prevent diabetes in those at high risk, specifically those patients with minimal physical activity, obesity, and genetic predisposition. Behavioral therapy can address alterations in lifestyle with goals for desired outcomes pertaining to nutrition and exercise while allowing care plan oversight by a trained provider. This code is reported for a minimum of 60 minutes per day of intense therapy.

97001-97002

97001   Physical therapy evaluation

97002   Physical therapy re-evaluation

Explanation

Physical therapy evaluation is a dynamic process in which the physical therapist makes clinical judgments based on data gathered during examination. Examination includes taking a comprehensive history, performing a systems review and conducting tests and measures. Tests and measures may include but are not limited to tests of range of motion, motor function, muscle performance, joint integrity, neuromuscular status, and review of orthotic or prosthetic devices. The PT will evaluate the examination findings, establish a physical therapy diagnosis, determine the prognosis, and develop a plan of care that includes anticipated goals and expected outcomes, interventions to be used, and anticipated discharge plans. Report 97001 for the initial evaluation. Report 97002 when the PT re-examines the patient.

97003-97004

97003   Occupational therapy evaluation

97004   Occupational therapy re-evaluation

Explanation

The health care provider evaluates the patient. Various movements required for activities of daily living are examined. Dexterity, range of movement, and other elements may also be studied. Report 97003 for the initial evaluation and 97004 for the re-evaluation.

99026-99027

99026   Hospital mandated on call service; in-hospital, each hour

99027   out-of-hospital, each hour

Explanation

The code reports the time for hospital mandated on call service provided by the physician. This code does not include prolonged physician attendance time for standby services or the time spent performing other reportable procedures or services. Report 99026 for each hour of hospital mandated on call service spent in the hospital and 99027 for each hour of hospital mandated on call service spent outside the hospital.

99050

99050   Services provided in the office at times other than regularly scheduled office hours, or days when the office is normally closed (eg, holidays, Saturday or Sunday), in addition to basic service

Explanation

This code is adjunct to basic services rendered. The physician reports this code to indicate services after posted office hours in addition to basic services.

99051

99051   Service(s) provided in the office during regularly scheduled evening, weekend, or holiday office hours, in addition to basic service

Explanation

This code is adjunct to basic services rendered. The physician reports this code to indicate services provided during posted evening, weekend, or holiday office hours in addition to basic services.

99053

99053   Service(s) provided between 10:00 PM and 8:00 AM at 24-hour facility, in addition to basic service

Explanation

This code is adjunct to basic services rendered. The physician reports this code to indicate services provided between 10 p.m. and 8 a.m. at a 24-hour facility in addition to basic services.

99056

99056   Service(s) typically provided in the office, provided out of the office at request of patient, in addition to basic service

Explanation

This code is adjunct to basic services rendered. The physician reports this code to indicate services typically provided in the office that are provided in a different location at the request of a patient.

99058

99058   Service(s) provided on an emergency basis in the office, which disrupts other scheduled office services, in addition to basic service

Explanation

This code is adjunct to basic services rendered. The physician reports this code to indicate services provided in the office on an emergency basis that disrupt other scheduled office services.

99060

99060   Service(s) provided on an emergency basis, out of the office, which disrupts other scheduled office services, in addition to basic service

Explanation

This code is adjunct to basic services rendered. The physician reports this code to indicate services provided on an emergency basis in a location other than the physician's office that disrupt other scheduled office services.

99070-99071

99070   Supplies and materials (except spectacles), provided by the physician or other qualified health care professional over and above those usually included with the office visit or other services rendered (list drugs, trays, supplies, or materials provided)

99071   Educational supplies, such as books, tapes, and pamphlets, for the patient's education at cost to physician or other qualified health care professional

Explanation

These codes are adjunct to basic services rendered. The physician or other qualified provider reports 99070 to indicate supplies and materials provided over and above those usually included with an office visit or services rendered. This code does not include eyeglasses; report the appropriate supply code if eyeglasses are provided. List drugs, trays, supplies, and other materials provided when using this code. Report 99071 when educational supplies are provided by the physician or other qualified provider for the patient's education.

99075

99075   Medical testimony

Explanation

This code is adjunct to basic services rendered. The physician reports this code to indicate medical testimony.

99078

99078   Physician or other qualified health care professional qualified by education, training, licensure/regulation (when applicable) educational services rendered to patients in a group setting (eg, prenatal, obesity, or diabetic instructions)

Explanation

The physician or other qualified health care professional provides educational services to patients in a group setting. The topics vary according to the group but may be related to prenatal care, diet, diabetic instruction, and smoking cessation.

99080

99080   Special reports such as insurance forms, more than the information conveyed in the usual medical communications or standard reporting form

Explanation

This code is adjunct to basic services rendered. The physician reports this code to indicate reports such as insurance forms, more than the information in standard communications methods or forms.

99082

99082   Unusual travel (eg, transportation and escort of patient)

Explanation

This code is adjunct to basic services rendered. The physician reports this code to indicate unusual travel for the purpose of transportation or accompanying the patient.

Correct Coding Initiative Update (21.3)

❖Indicates Mutually Exclusive Edit

0359T 36591-36592, 96101-96111, 96116, 96118-96127

0360T 36591-36592, 96101-96111, 96116, 96118-96127

0361T 36591-36592, 96101-96111, 96116, 96118-96127

0362T 36591-36592, 96101-96111, 96116, 96118-96127

0363T 36591-36592, 96101-96111, 96116, 96118-96127

0364T 36591-36592, 92507, 96101-96111, 96116, 96118-96127, 97532

0365T 36591-36592, 92507, 96101-96111, 96116, 96118-96127, 97532

0366T 36591-36592, 92508, 96101-96111, 96116, 96118-96127, 97150

0367T 36591-36592, 92508, 96101-96111, 96116, 96118-96127, 97150

0368T 36591-36592, 92507, 96101-96111, 96116, 96118-96127, 97532

0369T 36591-36592, 92507, 96101-96111, 96116, 96118-96127, 97532

0370T 36591-36592, 92508, 96101-96111, 96116, 96118-96127, 97150

0371T 36591-36592, 92508, 96101-96111, 96116, 96118-96127, 97150

0372T 36591-36592, 92508, 96101-96111, 96116, 96118-96127, 97150

0373T 36591-36592, 96101-96111, 96116, 96118-96127

0374T 36591-36592, 96101-96111, 96116, 96118-96127

80155 No CCI edits apply to this code.

80156 No CCI edits apply to this code.

80157 No CCI edits apply to this code.

80159 No CCI edits apply to this code.

80164 No CCI edits apply to this code.

80165 No CCI edits apply to this code.

80173 No CCI edits apply to this code.

80178 No CCI edits apply to this code.

80183 No CCI edits apply to this code.

80300 No CCI edits apply to this code.

80301 No CCI edits apply to this code.

80303 No CCI edits apply to this code.

80304 No CCI edits apply to this code.

80320 No CCI edits apply to this code.

80321 No CCI edits apply to this code.

80322 No CCI edits apply to this code.

80324 No CCI edits apply to this code.

80325 No CCI edits apply to this code.

80326 No CCI edits apply to this code.

80332 No CCI edits apply to this code.

80333 No CCI edits apply to this code.

80334 No CCI edits apply to this code.

80335 No CCI edits apply to this code.

80336 No CCI edits apply to this code.

80337 No CCI edits apply to this code.

80338 No CCI edits apply to this code.

80342 No CCI edits apply to this code.

80343 No CCI edits apply to this code.

80344 No CCI edits apply to this code.

80345 No CCI edits apply to this code.

80346 No CCI edits apply to this code.

80347 No CCI edits apply to this code.

80348 No CCI edits apply to this code.

80349 No CCI edits apply to this code.

80350 No CCI edits apply to this code.

80351 No CCI edits apply to this code.

80352 No CCI edits apply to this code.

80353 No CCI edits apply to this code.

80354 No CCI edits apply to this code.

80356 No CCI edits apply to this code.

80357 No CCI edits apply to this code.

80358 No CCI edits apply to this code.

80359 No CCI edits apply to this code.

80360 No CCI edits apply to this code.

80361 No CCI edits apply to this code.

80362 No CCI edits apply to this code.

80363 No CCI edits apply to this code.

80364 No CCI edits apply to this code.

80365 No CCI edits apply to this code.

80367 No CCI edits apply to this code.

80368 No CCI edits apply to this code.

80371 No CCI edits apply to this code.

80372 No CCI edits apply to this code.

80373 No CCI edits apply to this code.

80375 No CCI edits apply to this code.

80376 No CCI edits apply to this code.

80377 No CCI edits apply to this code.

82075 No CCI edits apply to this code.

83992 No CCI edits apply to this code.

84260 No CCI edits apply to this code.

84600 No CCI edits apply to this code.

90785 0359T-0374T, 36591-36592, 96150-96155

90791 0359T-0374T, 36591-36592, 90832-90834, 90836-90840, 90845-90853, 90863-90870, 90875-90889, 96116, 96127-96155, 97802-97804, 99184, 99201-99255, 99281-99288, 99291-99292, 99304-99310, 99315-99318, 99324-99328, 99334-99350, 99354-99360, 99363-99368, 99374-99375, 99377-99412, 99420, 99441-99480, 99485-99487, 99489-99496, 99605-99606, G0270-G0271, G0380-G0384, G0396-G0397, G0406-G0411❖, G0425-G0427, G0442-G0447, G0459, G0463, G0473

90792 0359T-0374T, 36591-36592, 90791, 90832-90834, 90836-90840, 90845-90853, 90863-90870, 90875-90889, 96116, 96127-96155, 97802-97804, 99184, 99201-99255, 99281-99288, 99291-99292, 99304-99310, 99315-99318, 99324-99328, 99334-99350, 99354-99360,

99363-99368, 99374-99375, 99377-99412, 99420, 99441-99480,
99485-99487, 99489-99496, 99605-99606, G0270-G0271,
G0380-G0384, G0396-G0397, G0406-G0411✦, G0425-G0427,
G0442-G0447, G0459, G0463, G0473

90832 0359T-0374T, 36591-36592, 36640, 90839-90840, 90867-90869✦,
96116, 96127-96155, 97802-97804, 99184, 99201-99255, 99281-99288,
99291-99292, 99304-99310, 99315-99318, 99324-99328, 99334-99350,
99354-99360, 99363-99368, 99374-99375, 99377-99412, 99420-99429,
99441-99480, 99485-99487, 99489-99496, 99605-99606, G0176-G0177,
G0270-G0271, G0380-G0384✦, G0396-G0397, G0406-G0407✦,
G0409-G0411✦, G0442-G0447, G0459, G0463, G0473

90833 0359T-0374T, 36591-36592, 36640, 90832✦, 90839-90840,
90867-90869✦, 96116, 96127-96155, 97802-97804, 99184,
99281-99288, 99291-99292, 99339-99340, 99354-99360, 99363-99368,
99374-99375, 99377-99412, 99420-99429, 99441-99480, 99485-99487,
99489-99496, 99605-99606, G0176-G0177, G0270-G0271,
G0380-G0384✦, G0396-G0397, G0406✦, G0409-G0411✦, G0442-G0447,
G0459, G0473

90834 0359T-0374T, 36591-36592, 36640, 90832-90833✦, 90839-90840,
90845✦, 90867-90869✦, 96116, 96127-96155, 97802-97804, 99184,
99201-99255, 99281-99288, 99291-99292, 99304-99310, 99315-99318,
99324-99328, 99334-99350, 99354-99360, 99363-99368, 99374-99375,
99377-99412, 99420-99429, 99441-99480, 99485-99487, 99489-99496,
99605-99606, G0176-G0177, G0270-G0271, G0380-G0384✦,
G0396-G0397, G0406-G0411✦, G0425✦, G0442-G0447, G0459, G0463,
G0473

90836 0359T-0374T, 36591-36592, 36640, 90832-90834✦, 90839-90840,
90867-90869✦, 96116, 96127-96155, 97802-97804, 99184,
99281-99288, 99291-99292, 99339-99340, 99354-99360, 99363-99368,
99374-99375, 99377-99412, 99420-99429, 99441-99480, 99485-99487,
99489-99496, 99605-99606, G0176-G0177, G0270-G0271,
G0380-G0384✦, G0396-G0397, G0406-G0407✦, G0409-G0411✦,
G0442-G0447, G0459, G0473

90837 0359T-0374T, 36591-36592, 36640, 90832-90834✦, 90836✦,
90839-90840, 90845✦, 90867-90869✦, 96116, 96127-96155,
97802-97804, 99184, 99201-99255, 99281-99288, 99291-99292,
99304-99310, 99315-99318, 99324-99328, 99334-99350, 99358-99360,
99363-99368, 99374-99375, 99377-99412, 99420-99429, 99441-99480,
99485-99487, 99489-99496, 99605-99606, G0176-G0177,
G0270-G0271, G0380-G0384✦, G0396-G0397, G0406-G0411✦,
G0425-G0426✦, G0442-G0447, G0459, G0463, G0473

90838 0359T-0374T, 36591-36592, 36640, 90832-90834✦, 90836-90837✦,
90839-90840, 90845✦, 90867-90869✦, 96116, 96127-96155,
97802-97804, 99184, 99281-99288, 99291-99292, 99339-99340,
99354-99360, 99363-99368, 99374-99375, 99377-99412, 99420-99429,
99441-99480, 99485-99487, 99489-99496, 99605-99606, G0176-G0177,
G0270-G0271, G0380-G0384✦, G0396-G0397, G0406-G0411✦,
G0425-G0426✦, G0442-G0447, G0459, G0473

90839 0359T-0374T, 36591-36592, 36640, 90785, 90845-90853, 90863-90870,
90875-90889, 96116, 96127-96155, 97802-97804, 99605-99606,
G0176-G0177, G0270-G0271, G0396-G0397, G0409-G0411✦,
G0442-G0447, G0459, G0473

90840 0359T-0374T, 36591-36592, 36640, 90785, 90845-90853, 90863-90870,
90875-90889, 96116, 96127-96155, 97802-97804, 99605-99606,
G0176-G0177, G0270-G0271, G0396-G0397, G0442-G0447, G0459,
G0473

90845 0359T-0374T, 36591-36592, 36640, 90832-90833✦, 90836✦,
90846-90847✦, 90865✦, 96116, 96127-96155, 97802-97804,
99201-99239, 99281-99285, 99291-99292, 99304-99310, 99315-99318,

99324-99328, 99334-99337, 99341-99350, 99354-99357, 99408-99409,
99605-99606, G0176-G0177, G0270-G0271, G0380-G0384,
G0396-G0397, G0406-G0408, G0425-G0427, G0442-G0447, G0459,
G0463, G0473

90846 0359T-0374T, 36591-36592, 90832-90834, 90836-90838, 90847✦,
90865✦, 90870✦, 96116, 96127-96155, 97802-97804, 99201-99239,
99281-99285, 99304-99310, 99315-99318, 99324-99328, 99334-99337,
99341-99350, 99354-99357, 99408-99409, 99605-99606, G0176-G0177,
G0270-G0271, G0380-G0384, G0396-G0397, G0442-G0447, G0463,
G0473

90847 0359T-0374T, 36591-36592, 36640, 90832-90834, 90836-90838,
90865✦, 90870✦, 96116, 96127-96155, 97802-97804, 99201-99239,
99281-99285, 99304-99310, 99315-99318, 99324-99328, 99334-99337,
99341-99350, 99354-99357, 99408-99409, 99605-99606, G0176-G0177,
G0270-G0271, G0380-G0384, G0396-G0397, G0406-G0408,
G0425-G0427, G0442-G0447, G0459, G0463, G0473

90849 0359T-0374T, 36591-36592, 90832-90834, 90836-90838,
90845-90847✦, 90865✦, 90870✦, 96116, 96127-96155, 97802-97804,
99201-99239, 99281-99285, 99304-99310, 99315-99318, 99324-99328,
99334-99337, 99341-99350, 99354-99357, 99408-99409, 99605-99606,
G0176-G0177, G0270-G0271, G0380-G0384, G0396-G0397,
G0406-G0408, G0425-G0427, G0442-G0447, G0459, G0463, G0473

90853 0359T-0374T, 36591-36592, 36640, 90832-90834, 90836-90838,
90845-90849✦, 90865✦, 90870✦, 96116, 96127-96155, 97802-97804,
99201-99239, 99281-99285, 99291-99292, 99307-99310, 99315-99318,
99324-99328, 99334-99337, 99341-99350, 99354-99357, 99408-99409,
99605-99606, G0176-G0177, G0270-G0271, G0380-G0384,
G0396-G0397, G0406-G0408, G0425-G0427, G0442-G0447, G0459,
G0463, G0473

90863 0359T-0374T, 36591-36592, 96127-96155

90865 0359T-0374T, 36591-36592, 90832-90834✦, 90836-90838✦, 96116,
96127-96155, 97802-97804, 99201-99239, 99281-99285, 99291-99292,
99304-99310, 99315-99318, 99324-99328, 99334-99337, 99341-99350,
99354-99357, 99605-99606, G0270-G0271, G0380-G0384,
G0406-G0408, G0425-G0427, G0444-G0447, G0459, G0463, G0473

90867 0333T, 0359T-0374T, 12001-12007, 12011-12057, 13100-13133,
13151-13153, 36591-36592, 64486-64489, 90845-90853✦, 90865✦,
90868-90870✦, 90880✦, 92012-92014, 95860-95870, 95907-95913,
95925-95930, 95938-95939, 96127-96155, 99201-99255, 99281-99285,
99291-99292, 99304-99310, 99315-99318, 99324-99328, 99334-99337,
99341-99350, 99374-99375, 99377-99378, 99446-99449, 99495-99496,
G0410-G0411✦, G0444-G0447, G0459, G0463, G0473

90868 0333T, 0359T-0374T, 12001-12007, 12011-12057, 13100-13133,
13151-13153, 36591-36592, 64486-64489, 90845-90853✦, 90865✦,
90870✦, 90880✦, 92012-92014, 95860-95870, 95907-95913,
95925-95930, 95938-95939, 96127-96155, 99201-99255, 99281-99285,
99291-99292, 99304-99310, 99315-99318, 99324-99328, 99334-99337,
99341-99350, 99374-99375, 99377-99378, 99446-99449, 99495-99496,
G0410-G0411✦, G0444-G0447, G0459, G0463, G0473

90869 0333T, 0359T-0374T, 12001-12007, 12011-12057, 13100-13133,
13151-13153, 36591-36592, 64486-64489, 90845-90853✦, 90865✦,
90868, 90870✦, 90880✦, 92012-92014, 95860-95870, 95907-95913,
95925-95930, 95938-95939, 96127-96155, 99201-99255, 99281-99285,
99291-99292, 99304-99310, 99315-99318, 99324-99328, 99334-99337,
99341-99350, 99354-99357, 99374-99375, 99377-99378, 99406-99407,
99446-99449, 99455-99480, 99485, 99495-99496, G0410-G0411✦,
G0444-G0447, G0459, G0463, G0473

90870 00104, 0213T, 0216T, 0228T, 0230T, 0359T-0374T, 12001-12007,
12011-12057, 13100-13133, 13151-13153, 36000, 36400-36410,

36420-36430, 36440, 36591-36592, 36600, 36640, 37202, 43752, 51701-51703, 62310-62319, 64400-64435, 64445-64450, 64479, 64483, 64486-64490, 64493, 64505-64530, 90832-90834✦, 90836-90838✦, 90845✦, 90865✦, 90880✦, 92012-92014, 93000-93010, 93040-93042, 93318, 93355, 94002, 94200, 94250, 94680-94690, 94770, 95812-95816, 95819, 95822, 95829, 95955, 96127-96360, 96365, 96372, 96374-96376, 97802-97804, 99148-99149, 99150, 99211-99223, 99231-99255, 99291-99292, 99304-99310, 99315-99316, 99334-99337, 99347-99350, 99374-99375, 99377-99378, 99446-99449, 99495-99496, 99605-99606, G0270-G0271, G0444-G0447, G0459, G0463, G0471, G0473

90875 0359T-0374T, 36591-36592, 96150-96155

90876 0359T-0374T, 36591-36592, 96150-96155

90880 0359T-0374T, 36591-36592, 90832-90834, 90836-90838, 90845-90853, 90865✦, 96116, 96127-96155, 97802-97804, 99201-99239, 99281-99285, 99291-99292, 99304-99310, 99315-99318, 99324-99328, 99334-99337, 99341-99350, 99354-99357, 99408-99409, G0176-G0177, G0270-G0271, G0380-G0384, G0396-G0397, G0406-G0408, G0410-G0411, G0425-G0427, G0442-G0447, G0463, G0473

90882 0359T-0374T, 36591-36592, 96150-96155

90885 0359T-0374T, 36591-36592, 96150-96155

90887 0359T-0374T, 36591-36592, 96150-96155

90889 0359T-0374T, 36591-36592, 96150-96155

90901 12001-12007, 12011-12057, 13100-13133, 13151-13153, 36000, 36400-36410, 36420-36430, 36440, 36591-36592, 36600, 36640, 37202, 43752, 51701-51703, 51784-51785, 62310-62319, 64400-64435, 64445-64450, 64479, 64483, 64486-64490, 64493, 64505-64550, 90832-90834, 90836-90839, 90845-90853, 90865, 90880, 91122, 92012-92014, 93000-93010, 93040-93042, 93318, 93355, 94002, 94200, 94250, 94680-94690, 94770, 95812-95816, 95819, 95822, 95829, 95955, 96360, 96365, 96372, 96374-96376, 99148-99149, 99150, 99211-99223, 99231-99255, 99291-99292, 99304-99310, 99315-99316, 99334-99337, 99347-99350, 99374-99375, 99377-99378, 99446-99449, 99495-99496, G0410-G0411, G0463, G0471

90911 12001-12007, 12011-12057, 13100-13133, 13151-13153, 36000, 36400-36410, 36420-36430, 36440, 36591-36592, 36600, 36640, 37202, 43752, 51701-51703, 51728-51729, 51784-51785, 62310-62319, 64400-64435, 64445-64450, 64479, 64483, 64486-64490, 64493, 64505-64550, 90832-90834, 90836-90839, 90845-90853, 90865, 90880, 90901, 91122, 92012-92014, 93000-93010, 93040-93042, 93318, 93355, 94002, 94200, 94250, 94680-94690, 94770, 95812-95816, 95819, 95822, 95829, 95860-95864, 95867-95872, 95955, 96360, 96365, 96372, 96374-96376, 97032, 97110-97112, 97530, 97535, 97750, 99148-99149, 99150, 99211-99223, 99231-99255, 99291-99292, 99304-99310, 99315-99316, 99334-99337, 99347-99350, 99374-99375, 99377-99378, 99446-99449, 99495-99496, G0410-G0411, G0463, G0471

96020 0333T, 36591-36592, 92558, 92585-92588, 95812-95816, 95819, 95829, 95831-95834, 95851-95852, 95860-95870, 95907-95913, 95925-95930, 95938-95940, 96101-96103, 96116, 96118-96127, 99446-99449, G0453

96101 36591-36592, 96102-96103✦, 96110✦, 96125-96127, G0451✦

96102 36591-36592, 96103✦, 96110✦, 96125-96127, G0451✦

96103 36591-36592, 96110✦, 96125-96127, G0451✦

96110 36591-36592, 96125

96111 36591-36592, 90791-90792, 90832-90834, 90836-90839, 90845-90853, 90865, 90870, 90880, 92002-92014, 96101-96103✦, 96110, 96118-96127, 97001-97004, 99201-99239, 99281-99285, 99291, 99304-99310, 99315-99318, 99324-99328, 99334-99337, 99341-99350,

99466-99480, 99485, G0380-G0384, G0406-G0408, G0410-G0411, G0425-G0427, G0451, G0459, G0463

96116 36591-36592, 96105-96111, 96125-96127, G0451

96118 36591-36592, 96110✦, 96119-96127, G0451✦

96119 36591-36592, 96110✦, 96120-96127, G0451✦

96120 36591-36592, 96110✦, 96125-96127, G0451✦

96125 36591-36592, 96127

96127 36591-36592

96150 0359T-0374T, 36591-36592, 96101-96111, 96116, 96118-96127, 96151-96154✦, 99406-99407, G0396-G0397, G0436-G0437, G0442-G0447, G0451, G0473

96151 0359T-0374T, 36591-36592, 96101-96111, 96116, 96118-96127, 99406-99407, G0396-G0397, G0436-G0437, G0442-G0447, G0451, G0473

96152 0359T-0374T, 36591-36592, 96151✦, 99406-99407, G0396-G0397, G0436-G0437, G0442-G0447, G0473

96153 0359T-0374T, 36591-36592, 96151-96152✦, 96154✦, 99406-99407, G0396-G0397, G0436-G0437, G0442-G0447, G0473

96154 0359T-0374T, 36591-36592, 96151-96152✦, 99406-99407, G0396-G0397, G0436-G0437, G0442-G0447, G0473

96155 0359T-0374T, 36591-36592

97001 0213T, 0216T, 0228T-0231T, 36591-36592, 62310-62319, 64400-64435, 64445-64450, 64479-64490, 64493, 64505-64530, 95831-95834, 95851-95852, 96101-96105, 96118-96125, 96150-96154, 97750, 97755, 97762, 97802-97804, 99201-99239✦, 99291-99292✦, 99304-99310✦, 99315-99318✦, 99324-99328✦, 99334-99337✦, 99341-99350✦, 99354-99357✦, 99455-99463✦, 99465-99466✦, 99468-99480✦, 99485✦, 99605-99606, G0270-G0271, G0406-G0408✦, G0425-G0427✦, G0463✦

97002 0213T, 0216T, 0228T-0231T, 36591-36592, 62310-62319, 64400-64435, 64445-64450, 64479-64490, 64493, 64505-64530, 95831-95834, 95851-95852, 96101-96105, 96118-96125, 96150-96154, 97001✦, 97750, 97755, 97762, 97802-97804, 99201-99239✦, 99291-99292✦, 99304-99310✦, 99315-99318✦, 99324-99328✦, 99334-99337✦, 99341-99350✦, 99354-99357✦, 99455-99463✦, 99465-99466✦, 99468-99480✦, 99605-99606, G0270-G0271, G0406-G0408✦, G0425-G0427✦, G0463✦

97003 0213T, 0216T, 0228T-0231T, 0359T-0363T, 36591-36592, 62310-62319, 64400-64435, 64445-64450, 64479-64490, 64493, 64505-64530, 95831-95834, 95851-95852, 96101-96105, 96118-96125, 96150-96154, 97750, 97755, 97762, 97802-97804, 99201-99239✦, 99291-99292✦, 99304-99310✦, 99315-99318✦, 99324-99328✦, 99334-99337✦, 99341-99350✦, 99354-99357✦, 99455-99463✦, 99465-99466✦, 99468-99480✦, 99485✦, 99605-99606, G0270-G0271, G0406-G0408✦, G0425-G0427✦, G0463✦

97004 0213T, 0216T, 0228T-0231T, 0359T-0363T, 36591-36592, 62310-62319, 64400-64435, 64445-64450, 64479-64490, 64493, 64505-64530, 95831-95834, 95851-95852, 96101-96105, 96118-96125, 96150-96154, 97003✦, 97750, 97755, 97762, 97802-97804, 99201-99239✦, 99291-99292✦, 99304-99310✦, 99315-99318✦, 99324-99328✦, 99334-99337✦, 99341-99350✦, 99354-99357✦, 99455-99463✦, 99465-99466✦, 99468-99480✦, 99605-99606, G0270-G0271, G0406-G0408✦, G0425-G0427✦, G0463✦

97532 0213T, 0216T, 0228T-0231T, 36591-36592, 62310-62319, 64400-64435, 64445-64450, 64479-64490, 64493, 64505-64530, 97002, 97004

97533 0213T, 0216T, 0228T-0231T, 36591-36592, 62310-62319, 64400-64435, 64445-64450, 64479-64490, 64493, 64505-64530, 97002, 97004

98960 36591-36592

98961 36591-36592

98962 36591-36592

98966 36591-36592

98967 36591-36592

98968 36591-36592

98969 36591-36592

99026 36591-36592

99027 36591-36592

99050 36591-36592

99051 36591-36592

99053 36591-36592

99056 36591-36592

99058 36591-36592

99060 36591-36592

99070 36591-36592

99071 36591-36592

99075 36591-36592

99078 36591-36592

99080 36591-36592

99082 36591-36592

99510 36591-36592

G0175 36591-36592, 90832-90834❖, 90836-90839❖, 90846-90847❖, 99446-99449

G0176 36591-36592

G0177 36591-36592

G0436 36591-36592, 92531-92532, 96101-96105, 96118-96125, 99406-99409, G0396-G0397

G0437 36591-36592, 92531-92532, 96101-96105, 96118-96125, 99406-99409, G0396-G0397, G0436

G0442 36591-36592, 99408-99409

G0443 36591-36592, 99408-99409, G0396-G0397

G0451 36591-36592, 96125-96127

G0469 36591-36592

G0470 36591-36592

S0220 No CCI edits apply to this code.

S0221 No CCI edits apply to this code.

S9453 No CCI edits apply to this code.

© 2015 Optum360, LLC

Evaluation and Management Services

This section provides an overview of evaluation and management (E/M) services, tables that identify the documentation elements associated with each code, and the federal documentation guidelines with emphasis on the 1997 exam guidelines. This set of guidelines represent the most complete discussion of the elements of the currently accepted versions. The 1997 version identifies both general multi-system physical examinations and single-system examinations, but providers may also use the original 1995 version of the E/M guidelines; both are currently supported by the Centers for Medicare and Medicaid Services (CMS) for audit purposes.

Although some of the most commonly used codes by physicians of all specialties, the E/M service codes are among the least understood. These codes, introduced in the 1992 CPT® manual, were designed to increase accuracy and consistency of use in the reporting of levels of non-procedural encounters. This was accomplished by defining the E/M codes based on the degree that certain common elements are addressed or performed and reflected in the medical documentation.

The Office of the Inspector General (OIG) Work Plan for physicians consistently lists these codes as an area of continued investigative review. This is primarily because Medicare payments for these services total approximately $33.5 billion per year and are responsible for close to half of Medicare payments for physician services.

The levels of E/M services define the wide variations in skill, effort, and time and are required for preventing and/or diagnosing and treating illness or injury, and promoting optimal health. These codes are intended to represent physician work, and because much of this work involves the amount of training, experience, expertise, and knowledge that a provider may bring to bear on a given patient presentation, the true indications of the level of this work may be difficult to recognize without some explanation.

At first glance, selecting an E/M code may appear to be difficult, but the system of coding clinical visits may be mastered once the requirements for code selection are learned and used.

Providers

The AMA advises coders that while a particular service or procedure may be assigned to a specific section, the service or procedure itself is not limited to use only by that specialty group (see paragraphs 2 and 3 under "Instructions for Use of the CPT Codebook" on page xii of the CPT Book). Additionally, the procedures and services listed throughout the book are for use by any qualified physician or other qualified health care professional or entity (e.g., hospitals, laboratories, or home health agencies).

The use of the phrase "physician or other qualified health care professional" (OQHCP) was adopted to identify a health care provider other than a physician. This type of provider is further described in CPT as an individual "qualified by education, training, licensure/regulation (when applicable), and facility privileging (when applicable)." State licensure guidelines determine the scope of practice and a qualified health care professional must practice within these guidelines, even if more restrictive than the CPT guidelines. The qualified health care professional may report services independently or under incident-to guidelines. The professionals within this definition are separate from

"clinical staff" and are able to practice independently. CPT defines clinical staff as "a person who works under the supervision of a physician or other qualified health care professional and who is allowed, by law, regulation, and facility policy to perform or assist in the performance of a specified professional service, but who does not individually report that professional service." Keep in mind that there may be other policies or guidance that can affect who may report a specific service.

Types of E/M Services

When approaching E/M, the first choice that a provider must make is what type of code to use. The following tables outline the E/M codes for different levels of care for:

- Office or other outpatient services—new patient
- Office or other outpatient services—established patient
- Hospital observation services—initial care, subsequent, and discharge
- Hospital inpatient services—initial care, subsequent, and discharge
- Observation or inpatient care (including admission and discharge services)
- Consultations—office or other outpatient
- Consultations—inpatient

The specifics of the code components that determine code selection are listed in the table and discussed in the next section. Before a level of service is decided upon, the correct type of service is identified.

Office or other outpatient services are E/M services provided in the physician or other qualified health care provider's office, the outpatient area, or other ambulatory facility. Until the patient is admitted to a health care facility, he/she is considered to be an outpatient.

A new patient is a patient who has not received any face-to-face professional services from the physician or other qualified health care provider within the past three years. An established patient is a patient who has received face-to-face professional services from the physician or other qualified health care provider within the past three years. In the case of group practices, if a physician or other qualified health care provider of the exact same specialty or subspecialty has seen the patient within three years, the patient is considered established.

If a physician or other qualified health care provider is on call or covering for another physician or other qualified health care provider, the patient's encounter is classified as it would have been by the physician or other qualified health care provider who is not available. Thus, a locum tenens physician or other qualified health care provider who sees a patient on behalf of the patient's attending physician or other qualified health care provider may not bill a new patient code unless the attending physician or other qualified health care provider has not seen the patient for any problem within three years.

Hospital observation services are E/M services provided to patients who are designated or admitted as "observation status" in a hospital.

Codes 99218-99220 are used to indicate initial observation care. These codes include the initiation of the observation status, supervision of patient care including writing orders, and the performance of periodic reassessments. These codes are used only by the provider "admitting" the patient for observation.

Codes 99234-99236 are used to indicate evaluation and management services to a patient who is admitted to and discharged from observation status or hospital inpatient on the same day. If the patient is admitted as an inpatient from observation on the same day, use the appropriate level of Initial Hospital Care (99221-99223).

Code 99217 indicates discharge from observation status. It includes the final physical examination of the patient, instructions, and preparation of the discharge records. It should not be used when admission and discharge are on the same date of service. As mentioned above, report codes 99234-99236 to appropriately describe same day observation services.

If a patient is in observation longer than one day, subsequent observation care codes 99224-99226 should be reported. If the patient is discharged on the second day, observation discharge code 99217 should be reported. If the patient status is changed to inpatient on a subsequent date, the appropriate inpatient code, 99221-99233, should be reported.

Initial hospital care is defined as E/M services provided during the first hospital inpatient encounter with the patient by the admitting provider. (If a physician other than the admitting physician performs the initial inpatient encounter, refer to consultations or subsequent hospital care in the CPT book.) Subsequent hospital care includes all follow-up encounters with the patient by all physicians or other qualified health care providers.

A consultation is the provision of a physician or other qualified health care provider's opinion or advice about a patient for a specific problem at the request of another physician or other appropriate source. The CPT book also states that a consultation may be performed when a physician or other qualified health care provider is determining whether to accept the transfer of patient care at the request of another physician or appropriate source. An office or other outpatient consultation is a consultation provided in the consultant's office, in the emergency department, or in an outpatient or other ambulatory facility including hospital observation services, home services, domiciliary, rest home, or custodial care. An inpatient consultation is a consultation provided in the hospital or partial hospital nursing facility setting. Report only one inpatient consultation by a consultant for each admission to the hospital or nursing facility.

If a consultant participates in the patient's management after the opinion or advice is provided, use codes for subsequent hospital or observation care or for office or other outpatient services (established patient), as appropriate.

CMS adopted new policies regarding the use of consultation codes beginning in 2010. Under these guidelines the inpatient and office/outpatient consultation codes contained in the CPT book will not be a covered service for CMS. However, Medicare will cover telehealth consultations when reported with the appropriate HCPCS Level II G code.

Additional changes regarding inpatient services were initiated in 2010 by CMS. All outpatient services will be reported using the appropriate new or established E/M codes. Inpatient services for the first initial encounter should be reported by the physician providing the service using initial hospital care codes 99221–99223, and subsequent inpatient care codes 99231–99233. As there may only be one admitting physician, CMS has added HCPCS Level II modifier AI, Principal physician of record, which may be appended to the initial hospital care code by the attending physician or other qualified health care provider.

Codes 99487, 99489, and 99490 are used to report evaluation and management services for chronic care management. These codes represent management and support services provided by clinical staff, under the direction of a physician or other qualified health care professional, to patients residing at home or in a domiciliary, rest home, or assisted living facility. The qualified provider oversees the management and/or coordination of services for all medical conditions, psychosocial needs, and activities of daily living. These codes are reported only once per calendar month and have specific time-based thresholds.

Codes 99497-99498 are used to report the discussion and explanation of advanced directives by a physician or other qualified health care professional. These codes represent a face-to-face service between the provider and a patient, family member, or surrogate. These codes are time-based codes and, since no active management of the problem(s) is undertaken during this time, may be reported on the same day as another E/M service.

Note: The E/M codes were revised for 2013 to indicate that the majority of these services may be provided by a physician or other qualified health care professional.

Office or Other Outpatient Services—New Patient

E/M Code	History[1]	Exam[1]	Medical Decision Making[1]	Problem Severity	Coordination of Care; Counseling	Time Spent Face-to-Face (avg.)
99201	Problem-focused	Problem-focused	Straight-forward	Minor or self-limited	Consistent with problem(s) and patient's needs	10 min.
99202	Expanded problem-focused	Expanded problem-focused	Straight-forward	Low to moderate	Consistent with problem(s) and patient's needs	20 min.
99203	Detailed	Detailed	Low complexity	Moderate	Consistent with problem(s) and patient's needs	30 min.
99204	Comprehensive	Comprehensive	Moderate complexity	Moderate to high	Consistent with problem(s) and patient's needs	45 min.
99205	Comprehensive	Comprehensive	High complexity	Moderate to high	Consistent with problem(s) and patient's needs	60 min.

1 Key component. For new patients, all three components (history, exam, and medical decision making) are crucial for selecting the correct code.

Office or Other Outpatient Services—Established Patient[1]

E/M Code	History[2]	Exam[2]	Medical Decision Making[2]	Problem Severity	Coordination of Care; Counseling	Time Spent Face-to-Face (avg.)
99211	—	—	Physician supervision, but presence not required	Minimal	Consistent with problem(s) and patient's needs	5 min.
99212	Problem-focused	Problem-focused	Straight-forward	Minor or self-limited	Consistent with problem(s) and patient's needs	10 min.
99213	Expanded problem-focused	Expanded problem-focused	Low complexity	Low to moderate	Consistent with problem(s) and patient's needs	15 min.
99214	Detailed	Detailed	Moderate complexity	Moderate to high	Consistent with problem(s) and patient's needs	25 min.
99215	Comprehensive	Comprehensive	High complexity	Moderate to high	Consistent with problem(s) and patient's needs	40 min.

1 Includes follow-up, periodic reevaluation, and evaluation and management of new problems.
2 Key component. For established patients, at least two of the three components (history, exam, and medical decision making) are needed to select the correct code.

Hospital Observation Services

E/M Code	History[1]	Exam[1]	Medical Decision Making[1]	Problem Severity	Coordination of Care; Counseling	Time Spent Bedside and on Unit/Floor (avg.)
99217	Observation care discharge day management					
99218	Detailed or comprehensive	Detailed or comprehensive	Straight-forward or low complexity	Low	Consistent with problem(s) and patient's needs	30 min.
99219	Comprehensive	Comprehensive	Moderate complexity	Moderate	Consistent with problem(s) and patient's needs	50 min.
99220	Comprehensive	Comprehensive	High complexity	High	Consistent with problem(s) and patient's needs	70 min.

1 Key component. All three components (history, exam, and medical decision making) are crucial for selecting the correct code.

Subsequent Hospital Observation Services[1]

E/M Code[2]	History[3]	Exam[3]	Medical Decision Making[3]	Problem Severity	Coordination of Care; Counseling	Time Spent Bedside and on Unit/Floor (avg.)
99224	Problem-focused interval	Problem-focused	Straight-forward or low complexity	Stable, recovering, or improving	Consistent with problem(s) and patient's needs	15 min.
99225	Expanded problem-focused interval	Expanded problem-focused	Moderate complexity	Inadequate response to treatment; minor complications	Consistent with problem(s) and patient's needs	25 min.
99226	Detailed interval	Detailed	High complexity	Unstable; significant new problem or significant complication	Consistent with problem(s) and patient's needs	35 min.

1 All subsequent levels of service include reviewing the medical record, diagnostic studies, and changes in the patient's status, such as history, physical condition, and response to treatment since the last assessment.
2 These codes are resequenced in CPT and are printed following codes 99217-99220.
3 Key component. For subsequent care, at least two of the three components (history, exam, and medical decision making) are needed to select the correct code.

Hospital Inpatient Services—Initial Care[1]

E/M Code	History[2]	Exam[2]	Medical Decision Making[2]	Problem Severity	Coordination of Care; Counseling	Time Spent Bedside and on Unit/Floor (avg.)
99221	Detailed or comprehensive	Detailed or comprehensive	Straight-forward or low complexity	Low	Consistent with problem(s) and patient's needs	30 min.
99222	Comprehensive	Comprehensive	Moderate complexity	Moderate	Consistent with problem(s) and patient's needs	50 min.
99223	Comprehensive	Comprehensive	High complexity	High	Consistent with problem(s) and patient's needs	70 min.

1 The admitting physician should append modifier AI, Principal physician of record, for Medicare patients
2 Key component. For initial care, all three components (history, exam, and medical decision making) are crucial for selecting the correct code.

Hospital Inpatient Services—Subsequent Care[1]

E/M Code	History[2]	Exam[2]	Medical Decision Making[2]	Problem Severity	Coordination of Care; Counseling	Time Spent Bedside and on Unit/Floor (avg.)
99231	Problem-focused interval	Problem-focused	Straight-forward or low complexity	Stable, recovering or Improving	Consistent with problem(s) and patient's needs	15 min.
99232	Expanded problem-focused interval	Expanded problem-focused	Moderate complexity	Inadequate response to treatment; minor complications	Consistent with problem(s) and patient's needs	25 min.
99233	Detailed interval	Detailed	High complexity	Unstable; significant new problem or significant complication	Consistent with problem(s) and patient's needs	35 min.
99238	Hospital discharge day management					30 min. or less
99239	Hospital discharge day management					> 30 min.

1 All subsequent levels of service include reviewing the medical record, diagnostic studies, and changes in the patient's status, such as history, physical condition, and response to treatment since the last assessment.
2 Key component. For subsequent care, at least two of the three components (history, exam, and medical decision making) are needed to select the correct code.

Observation or Inpatient Care Services (Including Admission and Discharge Services)

E/M Code	History[1]	Exam[1]	Medical Decision Making[1]	Problem Severity	Coordination of Care; Counseling	Time[2]
99234	Detailed or comprehensive	Detailed or comprehensive	Straight-forward or low complexity	Low	Consistent with problem(s) and patient's needs	40 min.
99235	Comprehensive	Comprehensive	Moderate	Moderate	Consistent with problem(s) and patient's needs	50 min.
99236	Comprehensive	Comprehensive	High	High	Consistent with problem(s) and patient's needs	55 min.

1 Key component. All three components (history, exam, and medical decision making) are crucial for selecting the correct code.
2 Typical times have not been established for this category of services.

Consultations—Office or Other Outpatient

E/M Code	History[1]	Exam[1]	Medical Decision Making[1]	Problem Severity	Coordination of Care; Counseling	Time Spent Face-to-Face (avg.)
99241	Problem-focused	Problem-focused	Straight-forward	Minor or self-limited	Consistent with problem(s) and patient's needs	15 min.
99242	Expanded problem-focused	Expanded problem-focused	Straight-forward	Low	Consistent with problem(s) and patient's needs	30 min.
99243	Detailed	Detailed	Low complexity	Moderate	Consistent with problem(s) and patient's needs	40 min.
99244	Comprehensive	Comprehensive	Moderate complexity	Moderate to high	Consistent with problem(s) and patient's needs	60 min.
99245	Comprehensive	Comprehensive	High complexity	Moderate to high	Consistent with problem(s) and patient's needs	80 min.

1 Key component. For office or other outpatient consultations, all three components (history, exam, and medical decision making) are crucial for selecting the correct code.

Consultations—Inpatient[1]

E/M Code	History[2]	Exam[2]	Medical Decision Making[2]	Problem Severity	Coordination of Care; Counseling	Time Spent Bedside and on Unit/Floor (avg.)
99251	Problem-focused	Problem-focused	Straight-forward	Minor or self-limited	Consistent with problem(s) and patient's needs	20 min.
99252	Expanded problem-focused	Expanded problem-focused	Straight-forward	Low	Consistent with problem(s) and patient's needs	40 min.
99253	Detailed	Detailed	Low complexity	Moderate	Consistent with problem(s) and patient's needs	55 min.
99254	Comprehensive	Comprehensive	Moderate complexity	Moderate to high	Consistent with problem(s) and patient's needs	80 min.
99255	Comprehensive	Comprehensive	High complexity	Moderate to high	Consistent with problem(s) and patient's needs	110 min.

1 These codes are used for hospital inpatients, residents of nursing facilities or patients in a partial hospital setting.
2 Key component. For initial inpatient consultations, all three components (history, exam, and medical decision making) are crucial for selecting the correct code.

Emergency Department Services, New or Established Patient

E/M Code	History[1]	Exam[1]	Medical Decision Making[1]	Problem Severity[3]	Coordination of Care; Counseling	Time Spent[2] Face-to-Face (avg.)
99281	Problem-focused	Problem-focused	Straight-forward	Minor or self-limited	Consistent with problem(s) and patient's needs	N/A
99282	Expanded problem-focused	Expanded problem-focused	Low complexity	Low to moderate	Consistent with problem(s) and patient's needs	N/A
99283	Expanded problem-focused	Expanded problem-focused	Moderate complexity	Moderate	Consistent with problem(s) and patient's needs	N/A
99284	Detailed	Detailed	Moderate complexity	High; requires urgent evaluation	Consistent with problem(s) and patient's needs	N/A
99285	Comprehensive	Comprehensive	High complexity	High; poses immediate/ significant threat to life or physiologic function	Consistent with problem(s) and patient's needs	N/A
99288[4]			High complexity			N/A

1 Key component. For emergency department services, all three components (history, exam, and medical decision making) are crucial for selecting the correct code and must be adequately documented in the medical record to substantiate the level of service reported.
2 Typical times have not been established for this category of services.
3 NOTE: The severity of the patient's problem, while taken into consideration when evaluating and treating the patient, does not automatically determine the level of E/M service unless the medical record documentation reflects the severity of the patient's illness, injury, or condition in the details of the history, physical examination, and medical decision making process. Federal auditors will "downcode" the level of E/M service despite the nature of the patient's problem when the documentation does not support the E/M code reported.
4 Code 99288 is used to report two-way communication with emergency medical services personnel in the field.

Critical Care

E/M Code	Patient Status	Physician Attendance	Time[1]
99291	Critically ill or critically injured	Constant	First 30–74 minutes
99292	Critically ill or critically injured	Constant	Each additional 30 minutes beyond the first 74 minutes

1 Per the guidelines for time in *CPT 2012*, "A unit of time is attained when the mid-point is passed. For example, an hour is attained when 31 minutes have elapsed (more than midway between zero and 60 minutes)."

Nursing Facility Services—Initial Nursing Facility Care[1]

E/M Code	History[1]	Exam[1]	Medical Decision Making[1]	Problem Severity	Coordination of Care; Counseling
99304	Detailed or comprehensive	Detailed or comprehensive	Straight-forward or low complexity	Low	25 min.
99305	Comprehensive	Comprehensive	Moderate complexity	Moderate	35 min.
99306	Comprehensive	Comprehensive	High complexity	High	45 min.

1 These services must be performed by the physician. See CPT Corrections Document – CPT 2013 page 2.
2 Key component. For new patients, all three components (history, exam, and medical decision making) are crucial for selecting the correct code.

Nursing Facility Services—Subsequent Nursing Facility Care

E/M Code	History[1]	Exam[1]	Medical Decision Making[2]	Problem Severity	Coordination of Care; Counseling
99307	Problem-focused interval	Problem-focused	Straight-forward	Stable, recovering or improving	10 min.
99308	Expanded problem-focused interval	Expanded problem-focused	Low complexity	Responding inadequately or has developed a minor complication	15 min.
99309	Detailed interval	Detailed	Moderate complexity	Significant complication or a significant new problem	25 min.
99310	Comprehensive interval	Comprehensive	High complexity	Developed a significant new problem requiring immediate attention	35 min.

1 Key component. For established patients, at least two of the three components (history, exam, and medical decision making) are needed for selecting the correct code.

Nursing Facility Discharge and Annual Assessment

E/M Code	History[1]	Exam[1]	Medical Decision Making[1]	Problem Severity	Time Spent Bedside and on Unit/Floor (avg.)
99315	Nursing facility discharge day management				30 min. or less
99316	Nursing facility discharge day management				more than 30 min.
99318	Detailed interval	Comprehensive	Low to moderate complexity	Stable, recovering or improving	30 min.

1 Key component. For annual nursing facility assessment, all three components (history, exam, and medical decision making) are crucial for selecting the correct code.

Domiciliary, Rest Home (e.g., Boarding Home) or Custodial Care Services—New Patient

E/M Code	History[1]	Exam[1]	Medical Decision Making[1]	Problem Severity	Coordination of Care; Counseling	Time Spent Face-to-Face (avg.)
99324	Problem-focused	Problem-focused	Straight-forward	Low	Consistent with problem(s) and patient's needs	20 min.
99325	Expanded problem-focused	Expanded problem-focused	Low complexity	Moderate	Consistent with problem(s) and patient's needs	30 min.
99326	Detailed	Detailed	Moderate complexity	Moderate to high	Consistent with problem(s) and patient's needs	45 min
99327	Comprehensive	Comprehensive	Moderate complexity	High	Consistent with problem(s) and patient's needs	60 min.
99328	Comprehensive	Comprehensive	High complexity	Unstable or developed a new problem requiring immediate physician attention	Consistent with problem(s) and patient's needs	75 min.

1 Key component. For new patients, all three components (history, exam, and medical decision making) are crucial for selecting the correct code and must be adequately documented in the medical record to substantiate the level of service reported.

Domiciliary, Rest Home (e.g., Boarding Home) or Custodial Care Services— Established Patient

E/M Code	History[1]	Exam[1]	Medical Decision Making[1]	Problem Severity	Coordination of Care; Counseling	Time Spent Face-to-Face (avg.)
99334	Problem-focused interval	Problem-focused	Straight-forward	Minor or self-limited	Consistent with problem(s) and patient's needs	15 min.
99335	Expanded problem-focused interval	Expanded problem-focused	Low complexity	Low to moderate	Consistent with problem(s) and patient's needs	25 min.
99336	Detailed interval	Detailed	Moderate complexity	Moderate to high	Consistent with problem(s) and patient's needs	40 min.
99337	Comprehensive interval	Comprehensive	Moderate to high complexity	Moderate to high	Consistent with problem(s) and patient's needs	60 min.

1 Key component. For established patients, at least two of the three components (history, exam, and medical decision making) are needed for selecting the correct code.

Domiciliary, Rest Home (e.g., Assisted Living Facility), or Home Care Plan Oversight Services

E/M Code	Intent of Service	Presence of Patient	Time
99339	Individual physician supervision of a patient (patient not present) in home, domiciliary or rest home (e.g., assisted living facility) requiring complex and multidisciplinary care modalities involving regular physician development and/or revision of care plans, review of subsequent reports of patient status, review of related laboratory and other studies, communication (including telephone calls) for purposes of assessment or care decisions with health care professional(s), family member(s), surrogate decision maker(s) (e.g., legal guardian) and/or key caregiver(s) involved in patient's care, integration of new information into the medical treatment plan and/or adjustment of medical therapy, within a calendar month	Patient not present	15–29 min.
99340	Same as 99339	Patient not present	30 min. or more

Home Services—New Patient

E/M Code	History[1]	Exam[1]	Medical Decision Making[1]	Problem Severity	Coordination of Care; Counseling	Time Spent Face-to-Face (avg.)
99341	Problem-focused	Problem-focused	Straight-forward complexity	Low	Consistent with problem(s) and patient's needs	20 min.
99342	Expanded problem-focused	Expanded problem-focused	Low complexity	Moderate	Consistent with problem(s) and patient's needs	30 min.
99343	Detailed	Detailed	Moderate complexity	Moderate to high	Consistent with problem(s) and patient's needs	45 min.
99344	Comprehensive	Comprehensive	Moderate complexity	High	Consistent with problem(s) and patient's needs	60 min.
99345	Comprehensive	Comprehensive	High complexity	Usually the patient has developed a significant new problem requiring immediate physician attention	Consistent with problem(s) and patient's needs	75 min.

1 Key component. For new patients, all three components (history, exam, and medical decision making) are crucial for selecting the correct code and must be adequately documented in the medical record to substantiate the level of service reported.

Home Services—Established Patient

E/M Code	History[1]	Exam[1]	Medical Decision Making[1]	Problem Severity	Coordination of Care; Counseling	Time Spent Face-to-Face (avg.)
99347	Problem-focused interval	Problem-focused	Straight-forward	Minor or self-limited	Consistent with problem(s) and patient's needs	15 min.
99348	Expanded problem-focused interval	Expanded problem-focused	Low complexity	Low to moderate	Consistent with problem(s) and patient's needs	25 min.
99349	Detailed interval	Detailed	Moderate complexity	Moderate to high	Consistent with problem(s) and patient's needs	40 min.
99350	Comprehensive interval	Comprehensive	Moderate to high complexity	Moderate to high Usually the patient has developed a significant new problem requiring immediate physician attention	Consistent with problem(s) and patient's needs	60 min.

1 Key component. For established patients, at least two of the three components (history, exam, and medical decision making) are needed to select the correct code and must be adequately documented in the medical record to substantiate the level of service reported.

Newborn Care Services

E/M Code	Patient Status	Type of Visit
99460	Normal newborn	Inpatient initial inpatient hospital or birthing center per day
99461	Normal newborn	Inpatient initial treatment not in hospital or birthing center per day
99462	Normal newborn	Inpatient subsequent per day
99463	Normal newborn	Inpatient initial inpatient and discharge in hospital or birthing center per day
99464	Unstable newborn	Attendance at delivery
99465	High-risk newborn at delivery	Resuscitation, ventilation, and cardiac treatment

Neonatal and Pediatric Interfacility Transportation

E/M Code	Patient Status	Type of Visit
99466	Critically ill or injured infant or young child, to 24 months	Face-to-face transportation from one facility to another, initial 30-74 minutes
99467	Critically ill or injured infant or young child, to 24 months	Face-to-face transportation from one facility to another, each additional 30 minutes
99485	Critically ill or injured infant or young child, to 24 months	Supervision of patient transport from one facility to another, initial 30 minutes
99486	Critically ill or injured infant or young child, to 24 months	Supervision of patient transport from one facility to another, each additional 30 minutes

Inpatient Neonatal and Pediatric Critical Care

E/M Code	Patient Status	Type of Visit
99468	Critically ill neonate, aged 28 days or less	Inpatient initial per day
99469	Critically ill neonate, aged 28 days or less	Inpatient subsequent per day
99471	Critically ill infant or young child, aged 29 days to 24 months	Inpatient initial per day
99472	Critically ill infant or young child, aged 29 days to 24 months	Inpatient subsequent per day
99475	Critically ill infant or young child, 2 to 5 years	Inpatient initial per day
99476	Critically ill infant or young child, 2 to 5 years	Inpatient subsequent per day

Initial and Continuing Intensive Care Services

E/M Code	Patient Status	Type of Visit
99477	Neonate, aged 28 days or less	Inpatient initial per day
99478	Infant with present body weight of less than 1500 grams, no longer critically ill	Inpatient subsequent per day
99479	Infant with present body weight of 1501-2500 grams, no longer critically ill	Inpatient subsequent per day
99480	Infant with present body weight of 2501-5000 grams, no longer critically ill	Inpatient subsequent per day

Levels of E/M Services

Confusion may be experienced when first approaching E/M due to the way that each description of a code component or element seems to have another layer of description beneath. The three key components—history, exam, and decision making—are each comprised of elements that combine to create varying levels of that component.

For example, an expanded problem-focused history includes the chief complaint, a brief history of the present illness, and a system review focusing on the patient's problems. The level of exam is not made up of different elements but rather distinguished by the extent of exam across body areas or organ systems.

The single largest source of confusion are the "labels" or names applied to the varying degrees of history, exam, and decision-making. Terms such as expanded problem-focused, detailed, and comprehensive are somewhat meaningless unless they are defined. The lack of definition in CPT guidelines relative to these terms is precisely what caused the first set of federal guidelines to be developed in 1995 and again in 1997.

Documentation Guidelines for Evaluation and Management Services

Both versions of the federal guidelines go well beyond CPT guidelines in defining specific code requirements. The current version of the CPT guidelines does not explain the number of history of present illness (HPI) elements or the specific number of organ systems or body areas to be examined as they are in the federal guidelines. Adherence to some version of the guidelines is required when billing E/M to federal payers, but at this time, the CPT guidelines do not incorporate this level of detail into the code definitions. Although that could be interpreted to mean that non-governmental payers have a lesser documentation standard, it is best to adopt one set of the federal versions for all payer types for both consistency and ease of use.

The 1997 guidelines supply a great amount of detail relative to history and exam and will give the provider clear direction to following documentation elements. With that stated, the 1995 guidelines are equally valid and place a lesser documentation burden on the provider in regards to the physical exam.

The 1995 guidelines ask only for a notation of "normal" on systems with normal findings. The only narrative required is for abnormal findings. The 1997 version calls for much greater detail, or an "elemental" or "bullet-point" approach to organ systems, although a notation of normal is sufficient when addressing the elements within a system. The 1997 version works well in a template or electronic health record (EHR) format for recording E/M services.

The 1997 version did produce the single system specialty exam guidelines. When reviewing the complete guidelines listed below, note the differences between exam requirements in the 1995 and 1997 versions.

A Comparison of 1995 and 1997 Exam Guidelines

There are four types of exams indicated in the levels of E/M codes. Although the descriptors or labels are the same under 1995 and 1997 guidelines, the degree of detail required is different. The remaining content on this topic references the 1997 general multi-system speciality examination, at the end of this chapter.

The levels under each set of guidelines are:

1995 Exam Guidelines:

Problem focused:	One body area or system
Expanded problem focused:	Two to seven body areas or organ systems
Detailed:	Two to seven body areas or organ systems
Comprehensive:	Eight or more organ systems or a complete single-system examination

1997 Exam Guidelines:

Problem-focused:	Perform and document examination of one to five bullet point elements in one or more organ systems/body areas from the general multi-system examination
OR	
	Perform or document examination of one to five bullet point elements from one of the 10 single-organ-system examinations, shaded or unshaded boxes
Expanded problem-focused:	Perform and document examination of at least six bullet point elements in one or more organ systems from the general multi-system examination
OR	
	Perform and document examination of at least six bullet point elements from one of the 10 single-organ-system examinations, shaded or unshaded boxes

Detailed:	Perform and document examination of at least six organ systems or body areas, including at least two bullet point elements for each organ system or body area from the general multi-system examination

OR

	Perform and document examination of at least 12 bullet point elements in two or more organ systems or body areas from the general multisystem examination

OR

	Perform and document examination of at least 12 bullet elements from one of the single-organ-system examinations, shaded or unshaded boxes

Comprehensive:	Perform and document examination of at least nine organ systems or body areas, with all bullet elements for each organ system or body area (unless specific instructions are expected to limit examination content with at least two bullet elements for each organ system or body area) from the general multi-system examination

OR

	Perform and document examination of all bullet point elements from one of the 10 single-organ system examinations with documentation of every element in shaded boxes and at least one element in each unshaded box from the single-organ-system examination.

The Documentation Guidelines

The following guidelines were developed jointly by the American Medical Association (AMA) and the Centers for Medicare and Medicaid Services (CMS). Their mutual goal was to provide physicians and claims reviewers with advice about preparing or reviewing documentation for evaluation and management (E/M) services.

I.   Introduction

What is Documentation and Why Is It Important?
Medical record documentation is required to record pertinent facts, findings, and observations about an individual's health history, including past and present illnesses, examinations, tests, treatments, and outcomes. The medical record chronologically documents the care of the patient and is an important element contributing to high quality care. The medical record facilitates:

- The ability of the physician and other health care professionals to evaluate and plan the patient's immediate treatment and to monitor his/her health care over time
- Communication and continuity of care among physicians and other health care professionals involved in the patient's care
- Accurate and timely claims review and payment
- Appropriate utilization review and quality of care evaluations
- Collection of data that may be useful for research and education

An appropriately documented medical record can reduce many of the problems associated with claims processing and may serve as a legal document to verify the care provided, if necessary.

What Do Payers Want and Why?
Because payers have a contractual obligation to enrollees, they may require reasonable documentation that services are consistent with the insurance coverage provided. They may request information to validate:

- The site of service
- The medical necessity and appropriateness of the diagnostic and/or therapeutic services provided
- Services provided have been accurately reported

II.   General Principles of Medical Record Documentation
The principles of documentation listed below are applicable to all types of medical and surgical services in all settings. For Evaluation and Management (E/M) services, the nature and amount of physician work and documentation varies by type of service, place of service, and the patient's status. The general principles listed below may be modified to account for these variable circumstances in providing E/M services.

- The medical record should be complete and legible
- The documentation of each patient encounter should include:
  — A reason for the encounter and relevant history, physical examination findings, and prior diagnostic test results
  — Assessment, clinical impression, or diagnosis
  — Plan for care
  — Date and legible identity of the practitioner
- If not documented, the rationale for ordering diagnostic and other ancillary services should be easily inferred
- Past and present diagnoses should be accessible to the treating and/or consulting physician
- Appropriate health risk factors should be identified
- The patient's progress, response to, and changes in treatment and revision of diagnosis should be documented
- The CPT and ICD-9-CM codes reported on the health insurance claim form or billing statement should be supported by the documentation in the medical record

III.   Documentation of E/M Services 1995 and 1997
The following information provides definitions and documentation guidelines for the three key components of E/M services and for visits that consist predominately of counseling or coordination of care. The three key components—history, examination, and medical decision making—appear in the descriptors for office and other outpatient services, hospital observation services, hospital inpatient services, consultations, emergency department services, nursing facility services, domiciliary care services, and home services. While some of

the text of the CPT guidelines has been repeated in this document, the reader should refer to CMS or CPT for the complete descriptors for E/M services and instructions for selecting a level of service. Documentation guidelines are identified by the symbol DG.

The descriptors for the levels of E/M services recognize seven components that are used in defining the levels of E/M services. These components are:

- History
- Examination
- Medical decision making
- Counseling
- Coordination of care
- Nature of presenting problem
- Time

The first three of these components (i.e., history, examination, and medical decision making) are the key components in selecting the level of E/M services. In the case of visits that consist predominately of counseling or coordination of care, time is the key or controlling factor to qualify for a particular level of E/M service.

Because the level of E/M service is dependent on two or three key components, performance and documentation of one component (e.g., examination) at the highest level does not necessarily mean that the encounter in its entirety qualifies for the highest level of E/M service.

These Documentation Guidelines for E/M services reflect the needs of the typical adult population. For certain groups of patients, the recorded information may vary slightly from that described here. Specifically, the medical records of infants, children, adolescents, and pregnant women may have additional or modified information, as appropriate, recorded in each history and examination area.

As an example, newborn records may include under history of the present illness (HPI) the details of the mother's pregnancy and the infant's status at birth; social history will focus on family structure; and family history will focus on congenital anomalies and hereditary disorders in the family. In addition, the content of a pediatric examination will vary with the age and development of the child. Although not specifically defined in these documentation guidelines, these patient group variations on history and examination are appropriate.

A. Documentation of History

The levels of E/M services are based on four types of history (Problem Focused, Expanded Problem Focused, Detailed, and Comprehensive). Each type of history includes some or all of the following elements:

- Chief complaint (CC)
- History of present illness (HPI)
- Review of systems (ROS)
- Past, family, and/or social history (PFSH)

The extent of history of present illness, review of systems, and past, family, and/or social history that is obtained and documented is dependent upon clinical judgment and the nature of the presenting problem.

The chart below shows the progression of the elements required for each type of history. To qualify for a given type of history all three elements in the table must be met. (A chief complaint is indicated at all levels.)

- DG: The CC, ROS, and PFSH may be listed as separate elements of history or they may be included in the description of the history of present illness

- DG: A ROS and/or a PFSH obtained during an earlier encounter does not need to be re-recorded if there is evidence that the physician reviewed and updated the previous information. This may occur when a physician updates his/her own record or in an institutional setting or group practice where many physicians use a common record. The review and update may be documented by:

  – Describing any new ROS and/or PFSH information or noting there has been no change in the information

  – Noting the date and location of the earlier ROS and/or PFSH

- DG: The ROS and/or PFSH may be recorded by ancillary staff or on a form completed by the patient. To document that the physician reviewed the information, there must be a notation supplementing or confirming the information recorded by others

- DG: If the physician is unable to obtain a history from the patient or other source, the record should describe the patient's condition or other circumstance that precludes obtaining a history

Definitions and specific documentation guidelines for each of the elements of history are listed below.

Chief Complaint (CC)
The CC is a concise statement describing the symptom, problem, condition, diagnosis, physician recommended return, or other factor that is the reason for the encounter, usually stated in the patient's words.

- DG: The medical record should clearly reflect the chief complaint

History of Present Illness	Review of systems (ROS)	PFSH	Type of History
Brief	N/A	N/A	Problem-focused
Brief	Problem Pertinent	N/A	Expanded Problem-Focused
Extended	Extended	Pertinent	Detailed
Extended	Complete	Complete	Comprehensive

History of Present Illness (HPI)

The HPI is a chronological description of the development of the patient's present illness from the first sign and/or symptom or from the previous encounter to the present. It includes the following elements:

- Location
- Quality
- Severity
- Duration
- Timing
- Context
- Modifying factors
- Associated signs and symptoms

Brief and extended HPIs are distinguished by the amount of detail needed to accurately characterize the clinical problem.

A brief HPI consists of one to three elements of the HPI.

- DG: The medical record should describe one to three elements of the present illness (HPI)

An extended HPI consists of at least four elements of the HPI or the status of at least three chronic or inactive conditions.

- DG: The medical record should describe at least four elements of the present illness (HPI) or the status of at least three chronic or inactive conditions

Beginning with services performed on or after September 10, 2013, CMS has stated that physicians and other qualified health care professionals will be able to use the 1997 guidelines for an extended history of present illness (HOPI) in combination with other elements from the 1995 documentation guidelines to document a particular level of evaluation and management service.

Review of Systems (ROS)

A ROS is an inventory of body systems obtained through a series of questions seeking to identify signs and/or symptoms that the patient may be experiencing or has experienced. For purposes of ROS, the following systems are recognized:

- Constitutional symptoms (e.g., fever, weight loss)
- Eyes
- Ears, nose, mouth, throat
- Cardiovascular
- Respiratory
- Gastrointestinal
- Genitourinary
- Musculoskeletal
- Integumentary (skin and/or breast)
- Neurological
- Psychiatric
- Endocrine
- Hematologic/lymphatic
- Allergic/immunologic

A problem pertinent ROS inquires about the system directly related to the problem identified in the HPI.

- DG: The patient's positive responses and pertinent negatives for the system related to the problem should be documented

An extended ROS inquires about the system directly related to the problem identified in the HPI and a limited number of additional systems.

- DG: The patient's positive responses and pertinent negatives for two to nine systems should be documented

A complete ROS inquires about the system directly related to the problem identified in the HPI plus all additional body systems.

- DG: At least 10 organ systems must be reviewed. Those systems with positive or pertinent negative responses must be individually documented. For the remaining systems, a notation indicating all other systems are negative is permissible. In the absence of such a notation, at least 10 systems must be individually documented

Past, Family, and/or Social History (PFSH)

The PFSH consists of a review of three areas:

- Past history (the patient's past experiences with illnesses, operations, injuries, and treatment)
- Family history (a review of medical events in the patient's family, including diseases that may be hereditary or place the patient at risk)
- Social history (an age appropriate review of past and current activities)

For certain categories of E/M services that include only an interval history, it is not necessary to record information about the PFSH. Those categories are subsequent hospital care, follow-up inpatient consultations, and subsequent nursing facility care.

A pertinent PFSH is a review of the history area directly related to the problem identified in the HPI.

- DG: At least one specific item from any of the three history areas must be documented for a pertinent PFSH

A complete PFSH is a review of two or all three of the PFSH history areas, depending on the category of the E/M service. A review of all three history areas is required for services that by their nature include a comprehensive assessment or reassessment of the patient. A review of two of the three history areas is sufficient for other services.

- DG: A least one specific item from two of the three history areas must be documented for a complete PFSH for the following categories of E/M services: office or other outpatient services, established patient; emergency department; domiciliary care, established patient; and home care, established patient

- DG: At least one specific item from each of the three history areas must be documented for a complete PFSH for the following categories of E/M services: office or other outpatient services, new patient; hospital observation services; hospital inpatient services, initial care; consultations; comprehensive nursing facility assessments; domiciliary care, new patient; and home care, new patient

B. Documentation of Examination 1997 Guidelines

The levels of E/M services are based on four types of examination:

- Problem Focused: A limited examination of the affected body area or organ system

- Expanded Problem Focused: A limited examination of the affected body area or organ system and any other symptomatic or related body area or organ system

- Detailed: An extended examination of the affected body area or organ system and any other symptomatic or related body area or organ system

- Comprehensive: A general multi-system examination or complete examination of a single organ system and other symptomatic or related body area or organ system

These types of examinations have been defined for general multi-system and the following single organ systems:

- Cardiovascular
- Ears, nose, mouth, and throat
- Eyes
- Genitourinary (Female)
- Genitourinary (Male)
- Hematologic/lymphatic/immunologic
- Musculoskeletal
- Neurological
- Psychiatric
- Respiratory
- Skin

Any physician regardless of specialty may perform a general multi-system examination or any of the single organ system examinations. The type (general multi-system or single organ system) and content of examination are selected by the examining physician and are based upon clinical judgment, the patient's history, and the nature of the presenting problem.

The content and documentation requirements for each type and level of examination are summarized below and described in detail in a table found later on in this document. In the table, organ systems and body areas recognized by CPT for purposes of describing examinations are shown in the left column. The content, or individual elements, of the examination pertaining to that body area or organ system are identified by bullets (•) in the right column.

Parenthetical examples "(e.g., ...)," have been used for clarification and to provide guidance regarding documentation. Documentation for each element must satisfy any numeric requirements (such as "Measurement of any three of the following seven...") included in the description of the element. Elements with multiple components but with no specific numeric requirement (such as "Examination of liver and spleen") require documentation of at least one component. It is possible for a given examination to be expanded beyond what is defined here. When that occurs, findings related to the additional systems and/or areas should be documented.

- DG: Specific abnormal and relevant negative findings from the examination of the affected or symptomatic body area or organ system should be documented. A notation of "abnormal" without elaboration is insufficient

- DG: Abnormal or unexpected findings from the examination of any asymptomatic body area or organ system should be described

- DG: A brief statement or notation indicating "negative" or "normal" is sufficient to document normal findings related to an unaffected areas or asymptomatic organ system

General Multi-System Examinations

General multi-system examinations are described in detail later in this document. To qualify for a given level of multi-system examination, the following content and documentation requirements should be met:

- Problem Focused Examination: It should include performance and documentation of one to five elements identified by a bullet (•) in one or more organ systems or body areas

- Expanded Problem Focused Examination: It should include performance and documentation of at least six elements identified by a bullet (•) in one or more organ systems or body areas

- Detailed Examination: It should include at least six organ systems or body areas. For each system/area selected, performance and documentation of at least two elements identified by a bullet (•) is expected. Alternatively, a detailed examination may include performance and documentation of at least 12 elements identified by a bullet (•) in two or more organ systems or body areas

- Comprehensive Examination: It should include at least nine organ systems or body areas. For each system/area selected, all elements of the examination identified by a bullet (•) should be performed, unless specific directions limit the content of the examination. For each area/system, documentation of at least two elements identified by a bullet (•) is expected

Single Organ System Examinations

The single organ system examinations recognized by CMS include eyes; ears, nose, mouth, and throat; cardiovascular; respiratory; genitourinary (male and female); musculoskeletal; neurologic; hematologic, lymphatic, and immunologic; skin; and psychiatric. Note that for each specific single organ examination type, the performance and documentation of the stated number of elements, identified by a bullet (•) should be included, whether in a box with a shaded or unshaded border. The following content and documentation requirements must be met to qualify for a given level:

- Problem Focused Examination: one to five elements
- Expanded Problem Focused Examination: at least six elements
- Detailed Examination: at least 12 elements (other than eye and psychiatric examinations)
- Comprehensive Examination: all elements (Documentation of every element in a box with a shaded border and at least one element in a box with an unshaded border is expected)

Content and Documentation Requirements

General Multisystem Examination 1997

System/Body Area	Elements of Examination
Constitutional	• Measurement of any three of the following seven vital signs: 1) sitting or standing blood pressure, 2) supine blood pressure, 3) pulse rate and regularity, 4) respiration, 5) temperature, 6) height, 7) weight (May be measured and recorded by ancillary staff). • General appearance of patient (e.g., development, nutrition, body habitus, deformities attention to grooming)
Eyes	• Inspection of conjunctivae and lids • Examination of pupils and irises (e.g., reaction to light and accommodation, size and symmetry) • Ophthalmoscopic examination of optic discs (e.g., size, C/D ratio, appearance) and posterior segments (e.g., vessel changes, exudates, hemorrhages)
Ears, nose, mouth, and throat	• External inspection of ears and nose (e.g., overall appearance, scars, lesions, masses) • Otoscopic examination of external auditory canals and tympanic membranes • Assessment of hearing (e.g., whispered voice, finger rub, tuning fork) • Inspection of nasal mucosa, septum and turbinates • Inspection of lips, teeth and gums • Examination of oropharynx: oral mucosa, salivary glands, hard and soft palates, tongue, tonsils and posterior pharynx
Neck	• Examination of neck (e.g., masses, overall appearance, symmetry, tracheal position, crepitus) • Examination of thyroid (e.g., enlargement, tenderness, mass)
Respiratory	• Assessment of respiratory effort (e.g., intercostal retractions, use of accessory muscles, diaphragmatic movement) • Percussion of chest (e.g., dullness, flatness, hyperresonance) • Palpation of chest (e.g., tactile fremitus) • Auscultation of lungs (e.g., breath sounds, adventitious sounds, rubs)
Cardiovascular	• Palpation of heart (e.g., location, size, thrills) • Auscultation of heart with notation of abnormal sounds and murmurs • Examination of: — carotid arteries (e.g., pulse amplitude, bruits) — abdominal aorta (e.g., size, bruits) — femoral arteries (e.g., pulse amplitude, bruits) — pedal pulses (e.g., pulse amplitude) — extremities for edema and/or varicosities
Chest (Breasts)	• Inspection of breasts (e.g., symmetry, nipple discharge) • Palpation of breasts and axillae (e.g., masses or lumps, tenderness)
Gastrointestinal (Abdomen)	• Examination of abdomen with notation of presence of masses or tenderness • Examination of liver and spleen • Examination for presence or absence of hernia • Examination (when indicated) of anus, perineum and rectum, including sphincter tone, presence of hemorrhoids, rectal masses • Obtain stool sample for occult blood test when indicated
Genitourinary	**Male:** • Examination of the scrotal contents (e.g., hydrocele, spermatocele, tenderness of cord, testicular mass) • Examination of the penis • Digital rectal examination of prostate gland (e.g., size, symmetry, nodularity tenderness) **Female:** • Pelvic examination (with or without specimen collection for smears and cultures), including: — examination of external genitalia (e.g., general appearance, hair distribution, lesions) and vagina (e.g., general appearance, estrogen effect, discharge, lesions, pelvic support, cystocele, rectocele) — examination of urethra (e.g., masses, tenderness, scarring) — examination of bladder (e.g., fullness, masses, tenderness) • Cervix (e.g., general appearance, lesions, discharge) • Uterus (e.g., size, contour, position, mobility, tenderness, consistency, descent or support) • Adnexa/parametria (e.g., masses, tenderness)

System/Body Area	Elements of Examination
Lymphatic	Palpation of lymph nodes in **two or more** areas: • Neck • Groin • Axillae • Other
Musculoskeletal	• Examination of gait and station *(if circled, add to total at bottom of column to the left) • Inspection and/or palpation of digits and nails (e.g., clubbing, cyanosis, inflammatory conditions, petechiae, ischemia, infections, nodes) *(if circled, add to total at bottom of column to the left) Examination of joints, bones and muscles of **one or more of the following six** areas: 1) head and neck; 2) spine, ribs, and pelvis; 3) right upper extremity; 4) left upper extremity; 5) right lower extremity; and 6) left lower extremity. The examination of a given area includes: • Inspection and/or palpation with notation of presence of any misalignment, asymmetry, crepitation, defects, tenderness, masses, effusions • Assessment of range of motion with notation of any pain, crepitation or contracture • Assessment of stability with notation of any dislocation (luxation), subluxation, or laxity • Assessment of muscle strength and tone (e.g., flaccid, cog wheel, spastic) with notation of any atrophy or abnormal movements
Skin	• Inspection of skin and subcutaneous tissue (e.g., rashes, lesions, ulcers) • Palpation of skin and subcutaneous tissue (e.g., induration, subcutaneous nodules, tightening)
Neurologic	• Test cranial nerves with notation of any deficits • Examination of deep tendon reflexes with notation of pathological reflexes (e.g., Babinski) • Examination of sensation (e.g., by touch, pin, vibration, proprioception)
Psychiatric	• Description of patient's judgment and insight • Brief assessment of mental status including: — Orientation to time, place and person — Recent and remote memory — Mood and affect (e.g., depression, anxiety, agitation)

Content and Documentation Requirements

Level of exam	Perform and document
Problem focused	**One to five** elements identified by a bullet.
Expanded problem focused	**At least six** elements identified by a bullet.
Detailed	**At least 12** elements identified by a bullet, whether in a box with a shaded or unshaded border
Comprehensive	Performance of **all** elements identified by a bullet; whether in a box or with a shaded or unshaded box. Documentation of every element in each with a shaded border and at least one element in a box with un shaded border is expected

C. Documentation of the Complexity of Medical Decision Making 1995 and 1997

The levels of E/M services recognize four types of medical decision-making (straightforward, low complexity, moderate complexity, and high complexity). Medical decision-making refers to the complexity of establishing a diagnosis and/or selecting a management option as measured by:

· The number of possible diagnoses and/or the number of management options that must be considered

· The amount and/or complexity of medical records, diagnostic tests, and/or other information that must be obtained, reviewed, and analyzed

· The risk of significant complications, morbidity, and/or mortality, as well as comorbidities, associated with the patient's presenting problem, the diagnostic procedure, and/or the possible management options

The following chart shows the progression of the elements required for each level of medical decision-making. To qualify for a given type of decision-making, two of the three elements in the table must be either met or exceeded.

Number of Diagnoses or Management Option	Amount and/or Complexity of Data to be Reviewed	Risk of Complications and/or Morbidity or Mortality	Type of Decision Making
Minimal	Minimal or None	Minimal	Straightforward
Limited	Limited	Low	Low Complexity
Multiple	Moderate	Moderate	Moderate Complexity
Extensive	Extensive	High	High Complexity

Each of the elements of medical decision-making is described below.

Number of Diagnoses or Management Options
The number of possible diagnoses and/or the number of management options that must be considered is based on the number and types of problems addressed during the encounter, the complexity of establishing a diagnosis, and the management decisions that are made by the physician.

Generally, decision making with respect to a diagnosed problem is easier than that for an identified but undiagnosed problem. The number and type of diagnostic tests employed may be an indicator of the number of possible diagnoses. Problems that are improving or resolving are less complex than those that are worsening or failing to change as expected. The need to seek advice from others is another indicator of complexity of diagnostic or management problems.

- DG: For each encounter, an assessment, clinical impression, or diagnosis should be documented. It may be explicitly stated or implied in documented decisions regarding management plans and/or further evaluation

    - For a presenting problem with an established diagnosis, the record should reflect whether the problem is: a) improved, well controlled, resolving, or resolved; or b) inadequately controlled, worsening, or failing to change as expected

    - For a presenting problem without an established diagnosis, the assessment or clinical impression may be stated in the form of a differential diagnosis or as a "possible," "probable," or "rule-out" (R/O) diagnosis

- DG: The initiation of, or changes in, treatment should be documented. Treatment includes a wide range of management options including patient instructions, nursing instructions, therapies, and medications

- DG: If referrals are made, consultations requested, or advice sought, the record should indicate to whom or where the referral or consultation is made or from whom the advice is requested

Amount and/or Complexity of Data to be Reviewed
The amount and complexity of data to be reviewed is based on the types of diagnostic testing ordered or reviewed. A decision to obtain and review old medical records and/or obtain history from sources other than the patient increases the amount and complexity of data to be reviewed.

Discussion of contradictory or unexpected test results with the physician who performed or interpreted the test is an indication of the complexity of data being reviewed. On occasion, the physician who ordered a test may personally review the image, tracing, or specimen to supplement information from the physician who prepared the test report or interpretation; this is another indication of the complexity of data being reviewed.

- DG: If a diagnostic service (test or procedure) is ordered, planned, scheduled, or performed at the time of the E/M encounter, the type of service (e.g., lab or x-ray) should be documented

- DG: The review of lab, radiology, and/or other diagnostic tests should be documented. A simple notation such as WBC elevated" or "chest x-ray unremarkable" is acceptable. Alternatively, the review may be documented by initialing and dating the report containing the test results

- DG: A decision to obtain old records or a decision to obtain additional history from the family, caretaker, or other source to supplement that obtained from the patient should be documented

- DG: Relevant findings from the review of old records and/or the receipt of additional history from the family, caretaker, or other source to supplement that obtained from the patient should be documented. If there is no relevant information beyond that already obtained, that fact should be documented. A notation of "old records reviewed" or "additional history obtained from family" without elaboration is insufficient

- DG: The results of discussion of laboratory, radiology, or other diagnostic tests with the physician who performed or interpreted the study should be documented

- DG: The direct visualization and independent interpretation of an image, tracing, or specimen previously or subsequently interpreted by another physician should be documented

Risk of Significant Complications, Morbidity, and/or Mortality
The risk of significant complications, morbidity, and/or mortality is based on the risks associated with the presenting problem, the diagnostic procedure, and the possible management options.

- DG: Comorbidities/underlying disease or other factors that increase the complexity of medical decision making by increasing the risk of complications, morbidity, and/or mortality should be documented

- DG: If a surgical or invasive diagnostic procedure is ordered, planned, or scheduled at the time of the E/M encounter, the type of procedure (e.g., laparoscopy) should be documented

- DG: If a surgical or invasive diagnostic procedure is performed at the time of the E/M encounter, the specific procedure should be documented

- DG: The referral for or decision to perform a surgical or invasive diagnostic procedure on an urgent basis should be documented or implied

The following Table of Risk may be used to help determine whether the risk of significant complications, morbidity, and/or mortality is minimal, low, moderate, or high. Because the determination of risk is complex and not readily quantifiable, the table includes common clinical examples rather than absolute measures of risk. The assessment of risk of the presenting problem is based on the risk related to the disease process anticipated between the present encounter and the next one. The assessment of risk of selecting diagnostic procedures and management options is based on the risk during and immediately following any procedures or treatment. The highest level of risk in any one category (presenting problem, diagnostic procedure, or management options) determines the overall risk.

Table of Risk.

Level of Risk	Presenting Problem(s)	Diagnostic Procedure(s) Ordered	Management Options Selected
Minimal	One self-limited or minor problem (e.g., cold, insect bite, tinea corporis)	Laboratory test requiring veinpuncture Chest x-rays EKG/EEG Urinalysis Ultrasound (e.g., echocardiography) KOH prep	Rest Gargles Elastic bandages Superficial dressings
Low	Two or more self-limited or minor problems One stable chronic illness (e.g., well controlled hypertension, non-insulin dependent diabetes, cataract, BPH) Acute, uncomplicated illness or injury (e.g., cystitis, allergic rhinitis, simple sprain)	Physiologic tests not under stress (e.g., pulmonary function tests) Non-cardiovascular imaging studies with contrast (e.g., barium enema) Superficial needle biopsies Clinical laboratory tests requiring arterial puncture Skin biopsies	Over-the-counter drugs Minor surgery with no identified risk factors Physical therapy Occupational therapy IV fluids without additives
Moderate	One or more chronic illnesses with mild exacerbation, progression or side effects of treatment Two or more stable chronic illnesses Undiagnosed new problem with uncertain prognosis (e.g., lump in breast) Acute illness with systemic symptoms (e.g., pyelonephritis, pneumonitis, colitis) Acute complicated injury (e.g., head injury with brief loss of consciousness)	Physiologic tests not under stress (e.g., cardiac stress test, fetal contraction stress test) Diagnostic endoscopies with no identified risk factors Deep needle or incisional biopsy Cardiovascular imaging studies with contrast and no identified risk factors (e.g., arteriogram, cardiac catheterization) Obtain fluid from body cavity (e.g., lumbar puncture, thoracentesis, culdocentesis)	Minor surgery with identified risk factors Effective major surgery (open, percutaneous or endoscopic) with no identified risk factors Prescription drug management Therapeutic nuclear medicine IV fluids with additives Closed treatment of fracture or dislocation without manipulation
High	One or more chronic illnesses with severe exacerbation, progression or side effects of treatment Acute/chronic illnesses that may pose a threat to life or bodily function (e.g., multiple trauma, acute MI, pulmonary embolus, severe respiratory distress, progressive severe rheumatoid arthritis, psychiatric illness with potential threat to self or others, peritonitis, acute renal failure An abrupt change in neurologic status (e.g., seizure, TIA, weakness or sensory loss)	Cardiovascular imaging studies with contrast with identified risk factors Cardiac electrophysiological tests Diagnostic endoscopies with identified risk factors Discography	Elective major surgery (open, percutaneous or endoscopic) with identified risk factors Emergency major surgery (open, percutaneous or endoscopic) Parenteral controlled substances Drug therapy requiring intensive monitoring for toxicity Decision not to resuscitate or to de-escalate care because of poor prognosis

D. Documentation of an Encounter Dominated by Counseling or Coordination of Care

In the case where counseling and/or coordination of care dominates (more than 50 percent) the physician/patient and/or family encounter (face-to-face time in the office or other outpatient setting or floor-unit time in the hospital or nursing facility), time is considered the key or controlling factor to qualify for a particular level of E/M service.

- DG: If the physician elects to report the level of service based on counseling and/or coordination of care, the total length of time of the encounter (face-to-face or floor time, as appropriate) should be documented and the record should describe the counseling and/or activities to coordinate care

General Surgery and Gastroenterology Specifics

Each provider specialty has differences that typically lie in the approach and are likely to revolve around the physical exam.

There are 11 types of exams specified in the 1997 guidelines. Some of these exams will work better for some specialties than others. Not all specialists will find that the organ-system exam related to their specialty is the most practical. Find below suggestions related to the most problematic E/M audit areas: history and exam.

Many suggestions may pertain to the higher levels of service, new patient or consult levels four and five, or level four and five established patients. This is not an effort to steer a provider toward the use of those codes, but rather recognition that this is where the more demanding documentation elements reside.

Hospital admissions require comprehensive histories and exams at the two higher levels of admits. This is where documentation deficiencies most often occur. All admits for levels two and three require a complete (10) ROS. This area probably yields more deficiencies than any other. Hospitals generally require a complete "H & P." Under current guidelines, the history element can be met by indicating "all other ROS negative" after reviewing problem pertinent systems, as well as any positive systems.

For subsequent hospital visits, the exam is often not very substantial (the patient just having had a complete H & P on admission). It is best to use the general system-level approach.

Physical Exam Section

Neither General Surgery nor Gastroenterolgy has a 1997 single system exam guideline developed specifically for their specialty. The approach to documentation may be somewhat different for each of these specialty areas. General surgeons, like most surgical specialties, have no specific single system exam identified for their use primarily because surgery can be performed on many areas of the body and therefore it would be difficult to come up with an exam that would be generally representative of these services. Given this situation, the 1995 general system exam or the 1997 general multi-system exam are probably the easiest guidelines to follow. Given the lack of specificity of the 1995 exam guidelines, almost all surgeons should find these easiest of all to use for new patients, consults, and follow up encounters. Even the highest levels only require a notation about each of eight organ systems, including notations of normal or negative.

For Gastroenterolgy, the 1995 multi-system exam guidelines are generally more friendly for follow-up patients. Again, there is no single system exam specifically for GI, but the Hematology/Lymphatic/Immunologic exam may be the closest of the single system exams. The Heme/Lymph exam may be the best fit for this specialty in terms of exam elements likely performed. The down side is that the 1997 Heme/Lymph comprehensive exam requires that 19 individual elements be addressed across 11 organ systems. GI providers may wish to review this single system exam in case it in fact approximates key exam elements in certain situations. A GI template could be rather easily created from the Heme/Lymph guidelines and may be of benefit to the GI provider. On the other hand, the 1995 general exam covers only eight systems and has no specific elemental requirements.

The table on following page is the 1997 single system Hematology/Lymphatic/Immunologic exam:

Remember that you can always use the 1995 general multi-system approach, it tends to be much simpler for many practices.

See the 1997 single system psychiatric exam below.

Content and Documentation Requirements—Psychiatric Examination

Constitutional	• Measurement of **any three of the following seven** vital signs: 1) sitting or standing blood pressure, 2) supine blood pressure, 3) pulse rate and regularity, 4) respiration, 5) temperature 6) height, 7) weight (May be measured and recorded by ancillary staff). • General appearance of patient (e.g., development, nutrition, body habitus, deformities, attention to grooming)
Head and face	
Eyes	
Ears, nose, mouth and throat	
Neck	
Respiratory	
Cardiovascular	
Chest (Breasts)	
Gastrointestinal (Abdomen)	
Genitourinary	
Lymphatic	
Musculoskeletal	• Assessment of muscle strength and tone (e.g., flaccid, cog wheel, spastic) with notation of any atrophy or abnormal movements • Examination of gait and station
Extremities	
Skin	
Neurological	
Psychiatric	• Description of speech including: rate; volume; articulation; coherence; and spontaneity with notation of abnormalities (e.g., perseveration, paucity of language) • Description of thought processes including: rate of thoughts; content of thoughts (e.g., logical vs. illogical, tangential); abstract reasoning; and computation • Description of associations (e.g., loose, tangential, circumstantial, intact) • Description of abnormal or psychotic thoughts including: hallucinations; delusions; preoccupation with violence; homicidal or suicidal ideation; and obsessions • Description of the patient's judgment (e.g., concerning everyday activities and social situations) and insight (e.g., concerning psychiatric condition) • Complete mental status examination including: — orientation to time, place and person — recent and remote memory — attention span and concentration — language (e.g., naming objects, repeating phrases) — fund of knowledge (e.g., awareness of current events, past history, vocabulary) — mood and affect (e.g., depression, anxiety, agitation, hypomania, lability)

Level of Exam Perform and Document:

Problem focused	**One to five** elements identified by a bullet.
Expanded problem focused	**At least six** elements identified by a bullet.
Detailed	**At least nine** elements identified by a bullet.
Comprehensive	Perform **all** elements identified by a bullet; document every element in each box with a shaded border and at least one element in each box with an unshaded border.

Remember that the 1995 general multi-system approach may also be used, it tends to be more simple for many practices to use.

CPT Index

A

Acetic Anhydrides, 84600
After Hours Medical Services, 99050, 99056–99058
Alcohol
  Breath, 82075
  Ethyl
    Glycol, 82693

B

Biofeedback Psychophysiological, 90875–90876
  Blood-flow, 90901
  Blood Pressure, 90901
  Brainwaves, 90901
  EEG (Electroencephalogram), 90901
  Electromyogram, 90901
  Electro-Oculogram, 90901
  Eyelids, 90901
  Nerve Conduction, 90901
  Other (unlisted) biofeedback, 90901
  Psychiatric Treatment, 90875–90876
Brain
  Mapping, 96020
Breath Test
  Alcohol, Ethyl, 82075

C

Carbamazepine
  Assay, 80156–80157
Carbon Tetrachloride, 84600
Care Plan Oversight Services
  Home Health Agency Care, 99374–99375
  Hospice, 99377–99378
  Nursing Facility, 99379–99380
Case Management Services
  Team Conferences, 99366–99368
  Telephone Calls
    Nonphysician, 98966–98968
    Physician, 99441–99443
CCL4, 84600
Cognitive Skills Development, 97532
Conference
  Medical
    with Interdisciplinary Team, 99366–99368
  Telephone
    Nonphysician, 98966–98968
    Physician, 99441–99443
Conjoint Psychotherapy, 90847
Counseling, home visit, 99510
Consultation
  Initial Inpatient
    New or Established Patient, 99251–99255
  Office and/or Other Outpatient
    New or Established Patient, 99241–99245
  Psychiatric, with Family, 90887
Crisis Psychotherapy 90839–90840

D

Developmental
  Screening, 96110
  Testing, 96111
Dichloroethane, 84600
Dichloromethane, 84600
Diethylether, 84600
Discharge Services
  Hospital, 99238–99239
  Nursing Facility, 99315–99316
  Observation Care, 99234–99236
Domiciliary Services
  Discharge Services, 99315–99316
Drug
  See also Drug Assay
  Administration For
    Cardiac Assessments, 93463
    Helicobacter Pylori Breath Test, 83014
    Infusion
      Epidural, 62360–62362
      Home Services, 99601–99602
      Intravenous, 4100F, 96365–96368, 96413–96417, 96422–96425
      Subcutaneous, 96369–96371
      Unlisted Infusion or Injection, 96379
    Antihistamines, *[80375, 80376, 80377]*
    Aspirin, 4084F, 4086F
    Confirmation, *[80320, 80321, 80322, 80323, 80324, 80325, 80326, 80327, 80328, 80329, 80330, 80331, 80332, 80333, 80334, 80335, 80336, 80337, 80338, 80339, 80340, 80341, 80342, 80343, 80344, 80345, 80346, 80347, 80348, 80349, 80350, 80351, 80352, 80353, 80354, 80355, 80356, 80357, 80358, 80359, 80360, 80361, 80362, 80363, 80364, 80365, 80366, 80367, 80368, 80369, 80370, 80371, 80372, 80373, 80374, 80375, 80376, 80377, 83992]*
    Implant Infusion Device, 62360–62362
    Infusion, 96365–96371, 96379, 96413–96417, 96422–96425
    Resistance Analysis HIV, 87903–87904
    Screening, *[80300, 80301, 80302, 80303, 80304]*
    Susceptibility Prediction, 87900
Drug Assay
  Amikacin, 80150
  Amitriptyline, *[80335, 80336, 80337]*
  Benzodiazepine, *[80346, 80347]*
  Caffeine, 80155
  Carbamazepine, 80156, 80157
  Clozapine, 80159
  Cyclosporine, 80158
  Desipramine, *[80335, 80336, 80337]*

Drug Assay—continued
  Digoxin, 80162–80163
  Dipropylacetic Acid, 80164
  Doxepin, *[80335, 80336, 80337]*
  Ethosuximide, 80168
  Everolimus, 80169
  Gabapentin, 80171
  Gentamicin, 80170
  Gold, *[80375]*
  Haloperidol, 80173
  Imipramine, *[80335, 80336, 80337]*
  Lamotrigine, 80175
  Levetiracetam, 80177
  Lidocaine, 80176
  Lithium, 80178
  Mycophenolate (mycophenolic acid), 80180
  Nortriptyline, *[80335, 80336, 80337]*
  Oxcarbazepine, 80183
  Phenobarbital, 80184
  Phenytoin, 80185, 80186
  Primidone, 80188
  Procainamide, 80190, 80192
  Quantitative
    Other, 80299
  Quinidine, 80194
  Salicylate, *[80329, 80330, 80331]*
  Sirolimus, 80195
  Tacrolimus, 80197
  Theophylline, 80198
  Therapeutic, 80150–80299 *[80164, 80165, 80171]*
  Tiagabine, 80199
  Tobramycin, 80200
  Topiramate, 80201
  Vancomycin, 80202
  Zonisamide, 80203
Drug Confirmation, *[80320, 80321, 80322, 80323, 80324, 80325, 80326, 80327, 80328, 80329, 80330, 80331, 80332, 80333, 80334, 80335, 80336, 80337, 80338, 80339, 80340, 80341, 80342, 80343, 80344, 80345, 80346, 80347, 80348, 80349, 80350, 80351, 80352, 80353, 80354, 80355, 80356, 80357, 80358, 80359, 80360, 80361, 80362, 80363, 80364, 80365, 80366, 80367, 80368, 80369, 80370, 80371, 80372, 80373, 80374, 80375, 80376, 80377, 83992]*
Drug Delivery Implant
  Insertion, 11981
  Irrigation, 96523
  Maintenance
    Brain, 95990, 95991
    Epidural, 95990, 95991
    Intra-arterial, 96522
    Intrathecal, 95990, 95991
    Intravenous, 96522
    Intraventricular, 95990, 95991
  Removal, 11982, 11983
    with Reinsertion, 11983
Drug Instillation
  See Instillation, Drugs
Drug Management
  Pharmacist, 99605–99607
  Psychiatric, 90863

Drugs, Anticoagulant
  See Clotting Inhibitors
Drug Screen, 99408–99409, *[80300, 80301, 80302, 80303, 80304]*
Drug Testing Definitive
  Alcohol Biomarkers, *[80321, 80322, 80323]*
  Alcohols, *[80320]*
  Alkaloids, Not Otherwise Specified, *[80323]*
  Amphetamines, *[80324, 80325, 80326]*
  Anabolic Steroids, *[80327, 80328]*
  Analgesics, Non Opioid, *[80329, 80330, 80331]*
  Antidepressants
    Not Otherwise Specified, *[80338]*
    Other Cyclicals, *[80335, 80336, 80337]*
    Serotonergic Class, *[80332, 80333, 80334]*
    Tricyclic, *[80335, 80336, 80337]*
  Antihistamines, *[80375, 80376, 80377]*
  Antipsychotics, *[80342, 80343, 80344]*
  Barbiturates, *[80345]*
  Benzodiazepines, *[80346, 80347]*
  Buprenorphine, *[80348]*
  Cannabinoids
    Natural, *[80349]*
    Synthetic, *[80350, 80351, 80352]*
  Cocaine, *[80353]*
  Drugs or Substances, Not Otherwise Specified, *[80375, 80376, 80377]*
  Fentanyl, *[80354]*
  Gabapentin, Non-Blood, *[80355]*
  Heroin Metabolite, *[80356]*
  Ketamine, *[80357]*
  MDA, *[80359]*
  MDEA, *[80359]*
  MDMA, *[80359]*
  Methadone, *[80358]*
  Methylenedioxyamphetamines (MDA, MDEA, MDMA), *[80359]*
  Methylphenidate, *[80360]*
  Norketamine, *[80357]*
  Opiates, *[80361]*
  Opioids and Opiate Analogs, *[80362, 80363, 80364]*
  Oxycodone, *[80365]*
  PCP, *[83992]*
  Phencyclidine (PCP), *[83992]*
  Phenobarbital, *[80345]*
  Pregabalin, *[80366]*
  Propoxyphene, *[80367]*
  Sedative Hypnotics, *[80368]*
  Skeletal Muscle Relaxants, *[80369, 80370]*
  Stereoisomer (Enantiomer) Analysis Single Drug Class, *[80374]*
  Stimulants, Synthetic, *[80371]*
  Tapentadol, *[80372]*
  Tramadol, *[80373]*

E

ECT (Electroconvulsive Therapy), 90870
ED, 99281–99285
Education, 99078
  Services (Group), 99078
  Supplies, 99071
Electroconvulsive Therapy, 90870
Emergency Department Services, 99281–99285
  Anesthesia
    in Office, 99058
Environmental Intervention
  for Psychiatric Patients, 90882
ER, 99281–99285
EST, 90870
Established Patient
  Emergency Department Services, 99281–99285
  Home Services, 99347–99350
  Hospital Inpatient Services, 99221–99239
  Hospital Observation Services, 99217–99220
  Inpatient Consultations, 99251–99255
  Office and/or Other Outpatient Consultations, 99241–99245
  Office Visit, 99211–99215
  Online Evaluation and Management Services
    Nonphysician, 98966–98968
    Physician, 99441–99443
  Outpatient Visit, 99211–99215
Ethanol
  Breath, 82075
Ethyl Alcohol (Ethanol)
  Breath, 82075
Evaluation and Management
  Care Plan Oversight Services, 99339–99340, 99374–99380
    Home Health Agency Care 99374–99375
    Home or Rest Care 99339–99340
    Hospice 99377–99378
    Nursing Facility 99379–99380
  Case Management Services, 99366–99368
  Consultation, 99241–99255
  Domiciliary or Rest Home
    Established Patient 99334–99337
    New Patient 99324–99328
  Emergency Department, 99281–99285
  Health Behavior
    Assessment, 96150
    Family Intervention, 96154–96155
    Group Intervention, 96153
    Individual Intervention, 96152
    Re-assessment, 96151
  Home Services, 99341–99350
  Hospital, 99221–99233
  Hospital Discharge, 99238–99239
  Hospital Services
    Observation Care, 99217–99220, 99224–99226, 99234–99236
  Internet Communication,
    Nonphysician, 98969
    Physician, 99444
  Nursing Facility, 99304–99318
  Observation Care, 99217–99220
  Office and Other Outpatient, 99201–99215
Evaluation and
  Management—*continued*
  Prolonged Services, 99356–99357
  Psychiatric/Records or Reports, 90889

F

Functional brain mapping, 96020

G

Group Health Education, 99078

H

Haloperidol
  Assay, 80173
HBcAb, 86704–86705
HBeAb, 86707
HBsAb, 86706
Heaf Test
  TB Test, 86580
Home Services
  Established Patient, 99347–99350
  New Patient, 99341–99345
Hospital Services
  Inpatient Services, 99238–99239
    Discharge Services, 99238–99239
    Initial Care New or Established Patient, 99221–99223
    Initial Hospital Care, 99221–99223
    Prolonged Services, 99356–99357
    Subsequent Hospital Care, 99231–99233
  Observation
    Discharge Services, 99234–99236
    Initial Care, 99218–99220
      New or Established Patient, 99218–99220
  Same Day Admission
    Discharge Services, 99234–99236
House Calls, 99341–99350
Hypnotherapy, 90880

I

Isopropyl Alcohol, 84600

L

Lithium
  Assay, 80178

M

Mandated Services
  Hospital, on call, 99026–99027
Mapping
  Functional brain, 96020
Medical Testimony, 99075
Methanol, 84600
Monitoring
  Prolonged, with Physician Attendance, 99354–99359

N

Narcosynthesis
  Diagnostic and Therapeutic, 90865

Neurology
  Central Motor
    Higher Cerebral Function
      Aphasia Test, 96105
      Developmental Tests, 96110–96111
New Patient
  Emergency Department Services, 99281–99285
  Home Services, 99341–99345
  Hospital Inpatient Services, 99221–99239
  Hospital Observation Services, 99217–99220
  Inpatient Consultations, 99251–99255
  Initial Office Visit, 99201–99205
  Office and/or Other Outpatient Consultations, 99241–99245
  Outpatient Visit, 99211–99215
Non-Office Medical Services, 99056
Nursing Facility Services
  Care Plan Oversight Services, 99379–99380
  Discharge Services, 99315–99316

O

Observation Services
  Initial, 99218–99220
  Same Date Admit/Discharge, 99234–99236
  Subsequent, 99224–99226
Office and/or Other Outpatient Visits
  Consultation, 99241–99245
  Established Patient, 99211–99215
  New Patient, 99201–99205
  Office Visit
    Established Patient, 99211–99215
    New Patient, 99201–99205
  Outpatient Visit
    Established Patient, 99211–99215
    New Patient, 99201–99205
  Prolonged Service, 99354–99355
Office Medical Services
  After Hours, 99050
  Emergency Care, 99058

P

Performance Measures
  Assessment
    Mental Status, 2014F
    Suicide Risk, 3085F
  Electroconvulsive therapy (ECT)
    Provided, 4066F
    Referral for, 4067F
  Major Depressive Disorder
    Criteria Documented 1040F
    Documentation New
      Initital/Recurrent episode, 3093F
      In Remission, 3092F
      Mild, 3088F
      Moderate, 3089F
      Severe,
        With Psychotic Features, 3091F
        Without Psychotic Features, 3090F
  Pharmacotherapy Prescribed
    Antidepressant, 4064F
    Antipsychotic, 4065F

Performance Measures—*continued*
  Psychotherapy Services
    Provided 4060F
    Referral for 4062F
  Tobacco Use
    Assessment, 1000F–1001F
    Counseling, 4000F
    Pharmacologic Therapy, 4001F
Phencyclidine, 83992
Phenytoin
  Assay, 80185–80186
Physical Examination
  Office and/or Other Outpatient Services, 99201–99205
Physical Medicine/Therapy/ Occupational Therapy
  Cognitive Skills Development, 97532
  Sensory Integration, 97533
Physician Services
  Care Plan Oversight Services, 99339–99340, 99374–99380
    Domiciliary Facility 99339–99340
    Home Health Agency Care 99374–99375
    Home or Rest Home Care 99339–99340
    Hospice, 99377–99378
    Nursing Facility, 99379–99380
  Case Management Services 99366–99368
  Online 99444
  Prolonged
    with Direct Patient Contact 99354–99357
    Inpatient 99356–99357
    Outpatient/Office 99354–99355
    without Direct Patient Contact 99358–99359
  Standby 99360
  Supervision, Care Plan Oversight Services 99339–99340, 99374–99380
  Team Conference 99367
  Telephone 99441–99443
Primidone
  Assay, 80188
Prolonged Services
  with Direct Patient Contact, 99354–99357
  without Direct Patient Contact, 99358–99359
Protein
  Western Blot, 84181–84182
Psychiatric Diagnosis
  Adaptive Behavior Assessments
    Behavioral Identification, 0359T
    Criteria Documented, 1040F
    Exposure Behavioral Followup, 0362T–0363T
    Observational Behavioral Followup, 0360T–0361T
  Evaluation, 90791–90792
  Evaluation of Records, Reports, and Tests, 90885
  Major Depressive Disorder (MDD), 3088F–3093F
  Diagnostic and Statistical Manual (DSM)
  Narcosynthesis, 90865
  Psychological Testing, 96101–96103
    Cognitive Performance, 96125
    Computer-Assisted, 96103

ICD-10-CM Index

The ICD-10-CM index is the means by which a diagnostic statement is translated into a diagnosis code. The index lists main diagnostic terms alphabetically and these main terms are then followed by subterms that are indented under the main term. Selecting the most specific main term and any subterms allow assignment of the most specific diagnosis code.

In addition to the main term and subterms, there are a number of conventions and symbols that must be understood to increase coding accuracy and efficiency. These conventions and symbols are discussed in this section.

Note: The 2016 ICD-10-CM codes for the 2016 *Coding and Payment Guide for Behavioral Health Services* are provided as a downloadable file and can be found on our website at: https://www.optumcoding.com/Product/Updates/specialty.

Password: **SPEC16DLC**

History of ICD-10-CM
The ICD-10-CM classification system was developed by the National Center for Health Statistics (NCHS) as a clinical modification to the ICD-10 system developed by the World Health Organization (WHO), primarily as a unique system for use in the United States for morbidity and mortality reporting. Although ICD-10 replaced ICD-9 for use in coding and classifying mortality data from death certificates beginning January 1, 1999, ICD-10-CM implementation was postponed many years until legislation to replace ICD-9-CM, volumes 1 and 2, with ICD-10-CM was approved.

ICD-10 is the copyrighted product of the World Health Organization (WHO), which has authorized the development of a clinical modification (CM) of ICD-10 for use in the United States. However, all modifications to the ICD-10 must conform to WHO conventions for ICD. The development of ICD-10-CM included comprehensive evaluation by a Technical Advisory Panel and extensive consultation with physician groups, clinical coders, and other industry experts.

The ICD-10-CM draft and crosswalk between ICD-9-CM and ICD-10-CM were made available on the Centers for Medicare and Medicaid Services (CMS) website for public comment. The initial public comment period extended from December 1997 through February 1998. A field test for ICD-10-CM was conducted in the summer of 2003 jointly by the American Hospital Association (AHA) and the American Health Information Management Association (AHIMA). Public comments and suggestions were reviewed and additional modifications to ICD-10-CM were made. Revisions were made to ICD-10-CM based on the established update process for ICD-10-CM (the ICD-10-CM Coordination and Maintenance Committee) and the World Health Organization's ICD-10 (the Update and Revision Committee).

These revisions to ICD-10-CM have included:

- information relevant to ambulatory and managed care encounters

- expanded injury codes

- creation of combination diagnosis/symptom codes to reduce the number of codes needed to fully describe a condition

- the addition of 6th and 7th character classifications

- incorporation of common 4th and 5th character classifications

- classifications specific to laterality

- classification refinement for increased data granularity

This new structure allows for further expansion than was possible with the ICD-9-CM classification system.

Legislative Steps to ICD-10-CM Implementation
January 16, 2009
The Department of Health and Human Services (DHHS) published the final rule regarding the adoption of ICD-10-CM in the *Federal Register*(45 CFR part 162 [CMS—0013—F]). The initial compliance date for implementation of ICD-10-CM as a replacement for the ICD-9-CM diagnosis code set was set as October 1, 2013.

April 17, 2012
DHHS released a notice to postpone the implementation date. The compliance date for implementation of ICD-10-CM as a replacement for ICD-9-CM diagnosis codes was changed to October 1, 2014.

April 1, 2014
Congress enacted the Protecting Access to Medicare Act of 2014, which contained a provision to delay the implementation of ICD-10-CM by a least one year, prohibiting DHHS from adopting the ICD-10-CM/PCS code sets as the mandatory standard until October 1, 2015.

August 4, 2014
DHHS issues a final rule changing the compliance date for the International Classification of Diseases, 10th Revision (ICD-10-CM) Medical Data Code Set to October 1, 2015.

ICD-10-CM Coding Conventions
The ICD-10-CM coding conventions, or rules, used in this book are outlined below. All ICD-10-CM coding rules can be found in the front of any ICD-10-CM code book.

Optum360 Additional Conventions
In addition to the official conventions, Optum360 code books use two additional conventions.

☑ This symbol is used to indicate when additional characters are required to complete a code.

Following **References**
The index includes *following* references to assist in locating "out-of-sequence" codes in the tabular list.
"Out-of-sequence" codes contain an alphabetic character (letter) in the 3rd or 4th character position. These codes are placed according to the classification rules—the placement of the codes according to condition—not according to alphabetic or numeric sequencing rules.

Example:

Carcinoma (malignant) (*see also,* Neoplasm, by site, malignant)
  neuroendocrine (*see also,* Tumor, neuroendocrine)
    high grade, any site C7A.1 (*following* C75)
    poorly differentiated, any site C7A.1 (*following* C75)

Official ICD-10-CM Conventions

The official ICD-10-CM conventions are incorporated into the alphabetic index and tabular list and an understanding of these conventions is needed to select and sequence codes. Key alphabetic index conventions are listed here. For a complete list of all conventions refer to your ICD-10-CM code book.

The provider's diagnostic statement usually contains several medical terms. To translate the terms into diagnosis codes, first identify the documented main term describing the condition. The other terms may be considered modifiers.

There are two types of modifiers, nonessential and essential:

- **Nonessential modifiers** are shown in parentheses after the term that they modify. Nonessential modifiers may be either present or absent in the medical record. These modifiers do not affect the code selection.

- **Essential modifiers** are indented under the main term. When there is only one essential modifier, it is listed next to the main term after a comma. Essential modifiers affect code assignment; therefore, they should be used in the coding process only if they are specified in the physician's diagnosis.

In the following example, "organic" and "spasmodic" are both nonessential modifiers, and "urethra" is an essential modifier.

Stricture (*see also* Stenosis)
    urethra (organic) (spasmodic) N35.9

Cross-References

Cross-references make locating a code easier. Two types of cross-references are used in this book: see and see also.

The *"see"* cross-reference directs the coder to seek another term elsewhere in the book. For example:

Tumor
    dermoid — *see* Neoplasm, benign, by site with malignant
        transformation C56- ☑

The *"see also"* cross-reference provides the coder with an alternative main term if the appropriate description is not found under the initial main term, such as:

Stricture (*see also* Stenosis)
    urethra (organic) (spasmodic) N35.9

Abbreviations

NEC—"Not elsewhere classifiable." Not every condition has its own ICD-10-CM code. The NEC abbreviation is used with those categories of codes for which a more specific code is not available. The NEC code describes all other specified forms of a condition. For example:

Disorder (of) (*see also* Disease)
    artery NEC I77.89

NOS—"Not otherwise specified." Coders should use an NOS code only when they lack the information necessary for assigning a more specific code.

Coding Neoplasms

The index contains a neoplasm table in which the codes for each particular type of neoplasm are listed for the body part, system, or tissue type affected. The columns divide the codes into neoplasm type:

malignant, benign, uncertain behavior, and unspecified with three distinct columns appearing under the malignant heading for primary, secondary, and carcinoma in situ.

Malignant neoplasms are uncontrolled new tissue growths or tumors that can progressively invade tissue in other parts of the body by spreading or metastasizing the disease producing cells from the initial site of malignancy. Primary defines the body site or tissue where the malignancy first began to grow and spread from there to other areas. Secondary malignancies are those sites that have been invaded by the cancer cells coming from another part of the body and are now exhibiting cancerous growth. Carcinoma in situ is confined to the epithelium of the vessels, glands, organs, or tissues in the body area where it originated and has not crossed the basement membrane to spread to the neighboring tissues.

Benign neoplasms are those found not to be cancerous in nature. The dividing cells adhere to each other in the tumor and remain a circumscribed lesion. Neoplasms of uncertain behavior are those whose subsequent behaviour cannot currently be predicted from the present appearance of the tumor and will require further study. Unspecified indicates simply a lack of documentation to support the selection of any more specific code.

Manifestation Codes

As in the following example, when two codes are required to indicate etiology and manifestation, the manifestation code appears in italics and brackets. The manifestation code is never a principal/primary diagnosis. Code the underlying disease (etiology) first. This is referred to as mandatory multiple coding of etiology and manifestation.

Arthritis, arthritic (acute) (chronic) (nonpyogenic) (subacute) M19.9Ø
    due to or associated with
        infectious disease NEC M01 ☑

Official ICD-10-CM Guidelines for Coding and Reporting

The Centers for Medicare and Medicaid Services (CMS) and the National Center for Health Statistics (NCHS), two departments within the U.S. federal government's Department of Health and Human Services (DHHS) present the following guidelines for coding and reporting using ICD-10-CM. These guidelines should be used as a companion document to the official versions of the ICD-10-CM.

These guidelines have been developed to assist the user in coding and reporting in situations where the ICD-10-CM book does not provide direction. These guidelines were developed to accompany and complement the official conventions and instructions provided within the index and tabular sections of ICD-10-CM. Any instructions within the ICD-10-CM classification take precedence over these guidelines.

These guidelines are not exhaustive. The cooperating parties are continuing to conduct review of these guidelines and to develop new guidelines as needed. Revisions of these guidelines and new guidelines will be published by DHHS when they are approved by the cooperating parties.

Diagnostic Coding and Reporting Guidelines for Outpatient Services

These coding guidelines for outpatient diagnoses have been approved for use by hospitals and physicians in coding and reporting hospital-based outpatient services and physician office visits.

The terms "encounter" and "visit" are often used interchangeably in describing outpatient service contacts and, therefore, appear together in these guidelines without distinguishing one from the other.

Though the conventions and general guidelines apply to all settings, coding guidelines for outpatient and physician reporting of diagnoses will vary in a number of instances from those for inpatient diagnoses, recognizing that: 1) the Uniform Hospital Discharge Data Set (UHDDS) definition of principal diagnosis applies only to inpatients in acute, short-term, long-term care, and general hospitals, and 2) coding guidelines for inconclusive diagnoses (probable, suspected, rule out, etc.) were developed for inpatient reporting and do not apply to outpatients.

A. **Selection of first-listed condition**

In the outpatient setting, the term "first-listed diagnosis" is used in lieu of principal diagnosis.

In determining the first-listed diagnosis, the coding conventions of ICD-10-CM, as well as the general and disease-specific guidelines, take precedence over the outpatient guidelines.

Diagnoses often are not established at the time of the initial encounter/visit. It may take two or more visits before the diagnosis is confirmed.

The most critical rule involves beginning the search for the correct code assignment through the Alphabetic Index. Never begin searching initially in the tabular list as this will lead to coding errors.

1. Outpatient Surgery

When a patient presents for outpatient surgery, code the reason for the surgery as the first-listed diagnosis (reason for the encounter), even if the surgery is not performed due to a contraindication.

2. Observation Stay

When a patient is admitted for observation for a medical condition, assign a code for the medical condition as the first-listed diagnosis.

When a patient presents for outpatient surgery and develops complications requiring admission to observation, code the reason for the surgery as the first reported diagnosis (reason for the encounter), followed by codes for the complications as secondary diagnoses.

B. **Codes from A00.0 through T88.9, Z00–Z99**

The appropriate code or codes from A00.0 through T88.9, Z00–Z99 must be used to identify diagnoses, symptoms, conditions, problems, complaints, or other reason(s) for the encounter/visit.

C. **Accurate reporting of ICD-10-CM diagnosis codes**

For accurate reporting of ICD-10-CM diagnosis codes, the documentation should describe the patient's condition, using terminology which includes specific diagnoses as well as symptoms, problems, or reasons for the encounter. There are ICD-10-CM codes to describe all of these.

D. **Codes that describe symptoms and signs**

Codes that describe symptoms and signs, as opposed to diagnoses, are acceptable for reporting purposes when a diagnosis has not been established (confirmed) by the provider. Chapter 18 of ICD-10-CM, "Symptoms, Signs, and Abnormal Clinical and Laboratory Finders Not Elsewhere Classified (R00-R99)" contains many, but not all, codes for symptoms.

E. **Encounters for circumstances other than a disease or injury**

ICD-10-CM provides codes to deal with encounters for circumstances other than a disease or injury. The Factors Influencing Health Status and Contact with Health Services codes (Z00–Z99) are provided to deal with occasions when circumstances other than a disease or injury are recorded as diagnosis or problems.

F. **Level of detail in coding**

1. ICD-10-CM codes with 3, 4, 5, 6, or 7 characters

ICD-10-CM is composed of codes with 3, 4, 5, 6, or 7 characters. Codes with three characters are included in ICD-10-CM as the heading of a category of codes that may be further subdivided by the use of fourth, fifth, sixth, or seventh characters to provide greater specificity.

2. Use of full number of characters required for a code

A three-character code is to be used only if it is not further subdivided. A code is invalid if it has not been coded to the full number of characters required for that code, including the 7th character, if applicable.

G. **ICD-10-CM code for the diagnosis, condition, problem, or other reason for encounter/visit**

List first the ICD-10-CM code for the diagnosis, condition, problem, or other reason for encounter/visit shown in the medical record to be chiefly responsible for the services provided. List additional codes that describe any coexisting conditions. In some cases the first-listed diagnosis may be a symptom when a diagnosis has not been established (confirmed) by the physician.

H. **Uncertain diagnosis**

Do not code diagnoses documented as "probable," "suspected," "questionable," "rule out," or "working diagnosis," or other similar terms indicating uncertainty. Rather, code the condition(s) to the highest degree of certainty for that encounter/visit, such as symptoms, signs, abnormal test results, or other reason for the visit.

Please note: This differs from the coding practices used by short-term care, acute care, long-term care, and psychiatric hospitals.

I. **Chronic diseases**

Chronic diseases treated on an ongoing basis may be coded and reported as many times as the patient receives treatment and care for the condition(s).

J. **Code all documented conditions that coexist**

Code all documented conditions that coexist at the time of the encounter/visit, and require or affect patient care treatment or management. Do not code conditions that were previously treated and no longer exist. However, history codes (categories Z80–Z87) may be used as secondary codes if the historical condition or family history has an impact on current care or influences treatment.

K. **Patients receiving diagnostic services only**

For patients receiving diagnostic services only during an encounter/visit, sequence first the diagnosis, condition, problem, or other reason for encounter/visit shown in the medical record to be chiefly responsible for the outpatient services provided during the encounter/visit. Codes for other diagnoses (e.g., chronic conditions) may be sequenced as additional diagnoses.

For encounters for routine laboratory or radiology testing in the absence of any signs, symptoms, or associated diagnoses, assign Z01.89 Encounter for other specified special examinations. If routine testing is performed during the same encounter as a test to evaluate a sign, symptom, or diagnosis, it is appropriate to assign both the Z code and describing the reason for the nonroutine test.

For outpatient encounters for diagnostic tests that have been interpreted by a physician, and the final report is available at the time of coding, code any confirmed or definitive diagnosis(es) documented in the interpretation. Do not code related signs and symptoms as additional diagnoses.

Please note: This differs from the coding practice in the hospital inpatient setting regarding abnormal findings on test results.

L. Patients receiving therapeutic services only

For patients receiving therapeutic services only during an encounter/visit, sequence first the diagnosis, condition, problem, or other reason for encounter/visit shown in the medical record to be chiefly responsible for the outpatient services provided during the encounter/visit. Codes for other diagnoses (e.g., chronic conditions) may be sequenced as additional diagnoses.

The only exception to this rule is that when the primary reason for the admission/encounter is chemotherapy or radiation therapy, the appropriate Z code for the service is listed first, and the diagnosis or problem for which the service is being performed listed second.

M. Patients receiving preoperative evaluations only

For patients receiving preoperative evaluations only, sequence a code from subcategory Z01.81 Encounter for pre-procedural examinations, to describe the pre-op consultations. Assign a code

for the condition to describe the reason for the surgery as an additional diagnosis. Code also any findings related to the pre-op evaluation.

N. Ambulatory surgery

For ambulatory surgery, code the diagnosis for which the surgery was performed. If the postoperative diagnosis is known to be different from the preoperative diagnosis at the time the diagnosis is confirmed, select the postoperative diagnosis for coding, since it is the most definitive.

O. Routine outpatient prenatal visits

See Section I.C.15. Routine outpatient prenatal visits, in your ICD-10-CM code book.

P. Encounters for general medical examinations with abnormal findings

The subcategories for encounters for general medical examinations, Z00.0-, provide codes for with and without abnormal findings. Should a general medical examination result in an abnormal finding, the code for general medical examination with abnormal finding should be assigned as the first-listed diagnosis. A secondary code for the abnormal finding should also be coded.

Q. Encounters for routine health screenings

See Section I.C.21.5 Factors influencing health status and contact with health services, screening, in your ICD-10-CM code book.

IMPORTANT

Note: The following URL and password will provide you access to download and view the complete list of CCI edits and the ICD-10-CM index:

https://www.optumcoding.com/Product/Updates/specialty

2016 password: **SPEC16DLC**

Please note that you should log in each quarter to ensure you receive the most current updates. An email reminder will be sent to you when the updates are available.

Medicare Official Regulatory Information

The CMS Online Manual System

The Centers for Medicare and Medicaid Services (CMS) restructured its paper-based manual system as a web-based system on October 1, 2003. Called the CMS Online Manual System, it combines all of the various program instructions into internet-only manuals (IOM), which are used by all CMS programs and contractors. Complete versions of all of the manuals can be found at http://www.cms.gov/manuals.

Effective with implementation of the IOMs, the former method of publishing program memoranda (PM) to communicate program instructions was replaced by the following four templates:

- One-time notification
- Manual revisions
- Business requirements
- Confidential requirements

The web-based system has been organized by functional area (e.g., eligibility, entitlement, claims processing, benefit policy, program integrity) in an effort to eliminate redundancy within the manuals, simplify updating, and make CMS program instructions available more quickly.

The web-based system contains the functional areas included below:

Pub. 100	Introduction
Pub. 100-01	Medicare General Information, Eligibility and Entitlement Manual
Pub. 100-02	Medicare Benefit Policy Manual
Pub. 100-03	Medicare National Coverage Determinations (NCD) Manual
Pub. 100-04	Medicare Claims Processing Manual
Pub. 100-05	Medicare Secondary Payer Manual
Pub. 100-06	Medicare Financial Management Manual
Pub. 100-07	State Operations Manual
Pub. 100-08	Medicare Program Integrity Manual
Pub. 100-09	Medicare Contractor Beneficiary and Provider Communications Manual
Pub. 100-10	Quality Improvement Organization Manual
Pub. 100-11	Programs of All-Inclusive Care for the Elderly (PACE) Manual
Pub. 100-12	State Medicaid Manual (under development)
Pub. 100-13	Medicaid State Children's Health Insurance Program (under development)
Pub. 100-14	Medicare ESRD Network Organizations Manual
Pub. 100-15	Medicaid Integrity Program (MIP)
Pub. 100-16	Medicare Managed Care Manual
Pub. 100-17	CMS/Business Partners Systems Security Manual
Pub. 100-18	Medicare Prescription Drug Benefit Manual
Pub. 100-19	Demonstrations
Pub. 100-20	One-Time Notification
Pub. 100-21	Reserved
Pub. 100-22	Medicare Quality Reporting Incentive Programs Manual
Pub. 100-23	Payment Error Rate Measurement (Under development)
Pub. 100-24	State Buy-In Manual
Pub. 100-25	Information Security Acceptable Risk Safeguards Manual

A brief description of the Medicare manuals primarily used for this publication follows:

The *National Coverage Determinations (NCD) Manual*, is organized according to categories such as diagnostic services, supplies, and medical procedures. The contents of the manual lists each category and subject within that category. Revision transmittals identify any new or background material, recap the changes, and provide an effective date for the change.

When complete, the manual will contain two chapters. Chapter 1 currently includes a description of CMS's national coverage determinations. When available, chapter 2 will contain a list of HCPCS codes related to each coverage determination. The manual is organized in accordance with CPT category sequences.

The *Medicare Benefit Policy Manual* contains Medicare general coverage instructions that are not national coverage determinations. As a general rule, in the past these instructions have been found in chapter II of the *Medicare Carriers Manual*, the *Medicare Intermediary Manual*, other provider manuals, and program memoranda.

The *Medicare Claims Processing Manual* contains instructions for processing claims for contractors and providers.

The *Medicare Program Integrity Manual* communicates the priorities and standards for the Medicare integrity programs.

Pub. 100 References

Pub. 100-1, Chapter 3, Section, 30
Outpatient Mental Health Treatment Limitation
Regardless of the actual expenses a beneficiary incurs in connection with the treatment of mental, psychoneurotic, and personality disorders while the beneficiary is not an inpatient of a hospital at the time such expenses are incurred, the amount of those expenses that may be recognized for Part B deductible and payment purposes is limited to 62.5 percent of the Medicare approved amount for those services. The limitation is called the outpatient mental health treatment limitation (the limitation). The 62.5 percent limitation has been in place since the inception of the Medicare Part B program and it will remain effective at this percentage amount until January 1, 2010. However, effective January 1, 2010, through January 1, 2014, the limitation will be phased out as follows:

- January 1, 2010—December 31, 2011, the limitation percentage is 68.75%.
  (Medicare pays 55% and the patient pays 45%).
- January 1, 2012—December 31, 2012, the limitation percentage is 75%.
  (Medicare pays 60% and the patient pays 40%).
- January 1, 2013—December 31, 2013, the limitation percentage is 81.25%.
  (Medicare pays 65% and the patient pays 35%).
- January 1, 2014—onward, the limitation percentage is 100%.
  (Medicare pays 80% and the patient pays 20%).

For additional details concerning the outpatient mental health treatment limitation, please see the Medicare Claims Processing Manual, Publication 100-04, chapter 9, section 60 and chapter 12, section 210.

Pub. 100-2, Chapter 15, Section 80.2
Psychological Tests and Neuropsychological Tests
(Rev. 85, Issued: 02-29-08, Effective: 01-01-06, Implementation: 12-28-06)

Medicare Part B coverage of psychological tests and neuropsychological tests is authorized under section 1861(s)(3) of the Social Security Act. Payment for psychological and neuropsychological tests is authorized under section 1842(b)(2)(A) of the Social Security Act. The payment amounts for the new psychological and neuropsychological tests (CPT codes 96102, 96103, 96119 and 96120) that are effective January 1, 2006, and are billed for tests administered by a technician or a computer reflect a site of service payment differential for the facility and non-facility settings. Additionally, there is no authorization for payment for diagnostic tests when performed on an "incident to" basis.

Under the diagnostic tests provision, all diagnostic tests are assigned a certain level of supervision. Generally, regulations governing the diagnostic tests provision require that only physicians can provide the assigned level of supervision for diagnostic tests. However, there is a regulatory exception to the supervision requirement for diagnostic psychological and neuropsychological tests in terms of who can provide the supervision. That is, regulations allow a clinical psychologist (CP) or a physician to perform the general supervision assigned to diagnostic psychological and neuropsychological tests.

In addition, nonphysician practitioners such as nurse practitioners (NPs), clinical nurse specialists (CNSs) and physician assistants (PAs) who personally perform diagnostic psychological and neuropsychological tests are excluded from having to perform these tests under the general supervision of a physician or a CP. Rather, NPs and CNSs must perform such tests under the requirements of their respective benefit instead of the requirements for diagnostic psychological and neuropsychological tests. Accordingly, NPs and CNSs must perform tests in collaboration (as defined under Medicare law at section 1861(aa)(6) of the Act) with a physician. PAs perform tests under the general supervision of a physician as required for services furnished under the PA benefit.

Furthermore, physical therapists (PTs), occupational therapists (OTs) and speech language pathologists (SLPs) are authorized to bill three test codes as "sometimes therapy" codes. Specifically, CPT codes 96105, 96110 and 96111 may be performed by these therapists. However, when PTs, OTs and SLPs perform these three tests, they must be performed under the general supervision of a physician or a CP.

Who May Bill for Diagnostic Psychological and Neuropsychological Tests

- CPs – see qualifications under chapter 15, section 160 of the Benefits Policy Manual, Pub. 100-02.
- NPs –to the extent authorized under State scope of practice. See qualifications under chapter 15, section 200 of the Benefits Policy Manual, Pub. 100-02.
- CNSs –to the extent authorized under State scope of practice. See qualifications under chapter 15, section 210 of the Benefits Policy Manual, Pub. 100-02.
- PAs – to the extent authorized under State scope of practice. See qualifications under chapter 15, section 190 of the Benefits Policy Manual, Pub. 100-02.
- Independently Practicing Psychologists (IPPs)
- PTs, OTs and SLPs – see qualifications under chapter 15, sections 220-230.6 of the Benefits Policy Manual, Pub. 100-02.

Psychological and neuropsychological tests performed by a psychologist (who is not a CP) practicing independently of an institution, agency, or physician's office are covered when a physician orders such tests. An IPP is any psychologist who is licensed or certified to practice psychology in the State or jurisdiction where furnishing services or, if the jurisdiction does not issue licenses, if provided by any practicing psychologist. (It is CMS' understanding that all States, the District of Columbia, and Puerto Rico license psychologists, but that some trust territories do not. Examples of psychologists, other than CPs, whose psychological and neuropsychological tests are covered under the diagnostic tests provision include, but are not limited to, educational psychologists and counseling psychologists.)

The carrier must secure from the appropriate State agency a current listing of psychologists holding the required credentials to determine whether the tests of a particular IPP are covered under Part B in States that have statutory licensure or certification. In States or territories that lack statutory licensing or certification, the carrier checks individual qualifications before provider numbers are issued. Possible reference sources are the national directory of membership of the American Psychological Association, which provides data about the educational background of individuals and indicates which members are board-certified, the records and directories of the State or territorial psychological association, and the National Register of Health Service Providers. If qualification is dependent on a doctoral degree from a currently accredited program, the carrier verifies the date of accreditation of the school involved, since such accreditation is not retroactive. If the listed reference sources do not provide enough information (e.g., the psychologist is not a member of one of these sources), the carrier contacts the psychologist personally for the required information. Generally, carriers maintain a continuing list of psychologists whose qualifications have been verified.

NOTE: When diagnostic psychological tests are performed by a psychologist who is not practicing independently, but is on the staff of an institution, agency, or clinic, that entity bills for the psychological tests.

The carrier considers psychologists as practicing independently when:

- They render services on their own responsibility, free of the administrative and professional control of an employer such as a physician, institution or agency;
- The persons they treat are their own patients; and
- They have the right to bill directly, collect and retain the fee for their services.

A psychologist practicing in an office located in an institution may be considered an independently practicing psychologist when both of the following conditions exist:

- The office is confined to a separately-identified part of the facility which is used solely as the psychologist's office and cannot be construed as extending throughout the entire institution; and
- The psychologist conducts a private practice, i.e., services are rendered to patients from outside the institution as well as to institutional patients.

Payment for Diagnostic Psychological and Neuropsychological Tests
Expenses for diagnostic psychological and neuropsychological tests are not subject to the outpatient mental health treatment limitation, that is, the payment limitation on treatment services for mental, psychoneurotic and personality disorders as authorized under Section 1833(c) of the Act. The payment amount for the new psychological and neuropsychological tests (CPT codes 96102, 96103, 96119 and 96120) that are billed for tests performed by a technician or a computer reflect a site of service payment differential for the facility and non-facility settings. CPs, NPs, CNSs and PAs are required by law to accept assigned payment for psychological and neuropsychological tests. However, while IPPs are not required by law to accept assigned payment for these tests, they must report the name and address of the physician who ordered the test on the claim form when billing for tests.

CPT Codes for Diagnostic Psychological and Neuropsychological Tests
The range of CPT codes used to report psychological and neuropsychological tests is 96101-96120. CPT codes 96101, 96102, 96103, 96105, 96110, and 96111 are appropriate for use when billing for psychological tests. CPT codes 96116, 96118, 96119 and 96120 are appropriate for use when billing for neuropsychological tests.

All of the tests under this CPT code range 96101-96120 are indicated as active codes under the physician fee schedule database and are covered if medically necessary.

Payment and Billing Guidelines for Psychological and Neuropsychological Tests
The technician and computer CPT codes for psychological and neuropsychological tests include practice expense, malpractice expense and professional work relative value units. Accordingly, CPT psychological test code 96101 should not be paid when billed for the same tests or services performed under psychological test codes 96102 or 96103. CPT neuropsychological test code 96118 should not be paid when billed for the same tests or services performed under neuropsychological test codes 96119 or 96120. However, CPT codes 96101 and 96118 can be paid separately on the rare occasion when billed on the same date of service for different and separate tests from 96102, 96103, 96119 and 96120.

Under the physician fee schedule, there is no payment for services performed by students or trainees. Accordingly, Medicare does not pay for services represented by CPT codes 96102 and 96119 when performed by a student or a trainee. However, the presence of a student or a trainee while the test is being administered does not prevent a physician, CP, IPP, NP, CNS or PA from performing and being paid for the psychological test under 96102 or the neuropsychological test under 96119.

Pub. 100-2, Chapter 15, Section 160
Clinical Psychologist Services
(Rev. 51, Issued: 06-23-06, Effective: 01-01-05, Implementation: 09-21-06)

A. Clinical Psychologist (CP) Defined
To qualify as a clinical psychologist (CP), a practitioner must meet the following requirements:

Hold a doctoral degree in psychology;

Be licensed or certified, on the basis of the doctoral degree in psychology, by the State in which he or she practices, at the independent practice level of psychology to furnish diagnostic, assessment, preventive, and therapeutic services directly to individuals.

B. Qualified Clinical Psychologist Services Defined
Effective July 1, 1990, the diagnostic and therapeutic services of CPs and services and supplies furnished incident to such services are covered as the services furnished by a physician or as incident to physician's services are covered. However, the CP must be legally authorized to perform the services under applicable licensure laws of the State in which they are furnished.

C. Types of Clinical Psychologist Services That May Be Covered
Diagnostic and therapeutic services that the CP is legally authorized to perform in accordance with State law and/or regulation. Carriers pay all qualified CPs based on the physician fee schedule for the diagnostic and therapeutic services. (Psychological tests

by practitioners who do not meet the requirements for a CP may be covered under the provisions for diagnostic tests as described in

§80.2.

Services and supplies furnished incident to a CP's services are covered if the requirements that apply to services incident to a physician's services, as described in §60 are met. These services must be:

- Mental health services that are commonly furnished in CPs' offices;
- An integral, although incidental, part of professional services performed by the CP;
- Performed under the direct personal supervision of the CP; i.e., the CP must be physically present and immediately available;
- Furnished without charge or included in the CP's bill; and
- Performed by an employee of the CP (or an employee of the legal entity that employs the supervising CP) under the common law control test of the Act, as set forth in 20 CFR 404.1007 and §RS 2101.020 of the Retirement and Survivors Insurance part of the Social Security Program Operations Manual System.
- Diagnostic psychological testing services when furnished under the general supervision of a CP.

Carriers are required to familiarize themselves with appropriate State laws and/or regulations governing a CP's scope of practice.

D. Noncovered Services
The services of CPs are not covered if the service is otherwise excluded from Medicare coverage even though a clinical psychologist is authorized by State law to perform them. For example, §1862(a)(1)(A) of the Act excludes from coverage services that are not "reasonable and necessary for the diagnosis or treatment of an illness or injury or to improve the functioning of a malformed body member." Therefore, even though the services are authorized by State law, the services of a CP that are determined to be not reasonable and necessary are not covered. Additionally, any therapeutic services that are billed by CPs under CPT psychotherapy codes that include medical evaluation and management services are not covered.

E. Requirement for Consultation
When applying for a Medicare provider number, a CP must submit to the carrier a signed Medicare provider/supplier enrollment form that indicates an agreement to the effect that, contingent upon the patient's consent, the CP will attempt to consult with the patient's

attending or primary care physician in accordance with accepted professional ethical norms, taking into consideration patient confidentiality.

If the patient assents to the consultation, the CP must attempt to consult with the patient's physician within a reasonable time after receiving the consent. If the CP's attempts to consult directly with the physician are not successful, the CP must notify the physician within a reasonable time that he or she is furnishing services to the patient. Additionally, the CP must document, in the patient's medical record, the date the patient consented or declined consent to consultations, the date of consultation, or, if attempts to consult did not succeed, that date and manner of notification to the physician.

The only exception to the consultation requirement for CPs is in cases where the patient's primary care or attending physician refers the patient to the CP. Also, neither a CP nor a primary care nor attending physician may bill Medicare or the patient for this required consultation.

F. Outpatient Mental Health Services Limitation
All covered therapeutic services furnished by qualified CPs are subject to the outpatient mental health services limitation in Pub 100-01, Medicare General Information, Eligibility, and Entitlement Manual, Chapter 3, "Deductibles, Coinsurance Amounts, and Payment Limitations," §30, (i.e., only 62 1/2 percent of expenses for these services are considered incurred expenses for Medicare purposes). The limitation does not apply to diagnostic services.

G. Assignment Requirement
Assignment is required.

Pub. 100-2, Chapter 15, Section, 170
Clinical Social Worker (CSW) Services
B3-2152

See the Medicare Claims Processing Manual Chapter 12, Physician/Nonphysician Practitioners, Sec.150, "Clinical Social Worker Services," for payment requirements.

A. Clinical Social Worker Defined
Section 1861(hh) of the Act defines a "clinical social worker" as an individual who:

- Possesses a master's or doctor's degree in social work;
- Has performed at least two years of supervised clinical social work; and
- Is licensed or certified as a clinical social worker by the State in which the services are performed; or
- In the case of an individual in a State that does not provide for licensure or certification, has completed at least 2 years or 3,000 hours of post master's degree supervised clinical social work practice under the supervision of a master's level social worker in an appropriate setting such as a hospital, SNF, or clinic.

B. Clinical Social Worker Services Defined
Section 1861(hh)(2) of the Act defines "clinical social worker services" as those services that the CSW is legally authorized to perform under State law (or the State regulatory mechanism provided by State law) of the State in which such services are performed for the diagnosis and treatment of mental illnesses. Services furnished to an inpatient of a hospital or an inpatient of a SNF that the SNF is required to provide as a requirement for participation are not included. The services that are covered are those that are otherwise covered if furnished by a physician or as incident to a physician's professional service.

C. Covered Services
Coverage is limited to the services a CSW is legally authorized to perform in accordance with State law (or State regulatory mechanism established by State law). The services of a CSW may be covered under Part B if they are:

- The type of services that are otherwise covered if furnished by a physician, or as incident to a physician's service. (See Sec.30 for a description of physicians' services and Sec.70 of Pub 100-1, the Medicare General Information, Eligibility, and Entitlement Manual, Chapter 5, for the definition of a physician.);
- Performed by a person who meets the definition of a CSW (See subsection A.); and
- Not otherwise excluded from coverage. Carriers should become familiar with the State law or regulatory mechanism governing a CSW's scope of practice in their service area.

D. Noncovered Services

Services of a CSW are not covered when furnished to inpatients of a hospital or to inpatients of a SNF if the services furnished in the SNF are those that the SNF is required to furnish as a condition of participation in Medicare. In addition, CSW services are not covered if they are otherwise excluded from Medicare coverage even though a CSW is authorized by State law to perform them. For example, the Medicare law excludes from coverage services that are not "reasonable and necessary for the diagnosis or treatment of an illness or injury or to improve the functioning of a malformed body member."

E. Outpatient Mental Health Services Limitation

All covered therapeutic services furnished by qualified CSWs are subject to the outpatient psychiatric services limitation in Pub 100-01, Medicare General Information, Eligibility, and Entitlement Manual, Chapter 3, "Deductibles, Coinsurance Amounts, and Payment Limitations," Sec.30, (i.e., only 62 1/2 percent of expenses for these services are considered incurred expenses for Medicare purposes). The limitation does not apply to diagnostic services.

F. Assignment Requirement

Assignment is required.

Pub. 100-2, Chapter 15, Section, 230.4

Services Furnished by a Physical or Occupational Therapist in Private Practice

A. General

See section 220 of this chapter for definitions. Therapist refers only to a qualified physical therapist, occupational therapist or speech-language pathologist. TPP refers to therapists in private practice (qualified physical therapists, occupational therapists and speech-language pathologists).

In order to qualify to bill Medicare directly as a therapist, each individual must be enrolled as a private practitioner and employed in one of the following practice types: an unincorporated solo practice, unincorporated partnership, unincorporated group practice, physician/NPP group or groups that are not professional corporations, if allowed by state and local law. Physician/NPP group practices may employ TPP if state and local law permits this employee relationship.

For purposes of this provision, a physician/NPP group practice is defined as one or more physicians/NPPs enrolled with Medicare who may bill as one entity. For further details on issues concerning enrollment, see the provider enrollment Web site at www.cms.hhs.gov/MedicareProviderSupEnroll and Pub. 100-08, Medicare Program Integrity Manual, chapter10, section 12.4.14.

Private practice also includes therapists who are practicing therapy as employees of another supplier, of a professional corporation or other incorporated therapy practice. Private practice does not include individuals when they are working as employees of an institutional provider.

Services should be furnished in the therapist's or group's office or in the patient's home. The office is defined as the location(s) where the practice is operated, in the state(s) where the therapist (and practice, if applicable) is legally authorized to furnish services, during the hours that the therapist engages in the practice at that location. If services are furnished in a private practice office space, that space shall be owned, leased, or rented by the practice and used for the exclusive purpose of operating the practice. For descriptions of aquatic therapy in a community center pool see section 220C of this chapter.

Therapists in private practice must be approved as meeting certain requirements, but do not execute a formal provider agreement with the Secretary.

If therapists who have their own Medicare National Provider Identifier (NPI) are employed by therapist groups, physician/NPP groups, or groups that are not professional organizations, the requirement that therapy space be owned, leased, or rented may be satisfied by the group that employs the therapist. Each therapist employed by a group should enroll as a TPP.

When therapists with a Medicare NPI provide services in the physician's/NPP's office in which they are employed, and bill using their NPI for each therapy service, then the direct supervision requirement for enrolled staff apply.

When the therapist who has a Medicare NPI is employed in a physician's/NPP's office the services are ordinarily billed as services of the therapist, with the therapist identified on the claim as the supplier of service. However, services of the therapist who has a Medicare NPI may also be billed by the physician/NPP as services incident to the physician's/NPP's service. (See §230.5 for rules related to

therapy services incident to a physician.) In that case, the physician/NPP is the supplier of service, the NPI of the supervising physician/NPP is reported on the claim with the service and all the rules for both therapy services and incident to services (§230.5) must be followed.

B. Private Practice Defined

Reference: Federal Register November, 1998, pages 58863-58869; 42CFR 410.38(b), 42CFR410.59, 42CFR410.60, 42CFR410.62

The contractor considers a therapist to be in private practice if the therapist maintains office space at his or her own expense and furnishes services only in that space or the patient's home. Or, a therapist is employed by another supplier and furnishes services in facilities provided at the expense of that supplier.

The therapist need not be in full-time private practice but must be engaged in private practice on a regular basis; i.e., the therapist is recognized as a private practitioner and for that purpose has access to the necessary equipment to provide an adequate program of therapy.

The therapy services must be provided either by or under the direct supervision of the TPP. Each TPP should be enrolled as a Medicare provider. If a therapist is not enrolled, the services of that therapist must be directly supervised by an enrolled therapist. Direct supervision requires that the supervising private practice therapist be present in the office suite at the time the service is performed. These direct supervision requirements apply only in the private practice setting and only for therapists and their assistants. In other outpatient settings, supervision rules differ. The services of support personnel must be included in the therapist's bill. The supporting personnel, including other therapists, must be W-2 or 1099 employees of the TPP or other qualified employer.

Coverage of outpatient therapy under Part B includes the services of a qualified TPP when furnished in the therapist's office or the beneficiary's home. For this purpose, "home" includes an institution that is used as a home, but not a hospital, CAH or SNF, (Federal Register Nov. 2, 1998, pg 58869). Place of Service (POS) includes:

- 03/School, only if residential,
- 04/Homeless Shelter,
- 12/Home, other than a facility that is a private residence,
- 14/Group Home,
- 33/Custodial Care Facility.

C. Assignment

Reference: Nov. 2, 1998 Federal Register, pg. 58863

See also Pub. 100-04 chapter 1, §30.2.

When physicians, NPPs, or TPPs obtain provider numbers, they have the option of accepting assignment (participating) or not accepting assignment (nonparticipating). In contrast, providers, such as outpatient hospitals, SNFs, rehabilitation agencies, and CORFs, do not have the option. For these providers, assignment is mandatory.

If physicians/NPPs, or TPPs accept assignment (are participating), they must accept the Medicare Physician Fee Schedule amount as payment. Medicare pays 80% and the patient is responsible for 20%. In contrast, if they do not accept assignment, Medicare will only pay 95% of the fee schedule amount. However, when these services are not furnished on an assignment-related basis, the limiting charge applies. (See §1848(g)(2)(c) of the Act.)

NOTE: Services furnished by a therapist in the therapist's office under arrangements with hospitals in rural communities and public health agencies (or services provided in the beneficiary's home under arrangements with a provider of outpatient physical or occupational therapy services) are not covered under this provision. See section 230.6.

Pub. 100-2, Chapter 15, Section 270

Telehealth Services

(Rev. 140, Issued: 02-28-11, Effective: 01-01-11, Implementation: 01-03-11 A/B MACs, Carriers/04-04-11 A/B MACs, FIs)

Background

Section 223 of the Medicare, Medicaid and SCHIP Benefits Improvement and Protection Act of 2000 (BIPA) - Revision of Medicare Reimbursement for Telehealth Services amended §1834 of the Act to provide for an expansion of Medicare payment for telehealth services.

Effective October 1, 2001, coverage and payment for Medicare telehealth includes consultation, office visits, individual psychotherapy, and pharmacologic management delivered via a telecommunications system. E ligible geographic areas include rural health professional shortage areas (HPSA) and counties not classified as a metropolitan statistical area (MSA). Additionally, Federal telemedicine demonstration projects as of December 31, 2000, may serve as the originating site regardless of geographic location.

An interactive telecommunications system is required as a condition of payment; however, BIPA does allow the use of asynchronous "store and forward" technology in delivering these services when the originating site is a Federal telemedicine demonstration program in Alaska or Hawaii. BIPA does not require that a practitioner present the patient for interactive telehealth services.

With regard to payment amount, BIPA specified that payment for the professional service performed by the distant site practitioner (i.e., where the expert physician or practitioner is physically located at time of telemedicine encounter) is equal to what would have been paid without the use of telemedicine. Distant site practitioners include only a physician as described in §1861(r) of the Act and a medical practitioner as described in §1842(b)(18)(C) of the Act. BIPA also expanded payment under Medicare to include a $20 originating site facility fee (location of beneficiary).

Previously, the Balanced Budget Act of 1997 (BBA) limited the scope of Medicare telehealth coverage to consultation services and the implementing regulation prohibited the use of an asynchronous 'store and forward' telecommunications system. The BBA of 1997 also required the professional fee to be shared between the referring and consulting practitioners, and prohibited Medicare payment for facility fees and line charges associated with the telemedicine encounter.

The BIPA required that Medicare Part B (Supplementary Medical Insurance) pay for this expansion of telehealth services beginning with services furnished on October 1, 2001.

Section 149 of the Medicare Improvements for Patients and Providers Act of 2008 (MIPPA) amended §1834(m) of the Act to add certain entities as originating sites for payment of telehealth services. Effective for services furnished on or after January 1, 2009, eligible originating sites include a hospital-based or critical access hospital-based renal dialysis center (including satellites); a skilled nursing facility (as defined in §1819(a) of the Act); and a community mental health center (as defined in §1861(ff)(3)(B) of the Act). MIPPA also amended§1888(e)(2)(A)(ii) of the Act to exclude telehealth services furnished under §1834(m)(4)(C)(ii)(VII) from the consolidated billing provisions of the skilled nursing facility prospective payment system (SNF PPS).

NOTE: MIPPA did not add independent renal dialysis facilities as originating sites for payment of telehealth services.

The telehealth provisions authorized by §1834(m) of the Act are implemented in 42 CFR 410.78 and 414.65.

Pub. 100-2, Chapter 15, Section 270.2

List of Medicare Telehealth Services
(Rev. 178, Issued: 12-30-13; Effective: 01-01-14, Implementation: 01-06-14)

The use of a telecommunications system may substitute for an in-person encounter for professional consultations, office visits, office psychiatry services, and a limited number of other physician fee schedule (PFS) services. These services are listed below.

Consultations (Effective October 1, 2001- December 31, 2009)

Telehealth consultations, emergency department or initial inpatient (Effective January 1, 2010)

Follow-up inpatient telehealth consultations (Effective January 1, 2009)

Office or other outpatient visits

Subsequent hospital care services (with the limitation of one telehealth visit every 3 days) (Effective January 1, 2011)

Subsequent nursing facility care services (with the limitation of one telehealth visit every 30 days) (Effective January 1, 2011)

Individual psychotherapy

Pharmacologic management (Effective March 1, 2003)

Psychiatric diagnostic interview examination (Effective March 1, 2003)

End stage renal disease related services (Effective January 1, 2005)

Individual and group medical nutrition therapy (Individual effective January 1, 2006; group effective January 1, 2011)

Neurobehavioral status exam (Effective January 1, 2008)

Individual and group health and behavior assessment and intervention (Individual effective January 1, 2010; group effective January 1, 2011)

Individual and group kidney disease education (KDE) services (Effective January 1, 2011)

Individual and group diabetes self-management training (DSMT) services (with a minimum of 1 hour of in-person instruction to be furnished in the initial year training period to ensure effective injection training) (Effective January 1, 2011)

Smoking Cessation Services (Effective January 1, 2012)

Alcohol and/or substance (other than tobacco) abuse structured assessment and intervention services (Effective January 1, 2013)

Annual alcohol misuse screening (Effective January 1, 2013)

Brief face-to-face behavioral counseling for alcohol misuse (Effective January 1, 2013).

Annual Depression Screening (Effective January 1, 2013)

High-intensity behavioral counseling to prevent sexually transmitted infections (Effective January 1, 2013)

Annual, face-to-face Intensive behavioral therapy for cardiovascular disease (Effective January 1, 2013)

Face-to-face behavioral counseling for obesity (Effective January 1, 2013)

Transitional Care Management Services (Effective January 1, 2014)

NOTE: Beginning January 1, 2010, CMS eliminated the use of all consultation codes, except for inpatient telehealth consultation G-codes. CMS no longer recognizes office/outpatient or inpatient consultation CPT codes for payment of office/outpatient or inpatient visits. Instead, physicians and practitioners are instructed to bill a new or established patient office/outpatient visit CPT code or appropriate hospital or nursing facility care code, as appropriate to the particular patient, for all office/outpatient or inpatient visits. For detailed instructions regarding reporting these and other telehealth services, see Pub. 100-04, Medicare Claims Processing Manual, chapter 12, section 190.3.

The conditions of payment for Medicare telehealth services, including qualifying originating sites and the types of telecommunications systems recognized by Medicare, are subject to the provisions of 42 CFR 410.78. Payment for these services is subject to the provisions of 42 CFR 414.65.

Pub. 100-2, Chapter 15, Section 270.4

Payment – Physician/Practitioner at a Distant Site
(Rev. 140, Issued: 02-28-11, Effective: 01-01-11, Implementation: 01-03-11 A/B MACs, Carriers/04-04-11 A/B MACs, FIs)

The term "distant site" means the site where the physician or practitioner providing the professional service is located at the time the service is provided via a telecommunications system.

The payment amount for the professional service provided via a telecommunications system by the physician or practitioner at the distant site is equal to the current physician fee schedule amount for the service. Payment for telehealth services (see section 270.2 of this chapter) should be made at the same amount as when these services are furnished without the use of a telecommunications system. For Medicare payment to occur, the service must be within a practitioner's scope of practice under State law. The beneficiary is responsible for any unmet deductible amount and applicable coinsurance.

Medicare Practitioners Who May Receive Payment at the Distant Site (i.e., at a Site Other Than Where the Beneficiary is Located)

As a condition of Medicare Part B payment for telehealth services, the physician or practitioner at the distant site must be licensed to provide the service under State law. When the physician or practitioner at the distant site is licensed under State law to provide a covered telehealth service (see section 270.2 of this chapter) then he or she may bill for and receive payment for this service when delivered via a telecommunications system.

Medicare practitioners who may bill for a covered telehealth service are listed below (subject to State law):

- Physician;
- Nurse practitioner;
- Physician assistant;
- Nurse midwife;
- Clinical nurse specialist;
- Clinical psychologist;
- Clinical social worker; and
- Registered dietitian or nutrition professional.

* Clinical psychologists and clinical social workers cannot bill for psychotherapy services that include medical evaluation and management services under Medicare. These practitioners may not bill or receive payment for the following CPT codes: 90805, 90807, and 90809.

Pub. 100-3, Section 10.3
Inpatient Hospital Pain Rehabilitation Programs

Since pain rehabilitation programs of a lesser scope than that described above would raise a question as to whether the program could be provided in a less intensive setting than on an inpatient hospital basis, carefully evaluate such programs to determine whether the program does, in fact, necessitate a hospital level of care. Some pain rehabilitation programs may utilize services and devices which are excluded from coverage, e.g., acupuncture (see 35-8), biofeedback (see 35-27), dorsal column stimulator (see 65-8), and family counseling services (see 35-I4). In determining whether the scope of a pain program does necessitate inpatient hospital care, evaluate only those services and devices which are covered. Although diagnostic tests may be an appropriate part of pain rehabilitation programs, such tests would be covered in an individual case only where they can be reasonably related to a patient's illness, complaint, symptom, or injury and where they do not represent an unnecessary duplication of tests previously performed.

An inpatient program of 4 weeks' duration is generally required to modify pain behavior. After this period it would be expected that any additional rehabilitation services which might be required could be effectively provided on an outpatient basis under an outpatient pain rehabilitation program (see 10.4 of the NCD Manual) or other outpatient program. The first 7 I0 days of such an inpatient program constitute, in effect, an evaluation period. If a patient is unable to adjust to the program within this period, it is generally concluded that it is unlikely that the program will be effective and the patient is discharged from the program. On occasions a program longer than 4 weeks may be required in a particular case. In such a case there should be documentation to substantiate that inpatient care beyond a 4-week period was reasonable and necessary. Similarly, where it appears that a patient participating in a program is being granted frequent outside passes, a question would exist as to whether an inpatient program is reasonable and necessary for the treatment of the patient's condition.

An inpatient hospital stay for the purpose of participating in a pain rehabilitation program would be covered as reasonable and necessary to the treatment of a patient's condition where the pain is attributable to a physical cause, the usual methods of treatment have not been successful in alleviating it, and a significant loss of ability to function independently has resulted from the pain. Chronic pain patients often have psychological problems which accompany or stem from the physical pain and it is appropriate to include psychological treatment in the multidisciplinary approach. However, patients whose pain symptoms result from a mental condition, rather than from any physical cause, generally cannot be successfully treated in a pain rehabilitation program.

Pub. 100-3, Section 10.4
Outpatient Hospital Pain Rehabilitation Programs
(Rev. 173, Issued: 09-04-14, Effective: Upon Implementation: of ICD-10, Implementation: Upon Implementation of ICD-10)

Some hospitals also provide pain rehabilitation programs for outpatients. In such programs, services frequently are provided in group settings even though they are being furnished pursuant to each patient's individualized plan of treatment.

Coverage of services furnished under outpatient hospital pain rehabilitation programs, including services furnished in group settings under individualized plans of treatment, is available if the patient's pain is attributable to a physical cause, the usual methods of treatment have not been successful in alleviating it,

and a significant loss of ability by the patient to function independently has resulted from the pain. If a patient meets these conditions and the program provides services of the types discussed in §10.3, the services provided under the program may be covered. Non-covered services (e.g., vocational counseling, meals for outpatients, or acupuncture) continue to be excluded from coverage, and A/B Medicare Administrative Contractors would not be precluded from finding, in the case of particular patients, that the pain rehabilitation program is not reasonable and necessary under §1862(a)(1) of the Social Security Act for the treatment of their conditions.

Pub. 100-3, Section 130.1
Inpatient Hospital Stays for the Treatment of Alcoholism (130.1)

A. Inpatient Hospital Stay for Alcohol Detoxification

Many hospitals provide detoxification services during the more acute stages of alcoholism or alcohol withdrawal. When the high probability or occurrence of medical complications (e.g., delirium, confusion, trauma, or unconsciousness) during detoxification for acute alcoholism or alcohol withdrawal necessitates the constant availability of physicians and/or complex medical equipment found only in the hospital setting, inpatient hospital care during this period is considered reasonable and necessary and is therefore covered under the program. Generally, detoxification can be accomplished within 2-3 days with an occasional need for up to 5 days where the patient's condition dictates. This limit (5 days) may be extended in an individual case where there is a need for a longer period for detoxification for a particular patient. In such cases, however, there should be documentation by a physician which substantiates that a longer period of detoxification was reasonable and necessary. When the detoxification needs of an individual no longer require an inpatient hospital setting, coverage should be denied on the basis that inpatient hospital care is not reasonable and necessary as required by section I862(a)(I) of the Act. Following detoxification a patient may be transferred to an inpatient rehabilitation unit or discharged to a residential treatment program or outpatient treatment setting.

B. Inpatient Hospital Stay for Alcohol Rehabilitation

Hospitals may also provide structured inpatient alcohol rehabilitation programs to the chronic alcoholic. These programs are composed primarily of coordinated educational and psychotherapeutic services provided on a group basis. Depending on the subject matter, a series of lectures, discussions, films, and group therapy sessions are led by either physicians, psychologists, or alcoholism counselors from the hospital or various outside organizations. In addition, individual psychotherapy and family counseling (see Sec.70.1 of the NCD Manual) may be provided in selected cases. These programs are conducted under the supervision and direction of a physician. Patients may directly enter an inpatient hospital rehabilitation program after having undergone detoxification in the same hospital or in another hospital or may enter an inpatient hospital rehabilitation program without prior hospitalization for detoxification.

Alcohol rehabilitation can be provided in a variety of settings other than the hospital setting. In order for an inpatient hospital stay for alcohol rehabilitation to be covered under Medicare it must be medically necessary for the care to be provided in the inpatient hospital setting rather than in a less costly facility or on an outpatient basis. Inpatient hospital care for receipt of an alcohol rehabilitation program would generally be medically necessary where either (I) there is documentation by the physician that recent alcohol rehabilitation services in a less intensive setting or on an outpatient basis have proven unsuccessful and, as a consequence, the patient requires the supervision and intensity of services which can only be found in the controlled environment of the hospital, or (2) only the hospital environment can assure the medical management or control of the patient's concomitant conditions during the course of alcohol rehabilitation. (However, a patient's concomitant condition may make the use of certain alcohol treatment modalities medically inappropriate.) In addition, the "active treatment" criteria (see the Medicare Benefit Policy Manual, Chapter 2, "Inpatient Psychiatric Hospital Services," Sec.20) should be applied to psychiatric care in the general hospital as well as to psychiatric care in a psychiatric hospital. Since alcoholism is classifiable as a psychiatric condition the "active treatment" criteria must also be met in order for alcohol rehabilitation services to be covered under Medicare. (Thus, it is the combined need for "active treatment" and for covered care which can only be provided in the inpatient hospital setting, rather than the fact that rehabilitation immediately follows a period of detoxification, which provides the basis for coverage of inpatient hospital alcohol rehabilitation programs.) Generally 16-19 days of rehabilitation services are sufficient to bring a patient to a point where care could be continued in other than an inpatient hospital setting. An inpatient hospital stay for alcohol rehabilitation may be extended beyond this limit in an individual case where a longer period of alcohol rehabilitation is medically necessary. In such cases, however, there should be documentation by a physician which substantiates the need for such care. Where the rehabilitation needs of an individual no longer require an inpatient hospital setting, coverage should be denied on the basis that inpatient hospital care is not reasonable and necessary as required by section l862(a)(l) of the Act.

Subsequent admissions to the inpatient hospital setting for alcohol rehabilitation followup, reinforcement, or "recap" treatments are considered to be readmissions (rather than an extension of the original stay) and must meet the requirements of this section for coverage under Medicare. Prior admissions to the inpatient hospital setting--either in the same hospital or in a different hospital--may be an indication that the "active treatment" requirements are not met (i.e., there is no reasonable expectation of improvement) and the stay should not be covered. Accordingly, there should be documentation to establish that "readmission" to the hospital setting for alcohol rehabilitation services can reasonably be expected to result in improvement of the patient's condition. For example, the documentation should indicate what changes in the patient's medical condition, social or emotional status, or treatment plan make improvement likely, or why the patient's initial hospital treatment was not sufficient.

C. Combined Alcohol Detoxification/Rehabilitation Programs.
iscal intermediaries should apply the guidelines in A. and B. above to both phases of a combined inpatient hospital alcohol detoxification/rehabilitation program. Not all patients who require the inpatient hospital setting for detoxification also need the inpatient hospital setting for rehabilitation. (See Sec.130.1 of the NCD Manual for coverage of outpatient hospital alcohol rehabilitation services.) Where the inpatient hospital setting is medically necessary for both alcohol detoxification and rehabilitation, generally a 3-week period is reasonable and necessary to bring the patient to the point where care can be continued in other than an inpatient hospital setting.

Decisions regarding reasonableness and necessity of treatment, the need for an inpatient hospital level of care, and length of treatment should be made by intermediaries based on accepted medical practice with the advice of their medical consultant. (In hospitals under PSRO review, PSRO determinations of medical necessity of services and appropriateness of the level of care at which services are provided are binding on the title XVIII fiscal intermediaries for purposes of adjudicating claims for payment.)

Pub. 100-3, Section 130.3
Chemical Aversion Therapy for Treatment of Alcoholism
Available evidence indicates that chemical aversion therapy may be an effective component of certain alcoholism treatment programs, particularly as part of multimodality treatment programs which include other behavioral techniques and therapies, such as psychotherapy. Based on this evidence, CMS's medical consultants have recommended that chemical aversion therapy be covered under Medicare. However, since chemical aversion therapy is a demanding therapy which may not be appropriate for all Medicare beneficiaries needing treatment for alcoholism, a physician should certify to the appropriateness of chemical aversion therapy in the individual case. Therefore, if chemical aversion therapy for treatment of alcoholism is determined to be reasonable and necessary for an individual patient, it is covered under Medicare.

When it is medically necessary for a patient to receive chemical aversion therapy as a hospital inpatient, coverage for care in that setting is available. (See Sec.130.1 regarding coverage of multimodality treatment programs.) Followup treatments for chemical aversion therapy can generally be provided on an outpatient basis. Thus, where a patient is admitted as an inpatient for receipt of chemical aversion therapy, there must be documentation by the physician of the need in the individual case for the inpatient hospital admission.

Decisions regarding reasonableness and necessity of treatment and the need for an inpatient hospital level of care should be made by intermediaries based on accepted medical practice with the advice of their medical consultant. (In hospitals under QIO review, QIO determinations of medical necessity of services and appropriateness of the level of care at which services are provided are binding on the title XVIII fiscal intermediaries for purposes of adjudicating claims for payment.)

Pub. 100-4, Chapter 5, Section 10
Part B Outpatient Rehabilitation and Comprehensive Outpatient Rehabilitation Facility (CORF) Services - General
Language in this section is defined or described in Pub. 100-02, chapter 15, sections 220 and 230.

Section 4541(a)(2) of the Balanced Budget Act (BBA) (P.L. 105-33), which added §1834(k)(5) to the Social Security Act (the Act), required that all claims for outpatient rehabilitation services and comprehensive outpatient rehabilitation facility (CORF) services, be reported using a uniform coding system. The CMS chose HCPCS (Healthcare Common Procedure Coding System) as the coding system to be used for the reporting of these services. This coding requirement is effective for all claims for outpatient rehabilitation services and CORF services submitted on or after April 1, 1998.

The BBA also required payment under a prospective payment system for outpatient rehabilitation services including CORF services. Effective for claims with dates of service on or after January 1, 1999, the Medicare Physician Fee Schedule (MPFS) became the method of payment for outpatient therapy services furnished by:

Comprehensive outpatient rehabilitation facilities (CORFs);

Outpatient physical therapy providers (OPTs);

Other rehabilitation facilities (ORFs);

Hospitals (to outpatients and inpatients who are not in a covered Part A stay);

Skilled nursing facilities (SNFs) (to residents not in a covered Part A stay and to nonresidents who receive outpatient rehabilitation services from the SNF); and

Home health agencies (HHAs) (to individuals who are not homebound or otherwise are not receiving services under a home health plan of care (POC)).

NOTE: No provider or supplier other than the SNF will be paid for therapy services during the time the beneficiary is in a covered SNF Part A stay. For information regarding SNF consolidated billing see chapter 6, section 10 of this manual.

Similarly, under the HH prospective payment system, HHAs are responsible to provide, either directly or under arrangements, all outpatient rehabilitation therapy services to beneficiaries receiving services under a home health POC. No other provider or supplier will be paid for these services during the time the beneficiary is in a covered Part A stay. For information regarding HH consolidated billing see chapter10, section 20 of this manual.

Section 143 of the Medicare Improvements for Patients and Provider's Act of 2008 (MIPPA) authorizes the Centers for Medicare & Medicaid Services (CMS) to enroll speech-language pathologists (SLP) as suppliers of Medicare services and for SLPs to begin billing Medicare for outpatient speech-language pathology services furnished in private practice beginning July 1, 2009. Enrollment will allow SLPs in private practice to bill Medicare and receive direct payment for their services. Previously, the Medicare program could only pay SLP services if an institution, physician or nonphysician practitioner billed them.

In Chapter 23, as part of the CY 2009 Medicare Physician Fee Schedule Database, the descriptor for PC/TC indicator "7", as applied to certain HCPCS/CPT codes, is described as specific to the services of privately practicing therapists. Payment may not be made if the service is provided to either a hospital outpatient or a hospital inpatient by a physical therapist, occupational therapist, or speech-language pathologist in private practice.

The MPFS is used as a method of payment for outpatient rehabilitation services furnished under arrangement with any of these providers.

In addition, the MPFS is used as the payment system for CORF services identified by the HCPCS codes in §20. Assignment is mandatory.

The Medicare allowed charge for the services is the lower of the actual charge or the MPFS amount. The Medicare payment for the services is 80 percent of the allowed charge after the Part B deductible is met. Coinsurance is made at 20 percent of the lower of the actual charge or the MPFS amount. The general coinsurance rule (20 percent of the actual charges) does not apply when making payment under the MPFS. This is a final payment.

The MPFS does not apply to outpatient rehabilitation services furnished by critical access hospitals (CAHs). CAHs are to be paid on a reasonable cost basis.

Contractors process outpatient rehabilitation claims from hospitals, including CAHs, SNFs, HHAs, CORFs, outpatient rehabilitation agencies, and outpatient physical therapy providers for which they have received a tie in notice from the RO. These provider types submit their claims to the contractors using the 837 Institutional electronic claim format or the UB-04 paper form when permissible. Contractors also process claims from physicians, certain nonphysician practitioners (NPPs), therapists in private practices (TPPs), (which are limited to physical and occupational therapists, and speech language pathologists in private practices), and physician-directed clinics that bill for services furnished incident to a physician's service (see Pub. 100-02, Medicare Benefit Policy Manual, chapter 15, for a definition of "incident to"). These provider types submit their claims to the contractor using the 837 Professional electronic claim format or the CMS-1500 paper form when permissible.

There are different fee rates for nonfacility and facility services. Chapter 23 describes the differences in these two rates. (See fields 28 and 29 of the record therein described). Facility rates apply to professional services performed in a facility other than the professional's office. Nonfacility rates apply when the service is performed in the professional's office. The nonfacility rate (that is paid when the provider performs the services in its own facility) accommodates overhead and indirect expenses the provider incurs by operating its own facility. Thus it is somewhat higher than the facility rate.

Contractors pay the nonfacility rate on institutional claims for services performed in the provider's facility. Contractors may pay professional claims using the facility or nonfacility rate depending upon where the service is performed (place of service on the claim), and the provider specialty.

Contractors pay the codes in §20 under the MPFS on professional claims regardless of whether they may be considered rehabilitation services. However, contractors must use this list for institutional claims to determine whether to pay under outpatient rehabilitation rules or whether payment rules for other types of service may apply, e.g., OPPS for hospitals, reasonable costs for CAHs.

Note that because a service is considered an outpatient rehabilitation service does not automatically imply payment for that service. Additional criteria, including coverage, plan of care and physician certification must also be met. These criteria are described in Pub. 100-02, Medicare Benefit Policy Manual, chapters 1 and 15.

Payment for rehabilitation services provided to Part A inpatients of hospitals or SNFs is included in the respective PPS rate. Also, for SNFs (but not hospitals), if the beneficiary has Part B, but not Part A coverage (e.g., Part A benefits are exhausted), the SNF must bill for any rehabilitation service.

Payment for rehabilitation therapy services provided by home health agencies under a home health plan of care is included in the home health PPS rate. HHAs may submit bill type 34X and be paid under the MPFS if there are no home health services billed under a home health plan of care at the same time, and there is a valid rehabilitation POC (e.g., the patient is not homebound).

An institutional employer (other than a SNF) of the TPPs, or physician performing outpatient services, (e.g., hospital, CORF, etc.), or a clinic billing on behalf of the physician or therapist may bill the contractor on a professional claim.

The MPFS is the basis of payment for outpatient rehabilitation services furnished by TPPs, physicians, and certain nonphysician practitioners or for diagnostic tests provided incident to the services of such physicians or nonphysician practitioners. (See Pub. 100-02, Medicare Benefit Policy Manual, chapter 15, for a definition of "incident to, therapist, therapy and related instructions.") Such services are billed to the contractor on the professional claim format. Assignment is mandatory.

The following table identifies the provider and supplier types, and identifies which claim format they may use to submit bills to the contractor. "Provider/Supplier Service" Type

Format	Bill Type	Comment
Inpatient hospital Part A Institutional	11X	Included in PPS
Inpatient SNF Part A Institutional	21X	Included in PPS
Inpatient hospital Part B Institutional	12X	Hospitals may obtain services under arrangements and bill, or rendering provider may bill.
Inpatient SNF Part B (audiology tests are not included) Institutional	22X	SNF must provide and bill, or obtain under arrangements and bill.
Outpatient hospital Institutional	13X	Hospital may provide and bill or obtain under arrangements and bill, or rendering provider may bill.

Format	Bill Type	Comment
Outpatient SNF Institutional	23X	SNF must provide and bill or obtain under arrangements and bill.
HHA billing for services rendered under a Part A or Part B home health plan of care. Institutional	32X	Service is included in PPS rate. CMS determines whether payment is from Part A or Part B trust fund.
HHA billing for services not rendered under a Part A or Part B home health plan of care, but rendered under a therapy plan of care. Institutional	34X	Service not under home health plan of care.
Other Rehabilitation Facility (ORF) Institutional	74X	Paid MPFS for outpatient rehabilitation services effective January 1, 1999, and all other services except drugs effective July 1, 2000. Starting April 1, 2002, drugs are paid 95% of the AWP. For claims with dates of service on or after July 1, 2003, drugs and biologicals do not apply in an OPT setting. Therefore, FIs are to advise their OPTs not to bill for them.
Comprehensive Outpatient Rehabilitation Facility (CORF) Institutional	75X	Paid MPFS for outpatient rehabilitation services effective January 1, 1999, and all other services except drugs effective July 1, 2000. Starting April 1, 2002, drugs are paid 95% of the AWP.
Physician, NPPs, TPPs, (service in hospital or SNF) Professional	See Chapter 26 for place of service, and type of service coding.	Payment may not be made for therapy services to Part A inpatients of hospitals or SNFs, or for Part B SNF residents. Otherwise, suppliers bill to the contractor using the professional claim format. Note that services of a physician/ NPP/TPP employee of a facility may be billed by the facility to a contractor.
Physician/NPP/TPPs office, independent clinic or patient's home Professional	See Chapter 26 for place of service, and type of service coding.	Paid via Physician fee schedule.
Critical Access Hospital - inpatient Part A Institutional	11X	Rehabilitation services are paid at cost.
Critical Access Hospital - inpatient Part B Institutional	85X	Rehabilitation services are paid at cost.
Critical Access Hospital – outpatient Part B Institutional	85X	Rehabilitation services are paid at cost.

Complete Claim form completion requirements are contained in chapters 25 and 26.

For a list of the outpatient rehabilitation HCPCS codes see §20.

If a contractor receives an institutional claim for one of these HCPCS codes with dates of service on or after July 1, 2003, that does not appear on the supplemental file it currently uses to pay the therapy claims, it contacts its professional claims area to obtain the non-facility price in order to pay the claim.

NOTE: The list of codes in §20 contains commonly utilized codes for outpatient rehabilitation services. Contractors may consider other codes on institutional claims for payment under the MPFS as outpatient rehabilitation services to the extent that such codes are determined to be medically reasonable and necessary and could be performed within the scope of practice of the therapist providing the service.

Pub. 100-4, Chapter 5, Section 10.2
The Financial Limitation Legislation
(Rev. 2073, Issued: 10-22-10, Effective: 01-01-11, Implementation: 01-03-11)

A. Legislation on Limitations
The dollar amount of the limitations (caps) on outpatient therapy services is established by statute. The updated amount of the caps is released annually via Recurring Update Notifications and posted on the CMS Website www.cms.gov/TherapyServices, on contractor Websites, and on each beneficiary's Medicare Summary Notice. Medicare contractors shall publish the financial limitation amount in educational articles. It is also available at 1-800-Medicare.

Section 4541(a)(2) of the Balanced Budget Act (BBA) (P.L. 105-33) of 1997, which added §1834(k)(5) to the Act, required payment under a prospective payment system (PPS) for outpatient rehabilitation services (except those furnished by or under arrangements with a hospital). Outpatient rehabilitation services include the following services:

- Physical therapy
- Speech-language pathology; and
- Occupational therapy.

Section 4541(c) of the BBA required application of financial limitations to all outpatient rehabilitation services (except those furnished by or under arrangements with a hospital). In 1999, an annual per beneficiary limit of $1,500 was applied, including all outpatient physical therapy services and speech-language pathology services. A separate limit applied to all occupational therapy services. The limits were based on incurred expenses and included applicable deductible and coinsurance. The BBA provided that the limits be indexed by the Medicare Economic Index (MEI) each year beginning in 2002.

Since the limitations apply to outpatient services, they do not apply to skilled nursing facility (SNF) residents in a covered Part A stay, including patients occupying swing beds. Rehabilitation services are included within the global Part A per diem payment that the SNF receives under the prospective payment system (PPS) for the covered stay. Also, limitations do not apply to any therapy services covered under prospective payment systems for home health or inpatient hospitals, including critical access hospitals.

The limitation is based on therapy services the Medicare beneficiary receives, not the type of practitioner who provides the service. Physical therapists, speech-language pathologists, and occupational therapists, as well as physicians and certain nonphysician practitioners, could render a therapy service.

B. Moratoria and Exceptions for Therapy Claims
Since the creation of therapy caps, Congress has enacted several moratoria. The Deficit Reduction Act of 2005 directed CMS to develop exceptions to therapy caps for calendar year 2006 and the exceptions have been extended periodically. The cap exception for therapy services billed by outpatient hospitals was part of the original legislation and applies as long as caps are in effect. Exceptions to caps based on the medical necessity of the service are in effect only when Congress legislates the exceptions.

Pub. 100-4, Chapter 5, Section 10.6
Functional Reporting
(Rev. 2859, Issued: 01-17-14, Effective: 01-01-14, Implementation: 01-31-14)

A. General
Section 3005(g) of the Middle Class Tax Relief and Jobs Creation Act (MCTRJCA) amended Section 1833(g) of the Act to require a claims-based data collection system for outpatient therapy services, including physical therapy (PT), occupational therapy (OT) and speech-language pathology (SLP) services. 42 CFR 410.59, 410.60, 410.61, 410.62 and 410.105 implement this requirement. The system will collect data on beneficiary function during the course of therapy services in order to better understand beneficiary conditions, outcomes, and expenditures.

Beneficiary unction information is reported using 42 nonpayable functional G-codes and seven severity/complexity modifiers on claims for PT, OT, and SLP services. Functional reporting on one functional limitation at a time is required periodically throughout an entire PT, OT, or SLP therapy episode of care.

The nonpayable G-codes and severity modifiers provide information about the beneficiary's functional status at the outset of the therapy episode of care, including projected goal status, at specified points during treatment, and at the time of discharge. These G-codes, along with the associated modifiers, are required at specified intervals on all claims for outpatient therapy services – not just those over the cap.

B. Application of New Coding Requirements
This functional data reporting and collection system is effective for therapy services with dates of service on and after January 1, 2013. A testing period will be in effect from January 1, 2013, until July 1, 2013, to allow providers and practitioners to use the new coding requirements to assure that systems work. Claims for therapy services furnished on and after July 1, 2013, that do not contain the required functional G-code/modifier information will be returned or rejected, as applicable.

C. Services Affected
These requirements apply to all claims for services furnished under the Medicare Part B outpatient therapy benefit and the PT, OT, and SLP services furnished under the CORF benefit. They also apply to the therapy services furnished personally by and incident to the service of a physician or a nonphysician practitioner (NPP), including a nurse practitioner (NP), a certified nurse specialist (CNS), or a physician assistant (PA), as applicable.

D. Providers and Practitioners Affected.
The functional reporting requirements apply to the therapy services furnished by the following providers: hospitals, CAHs, SNFs, CORFs, rehabilitation agencies, and HHAs (when the beneficiary is not under a home health plan of care). It applies to the following practitioners: physical therapists, occupational therapists, and speech-language pathologists in private practice (TPPs), physicians, and NPPs as noted above. The term "clinician" is applied to these practitioners throughout this manual section. (See definition section of Pub. 100-02, Chapter 15, section 220.)

E. Function-related G-codes
There are 42 functional G-codes, 14 sets of three codes each. Six of the G-code sets are generally for PT and OT functional limitations and eight sets of G-codes are for SLP functional limitations.

The following G-codes are for functional limitations typically seen in beneficiaries receiving PT or OT services. The first four of these sets describe categories of functional limitations and the final two sets describe "other" functional limitations, which are to be used for functional limitations not described by one of the four categories.

NONPAYABLE G-CODES FOR FUNCTIONAL LIMITATIONS

Code	Long Descriptor	Short Descriptor
Mobility G-code Set		
G8978	Mobility: walking & moving around functional limitation, current status, at therapy episode outset and at reporting intervals	Mobility current status
G8979	Mobility: walking & moving around functional limitation, projected goal status, at therapy episode outset, at reporting intervals, and at discharge or to end reporting	Mobility goal status
G8980	Mobility: walking & moving around functional limitation, discharge status, at discharge from therapy or to end reporting	Mobility D/C status
Changing & Maintaining Body Position G-code Set		
G8981	Changing & maintaining body position functional limitation, current status, at therapy episode outset and at reporting intervals	Body pos current status

|

Code	Long Descriptor	Short Descriptor
G8982	Changing & maintaining body position functional limitation, projected goal status, at therapy episode outset, at reporting intervals, and at discharge or to end reporting	Body pos goal status
G8983	Changing & maintaining body position functional limitation, discharge status, at discharge from therapy or to end reporting	Body pos D/C status

Carrying, Moving & Handling Objects G-code Set

Code	Long Descriptor	Short Descriptor
G8984	Carrying, moving & handling objects functional limitation, current status, at therapy episode outset and at reporting intervals	Carry current status
G8985	Carrying, moving & handling objects functional limitation, projected goal status, at therapy episode outset, at reporting intervals, and at discharge or to end reporting	Carry goal status
G8986	Carrying, moving & handling objects functional limitation, discharge status, at discharge from therapy or to end reporting	Carry D/C status

Self Care G-code Set

Code	Long Descriptor	Short Descriptor
G8987	Self care functional limitation, current status, at therapy episode outset and at reporting intervals	Self care current status
G8988	Self care functional limitation, projected goal status, at therapy episode outset, at reporting intervals, and at discharge or to end reporting	Self care goal status
G8989	Self care functional limitation, discharge status, at discharge from therapy or to end reporting	Self care D/C status

The following "other PT/OT" functional G-codes are used to report:

- a beneficiary's functional limitation that is not defined by one of the above four categories;
- a beneficiary whose therapy services are not intended to treat a functional limitation;
- or a beneficiary's functional limitation when an overall, composite or other score from a functional assessment too is used and it does not clearly represent a functional limitation defined by one of the above four code sets.

Code	Long Descriptor	Short Descriptor
Other PT/OT Primary G-code Set		
G8990	Other physical or occupational therapy primary functional limitation, current status, at therapy episode outset and at reporting intervals	Other PT/OT current status
G8991	Other physical or occupational therapy primary functional limitation, projected goal status, at therapy episode outset, at reporting intervals, and at discharge or to end reporting	Other PT/OT goal status
G8992	Other physical or occupational therapy primary functional limitation, discharge status, at discharge from therapy or to end reporting	Other PT/OT D/C status

Code	Long Descriptor	Short Descriptor
Other PT/OT Subsequent G-code Set		
G8993	Other physical or occupational therapy subsequent functional limitation, current status, at therapy episode outset and at reporting intervals	Sub PT/OT current status
G8994	Other physical or occupational therapy subsequent functional limitation, projected goal status, at therapy episode outset, at reporting intervals, and at discharge or to end reporting	Sub PT/OT goal status

The following G-codes are for functional limitations typically seen in beneficiaries receiving SLP services. Seven are for specific functional communication measures, which are modeled after the National Outcomes Measurement System (NOMS), and one is for any "other" measure not described by one of the other seven.

Code	Long Descriptor	Short Descriptor
Swallowing G-code Set		
G8996	Swallowing functional limitation, current status, at therapy episode outset and at reporting intervals	Swallow current status
G8997	Swallowing functional limitation, projected goal status, at therapy episode outset, at reporting intervals, and at discharge or to end reporting	Swallow goal status
G8998	Swallowing functional limitation, discharge status, at discharge from therapy or to end reporting	Swallow D/C status
Motor Speech G-code Set (Note: These codes are not sequentially numbered)		
G8999	Motor speech functional limitation, current status, at therapy episode outset and at reporting intervals	Motor speech current status
G9186	Motor speech functional limitation, projected goal status at therapy episode outset, at reporting intervals, and at discharge or to end reporting	Motor speech goal status
G9158	Motor speech functional limitation, discharge status, at discharge from therapy or to end reporting	Motor speech D/C status
Spoken Language Comprehension G-code Set		
G9159	Spoken language comprehension functional limitation, current status, at therapy episode outset and at reporting intervals	Lang comp current status
G9160	Spoken language comprehension functional limitation, projected goal status, at therapy episode outset, at reporting intervals, and at discharge or to end reporting	Lang comp goal status
G9161	Spoken language comprehension functional limitation, discharge status, at discharge from therapy or to end reporting	Lang comp D/C status
Spoken Language Expressive G-code Set		
G9162	Spoken language expression functional limitation, current status, at therapy episode outset and at reporting intervals	Lang express current status

Code	Long Descriptor	Short Descriptor
G9163	Spoken language expression functional limitation, projected goal status, at therapy episode outset, at reporting intervals, and at discharge or to end reporting	Lang press goal status
G9164	Spoken language expression functional limitation, discharge status, at discharge from therapy or to end reporting	Lang express D/C status

Attention G-code Set

Code	Long Descriptor	Short Descriptor
G9165	Attention functional limitation, current status, at therapy episode outset and at reporting intervals	Atten current status
G9166	Attention functional limitation, projected goal status, at therapy episode outset, at reporting intervals, and at discharge or to end reporting	Atten goal status
G9167	Attention functional limitation, discharge status, at discharge from therapy or to end reporting	Atten D/C status

Memory G-code Set

Code	Long Descriptor	Short Descriptor
G9168	Memory functional limitation, current status, at therapy episode outset and at reporting intervals	Memory current status
G9169	Memory functional limitation, projected goal status, at therapy episode outset, at reporting intervals, and at discharge or to end reporting	Memory goal status
G9170	Memory functional limitation, discharge status, at discharge from therapy or to end reporting	Memory D/C status

Voice G-code Set

Code	Long Descriptor	Short Descriptor
G9171	Voice functional limitation, current status, at therapy episode outset and at reporting intervals	Voice current status
G9172	Voice functional limitation, projected goal status, at therapy episode outset, at reporting intervals, and at discharge or to end reporting	Voice goal status
G9173	Voice functional limitation, discharge status, at discharge from therapy or to end reporting	Voice D/C status

The following "other SLP" G-code set is used to report:

- on one of the other eight NOMS-defined functional measures not described by the above code sets; or
- to report an overall, composite or other score from assessment tool that does not clearly represent one of the above seven categorical SLP functional measures.

Code	Long Descriptor	Short Descriptor
Other Speech Language Pathology G-code Set		
G9174	Other speech language pathology functional limitation, current status, at therapy episode outset and at reporting intervals	Speech lang current status
G9175	Other speech language pathology functional limitation, projected goal status, at therapy episode outset, at reporting intervals, and at discharge or to end reporting	Speech lang goal status

Code	Long Descriptor	Short Descriptor
G9176	Other speech language pathology functional limitation, discharge status, at discharge from therapy or to end reporting	Speech lang D/C status

F. Severity/Complexity Modifiers

For each nonpayable functional G-code, one of the modifiers listed below must be used to report the severity/complexity for that functional limitation.

Modifier	Impairment Limitation Restriction
CH	0 percent impaired, limited or restricted
CI	At least 1 percent but less than 20 percent impaired, limited or restricted
CJ	At least 20 percent but less than 40 percent impaired, limited or restricted
CK	At least 40 percent but less than 60 percent impaired, limited or restricted
CL	At least 60 percent but less than 80 percent impaired, limited or restricted
CM	At least 80 percent but less than 100 percent impaired, limited or restricted
CN	100 percent impaired, limited or restricted

The severity modifiers reflect the beneficiary's percentage of functional impairment as determined by the clinician furnishing the therapy services.

G. Required Reporting of Functional G-codes and Severity Modifiers

The functional G-codes and severity modifiers listed above are used in the required reporting on therapy claims at certain specified points during therapy episodes of care. Claims containing these functional G-codes must also contain another billable and separately payable (non-bundled) service. Only one functional limitation shall be reported at a given time for each related therapy plan of care (POC).

Functional reporting using the G-codes and corresponding severity modifiers is required reporting on specified therapy claims. Specifically, they are required on claims:

- At the outset of a therapy episode of care (i.e., on the claim for the date of service (DOS) of the initial therapy service);
- At least once every 10 treatment days, which corresponds with the progress reporting period;
- When an evaluative procedure, including a re-evaluative one, (HCPCS/CPT codes 92521, 92522, 92523, 92524, 92597, 92607, 92608, 92610, 92611, 92612, 92614, 92616, 96105, 96125, 97001, 97002, 97003, 97004) is furnished and billed;
- At the time of discharge from the therapy episode of care–(i.e., on the date services related to the discharge [progress] report are furnished); and
- At the time reporting of a particular functional limitation is ended in cases where the need for further therapy is necessary.
- At the time reporting is begun for a new or different functional limitation within the same episode of care (i.e., after the reporting of the prior functional limitation is ended)

Functional reporting is required on claims throughout the entire episode of care. When the beneficiary has reached his or her goal or progress has been maximized on the initially selected functional limitation, but the need for treatment continues, reporting is required for a second functional limitation using another set of G-codes. In these situations two or more functional limitations will be reported for a beneficiary during the therapy episode of care. Thus, reporting on more than one functional limitation may be required for some beneficiaries but not simultaneously.

When the beneficiary stops coming to therapy prior to discharge, the clinician should report the functional information on the last claim. If the clinician is unaware that the beneficiary is not returning for therapy until after the last claim is submitted, the clinician cannot report the discharge status.

When functional reporting is required on a claim for therapy services, two G-codes will generally be required.

Two exceptions exist:

1. Therapy services under more than one therapy POC-- Claims may contain more than two nonpayable functional G-codes when in cases where a beneficiary receives therapy services under multiple POCs (PT, OT, and/or SLP) from the same therapy provider.

2. One-Time Therapy Visit-- When a beneficiary is seen and future therapy services are either not medically indicated or are going to be furnished by another provider, the clinician reports on the claim for the DOS of the visit, all three G-codes in the appropriate code set (current status, goal status and discharge status), along with corresponding severity modifiers.

Each reported functional G-code must also contain the following line of service information:

- Functional severity modifier
- Therapy modifier indicating the related discipline/POC -- GP, GO or GN -- for PT, OT, and SLP services, respectively
- Date of the related therapy service
- Nominal charge, e.g., a penny, for institutional claims submitted to the A/B MACs (A). For professional claims, a zero charge is acceptable for the service line. If provider billing software requires an amount for professional claims, a nominal charge, e.g., a penny, may be included.

NOTE: The KX modifier is not required on the claim line for nonpayable G-codes, but would be required with the procedure code for medically necessary therapy services furnished once the beneficiary's annual cap has been reached.

The following example demonstrates how the G-codes and modifiers are used. In this example, the clinician determines that the beneficiary's mobility restriction is the most clinically relevant functional limitation and selects the Mobility G-code set (G8978 – G8980) to represent the beneficiary's functional limitation. The clinician also determines the severity/complexity of the beneficiary's functional limitation and selects the appropriate modifier. In this example, the clinician determines that the beneficiary has a 75 percent mobility restriction for which the CL modifier is applicable. The clinician expects that at the end of therapy the beneficiaries will have only a 15 percent mobility restriction for which the CI modifier is applicable. When the beneficiary attains the mobility goal, therapy continues to be medically necessary to address a functional limitation for which there is no categorical G-code. The clinician reports this using (G8990 – G8992).

At the outset of therapy-- On the DOS for which the initial evaluative procedure is furnished or the initial treatment day of a therapy POC, the claim for the service will also include two G-codes as shown below.

- G8978-CL to report the functional limitation (Mobility with current mobility limitation of "at least 60 percent but less than 80 percent impaired, limited or restricted")
- G8979-CI to report the projected goal for a mobility restriction of "at least 1 percent but less than 20 percent impaired, limited or restricted."

At the end of each progress reporting period-- On the claim for the DOS when the services related to the progress report (which must be done at least once each 10 treatment days) are furnished, the clinician will report the same two G-codes but the modifier for the current status may be different.

- G8978 with the appropriate modifier are reported to show the beneficiary's current status as of this DOS. So if the beneficiary has made no progress, this claim will include G8978-CL. If the beneficiary made progress and now has a mobility restriction of 65 percent CL would still be the appropriate modifier for 65 percent, and G8978-CL would be reported in this case. If the beneficiary now has a mobility restriction of 45 percent, G8978-CK would be reported.
- G8979-CI would be reported to show the projected goal. This severity modifier would not change unless the clinician adjusts the beneficiary's goal.

This step is repeated as necessary and clinically appropriate, adjusting the current status modifier used as the beneficiary progresses through therapy.

At the time the beneficiary is discharged from the therapy episode. The final claim for therapy episode will include two G-codes.

- G8979-CI would be reported to show the projected goal. G8980-CI would be reported if the beneficiary attained the 15 percent mobility goal. Alternatively, if the beneficiary's mobility restriction only reached 25 percent; G8980-CJ would be reported.

To end reporting of one functional limitation-- As noted above, functional reporting is required to continue throughout the entire episode of care. Accordingly, when further therapy is medically necessary after the beneficiary attains the goal for the first reported functional limitation, the clinician would end reporting of the first functional limitation by using the same G-codes and modifiers that would be used at the time of discharge. Using the mobility example, to end reporting of the mobility functional limitation, G8979-CI and G8980-CI would be reported on the same DOS that coincides with end of that progress reporting period.

To begin reporting of a second functional limitation. At the time reporting is begun for a new and different functional limitation, within the same episode of care (i.e., after the reporting of the prior functional limitation is ended). Reporting on the second functional limitation, however, is not begun until the DOS of the next treatment day -- which is day one of the new progress reporting period. When the next functional limitation to be reported is NOT defined by one of the other three PT/OT categorical codes, the G-code set (G8990 - G8992) for the "other PT/OT primary" functional limitation is used, rather than the G-code set for the "other PT/OT subsequent" because it is the first reported "other PT/OT" functional limitation. This reporting begins on the DOS of the first treatment day following the mobility "discharge" reporting, which is counted as the initial service for the "other PT/OT primary" functional limitation and the first treatment day of the new progress reporting period. In this case, G8990 and G8991, along with the corresponding modifiers, are reported on the claim for therapy services.

The table below illustrates when reporting is required using this example and what G-codes would be used.

Example of Required Reporting

Key: Reporting Period (RP)	Begin RP #1 for Mobility at Episode Outset	End RP#1for Mobility at Progress Report	Mobility RP #2 Begins Next Treatment Day	End RP #2 for Mobility at Progress Report	Mobility RP #3 Begins Next Treatment Day	D/C or End Reporting for Mobility	Begin RP #1 for Other PT/OT Primary
Mobility: Walking & Moving Around							
G8978 – Current Status	X	X		X			
G8979– Goal Status	X	X		X		X	
G8980 – Discharge Status						X	
Other PT/OT Primary							
G8990 – Current Status							X
G8991 – Goal Status							X
G8992 – Discharge Status							
No Functional Reporting Required			X		X		

H. Required Tracking and Documentation of Functional G-codes and Severity Modifiers

The clinician who furnishes the services must not only report the functional information on the therapy claim, but, he/she must track and document the G-codes and severity modifiers used for this reporting in the beneficiary's medical record of therapy services.

For details related to the documentation requirements, refer to, Medicare Benefit Policy Manual, Pub. 100-02, Chapter 15, section 220.4 - Functional Reporting. For coverage rules related to MCTRJCA and therapy goals, refer to Pub. 100-02: a) for outpatient therapy services, see Chapter 15, section 220.1.2 B and b) for instructions specific to PT, OT, and SLP services in the CORF, see Chapter 12, section 10.

Pub. 100-4, Chapter 12, Section 190.3
List of Medicare Telehealth Services
(Rev. 2848, Issued 12-30-13; Effective 01-01-14; Implementation 01-06-14)

The use of a telecommunications system may substitute for an in-person encounter for professional consultations, office visits, office psychiatry services, and a limited number of other physician fee schedule (PFS) services. The various services and corresponding

current procedure terminology (CPT) or Healthcare Common Procedure Coding System (HCPCS) codes are listed below.

- Consultations (CPT codes 99241 - 99275) - Effective October 1, 2001 – December 31, 2005;

- Consultations (CPT codes 99241 - 99255) - Effective January 1, 2006 – December 31, 2009;

- Telehealth consultations, emergency department or initial inpatient (HCPCS codes G0425 – G0427) - Effective January 1, 2010;

- Follow-up inpatient telehealth consultations (HCPCS codes G0406, G0407, and G0408) - Effective January 1, 2009;

- Office or other outpatient visits (CPT codes 99201 - 99215);

- Subsequent hospital care services, with the limitation of one telehealth visit every 3 days (CPT codes 99231, 99232, and 99233) – Effective January 1, 2011;

- Subsequent nursing facility care services, with the limitation of one telehealth visit every 30 days (CPT codes 99307, 99308, 99309, and 99310) – Effective January 1, 2011;

- Pharmacologic management (CPT code 90862) – Effective March 1, 2003 – December 31, 2012; (HCPCS code G0459) – Effective January 1, 2013;

- Individual psychotherapy (CPT codes 90804 - 90809); Psychiatric diagnostic interview examination (CPT code 90801) – Effective March 1, 2003 – December 31, 2012;

- Individual psychotherapy (CPT codes 90832 – 90834, 90836 – 90838); Psychiatric diagnostic interview examination (CPT codes 90791 -- 90792) – Effective January 1, 2013.

- Neurobehavioral status exam (CPT code 96116) - Effective January 1, 2008;

- End Stage Renal Disease (ESRD) related services (HCPCS codes G0308, G0309, G0311, G0312, G0314, G0315, G0317, and G0318) – Effective January 1, 2005 – December 31, 2008;

- End Stage Renal Disease (ESRD) related services (CPT codes 90951, 90952, 90954, 90955, 90957, 90958, 90960, and 90961) – Effective January 1, 2009;

- Individual and group medical nutrition therapy (HCPCS codes G0270, 97802, 97803, and 97804) – Individual effective January 1, 2006; group effective January 1, 2011;

- Individual and group health and behavior assessment and intervention (CPT codes 96150 – 96154) – Individual effective January 1, 2010; group effective January 1, 2011.

- Individual and group kidney disease education (KDE) services (HCPCS codes G0420 and G0421) – Effective January 1, 2011; and

- Individual and group diabetes self-management training (DSMT) services, with a minimum of 1 hour of in-person instruction to be furnished in the initial year training period to ensure effective injection training (HCPCS codes G0108 and G0109) - Effective January 1, 2011.

- Smoking Cessation Services (CPT codes 99406 and 99407 and HCPCS codes G0436 and G0437) – Effective January 1, 2012.

- Alcohol and/or substance (other than tobacco) abuse structured assessment and intervention services (HCPCS codes G0396 and G0397) – Effective January 1, 2013.

- Annual alcohol misuse screening (HCPCS code G0442) – Effective January 1, 2013.

- Brief face-to-face behavioral counseling for alcohol misuse (HCPCS code G0443) – Effective January 1, 2013.

- Annual Depression Screening (HCPCS code G0444) – Effective January 1, 2013.

- High-intensity behavioral counseling to prevent sexually transmitted infections (HCPCS code G0445) – Effective January 1, 2013.

- Annual, face-to-face Intensive behavioral therapy for cardiovascular disease (HCPCS code G0446) – Effective January 1, 2013.

- Face-to-face behavioral counseling for obesity (HCPCS code G0447) – Effective January 1, 2013.

- Transitional Care Management Services (CPT codes 99495 -99496) – Effective January 1, 2014.

NOTE: Beginning January 1, 2010, CMS eliminated the use of all consultation codes, except for inpatient telehealth consultation G-codes. CMS no longer

recognizes office/outpatient or inpatient consultation CPT codes for payment of office/outpatient or inpatient visits. Instead, physicians and practitioners are instructed to bill a new or established patient office/outpatient visit CPT code or appropriate hospital or nursing facility care code, as appropriate to the particular patient, for all office/outpatient or inpatient visits.

Pub. 100-4, Chapter 12, Section 190.7
Contractor Editing of Telehealth Claims
(Rev. 997, Issued: 07-07-06; Effective: 01-01-06; Implementation: 08-07-06)

Medicare telehealth services (as listed in section 190.3) are billed with either the "GT" or "GQ" modifier. The contractor shall approve covered telehealth services if the physician or practitioner is licensed under State law to provide the service. Contractors must familiarize themselves with licensure provisions of States for which they process claims and disallow telehealth services furnished by physicians or practitioners who are not authorized to furnish the applicable telehealth service under State law. For example, if a nurse practitioner is not licensed to provide individual psychotherapy under State law, he or she would not be permitted to receive payment for individual psychotherapy under

Medicare. The contractor shall install edits to ensure that only properly licensed physicians and practitioners are paid for covered telehealth services.

If a contractor receives claims for professional telehealth services coded with the "GQ" modifier (representing "via asynchronous telecommunications system"), it shall approve/pay for these services only if the physician or practitioner is affiliated with a Federal telemedicine demonstration conducted in Alaska or Hawaii. The contractor may require the physician or practitioner at the distant site to document his or her participation in a Federal telemedicine demonstration program conducted in Alaska or Hawaii prior to paying for telehealth services provided via asynchronous, store and forward technologies.

If a contractor denies telehealth services because the physician or practitioner may not bill for them, the contractor uses MSN message 21.18: "This item or service is not covered when performed or ordered by this practitioner." The contractor uses remittance advice message 52 when denying the claim based upon MSN message 21.18.

If a service is billed with one of the telehealth modifiers and the procedure code is not designated as a covered telehealth service, the contractor denies the service using MSN message 9.4: "This item or service was denied because information required to make payment was incorrect." The remittance advice message depends on what is incorrect, e.g., B18 if procedure code or modifier is incorrect, 125 for submission billing errors, 4-12 for difference inconsistencies. The contractor uses B18 as the explanation for the denial of the claim.

The only claims from institutional facilities that FIs shall pay for telehealth services at the distant site, except for MNT services, are for physician or practitioner services when the distant site is located in a CAH that has elected Method II, and the physician or practitioner has reassigned his/her benefits to the CAH. The CAH bills its regular FI for the professional services provided at the distant site via a telecommunications system, in any of the revenue codes 096x, 097x or 098x. All requirements for billing distant site telehealth services apply.

Claims from hospitals or CAHs for MNT services are submitted to the hospital's or CAH's regular FI. Payment is based on the non-facility amount on the Medicare Physician Fee Schedule for the particular HCPCS codes.

Pub. 100-4, Chapter 12, Section 100
Teaching Physician Services
Definitions
For purposes of this section, the following definitions apply.

Resident -An individual who participates in an approved graduate medical education (GME) program or a physician who is not in an approved GME program but who is authorized to practice only in a hospital setting. The term includes interns and fellows in GME programs recognized as approved for purposes of direct GME payments made by the FI. Receiving a staff or faculty appointment or participating in a fellowship does not by itself alter the status of "resident". Additionally, this status remains unaffected regardless of whether a hospital includes the physician in its full time equivalency count of residents.

Student- An individual who participates in an accredited educational program (e.g., a medical school) that is not an approved GME program. A student is never considered to be an intern or a resident. Medicare does not pay for any service furnished by a student. See 100.1.1B for a discussion concerning E/M service documentation performed by students.

Teaching Physician -A physician (other than another resident) who involves residents in the care of his or her patients.

Direct Medical and Surgical Services -Services to individual beneficiaries that are either personally furnished by a physician or furnished by a resident under the supervision of a physician in a teaching hospital making the reasonable cost election for physician services furnished in teaching hospitals. All payments for such services are made by the FI for the hospital.

Teaching Hospital -A hospital engaged in an approved GME residency program in medicine, osteopathy, dentistry, or podiatry.

Teaching Setting -Any provider, hospital-based provider, or nonprovider setting in which Medicare payment for the services of residents is made by the FI under the direct graduate medical education payment methodology or freestanding SNF or HHA in which such payments are made on a reasonable cost basis.

Critical or Key Portion- That part (or parts) of a service that the teaching physician determines is (are) a critical or key portion(s). For purposes of this section, these terms are interchangeable.

Documentation- Notes recorded in the patient's medical records by a resident, and/or teaching physician or others as outlined in the specific situations below regarding the service furnished. Documentation may be dictated and typed or hand-written, or computer-generated and typed or handwritten. Documentation must be dated and include a legible signature or identity. Pursuant to 42 CFR 415.172 (b), documentation must identify, at a minimum, the service furnished, the participation of the teaching physician in providing the service, and whether the teaching physician was physically present. In the context of an electronic medical record, the term 'macro' means a command in a computer or dictation application that automatically generates predetermined text that is not edited by the user.

When using an electronic medical record, it is acceptable for the teaching physician to use a macro as the required personal documentation if the teaching physician adds it personally in a secured (password protected) system. In addition to the teaching physician's macro, either the resident or the teaching physician must provide customized information that is sufficient to support a medical necessity determination. The note in the electronic medical record must sufficiently describe the specific services furnished to the specific patient on the specific date. It is insufficient documentation if both the resident and the teaching physician use macros only.

Physically Present- The teaching physician is located in the same room (or partitioned or curtained area, if the room is subdivided to accommodate multiple patients) as the patient and/or performs a face-to-face service.

Pub. 100-4, Chapter 12, Section 160.1
Payment
Diagnostic testing services are not subject to the outpatient mental health limitation. Refer to §210, below, for a discussion of the outpatient mental health limitation.

The diagnostic testing services performed by a psychologist (who is not a clinical psychologist) practicing independently of an institution, agency, or physician's office are covered as other diagnostic tests if a physician orders such testing. Medicare covers this type of testing as an outpatient service if furnished by any psychologist who is licensed or certified to practice psychology in the State or jurisdiction where he or she is furnishing services or, if the jurisdiction does not issue licenses, if provided by any practicing psychologist. (It is CMS' understanding that all States, the District of Columbia, and Puerto Ricolicense psychologists, but that some trust territories do not. Examples of psychologists, other than clinical psychologists, whose services are covered under this provision include, but are not limited to, educational psychologists and counseling psychologists.)

To determine whether the diagnostic psychological testing services of a particular independent psychologist are covered under Part B in States which have statutory licensure or certification, carriers must secure from the appropriate State agency a current listing of psychologists holding the required credentials. In States or territories which lack statutory licensing and certification, carriers must check individual qualifications as claims are submitted. Possible reference sources are the national directory of membership of the American Psychological Association, which provides data about the educational background of individuals and indicates which members are board-certified, and records and directories of the State or territorial psychological association. If qualification is dependent on a doctoral degree from a currently accredited program, carriers must verify the date of accreditation of the school involved, since such accreditation is not retroactive. If the reference sources listed above do not provide enough information (e.g., the psychologist is not a member of the association), carriers must contact the psychologist personally for the required information. Carriers may wish to maintain a continuing list of psychologists whose qualifications have been verified.

Medicare excludes expenses for diagnostic testing from the payment limitation on treatment for mental/psychoneurotic/personality disorders.

Carriers must identify the independent psychologist's choice whether or not to accept assignment when performing psychological tests.

Carriers must accept an independent psychologist claim only if the psychologist reports the name/UPIN of the physician who ordered a test.

Carriers pay nonparticipating independent psychologists at 95 percent of the physician fee schedule allowed amount. Carriers pay participating independent psychologists at 100 percent of the physician fee schedule allowed amount.

Independent psychologists are identified on the provider file by specialty code 62 and provider type 35.

Pub. 100-4, Chapter 12, Section 170
Clinical Psychologist Services
B3-2150 See Medicare Benefit Policy Manual, Chapter 15, for general coverage requirements.

Direct payment may be made under Part B for professional services. However, services furnished incident to the professional services of CPs to hospital patients remain bundled.

Therefore, payment must continue to be made to the hospital (by the FI) for such "incident to" services.

Pub. 100-4, Chapter 12, Section 210.1
Application of the Limitation
(Rev. 2166, Issued: 02-25-11, Effective: 03-25-11, Implementation: 03-25-11)

A. Status of Patient
The limitation is applicable to expenses incurred in connection with the treatment of an individual who is not an inpatient of a hospital. Thus, the limitation applies to mental health services furnished to a person in a physician's office, in the patient's home, in a skilled nursing facility, as an outpatient, and so forth. The term "hospital" in this context

means an institution, which is primarily engaged in providing to inpatients, by or under the supervision of a physician(s):

- Diagnostic and therapeutic services for medical diagnosis, treatment and care of injured, disabled, or sick persons;
- Rehabilitation services for injured, disabled, or sick persons; or
- Psychiatric services for the diagnosis and treatment of mentally ill patients.

B. Disorders Subject to the Limitation
The term "mental, psychoneurotic, and personality disorders" is defined as the specific psychiatric diagnoses described in the International Classification of Diseases, 9th Revision (ICD-9), under the code range 290-319.

When the treatment services rendered are both for a psychiatric diagnosis as defined in the ICD-9 and one or more nonpsychiatric conditions, separate the expenses for the psychiatric aspects of treatment from the expenses for the nonpsychiatric aspects of treatment. However, in any case in which the psychiatric treatment component is not readily distinguishable from the nonpsychiatric treatment component, all of the expenses are allocated to whichever component constitutes the primary diagnosis.

1. Diagnosis Clearly Meets Definition - If the primary diagnosis reported for a particular service is the same as or equivalent to a condition described in the ICD-9 under the code range 290-319 that represents mental, psychoneurotic and personality disorders, the expense for the service is subject to the limitation except as described in subsection D.

2. Diagnosis Does Not Clearly Meet Definition - When it is not clear whether the primary diagnosis reported meets the definition of mental, psychoneurotic, and personality disorders, it may be necessary to contact the practitioner to clarify the diagnosis. In deciding whether contact is necessary in a given case, give consideration to such factors as the type of services rendered, the diagnosis, and the individual's previous utilization history.

C. Services Subject to the Limitation

Medicare Contractors must apply the limitation to claims for professional services that represent mental health treatment furnished to individuals who are not hospital inpatients by physicians, clinical psychologists, clinical social workers, nurse practitioners, clinical nurse specialists and physician assistants. Items and supplies furnished by physicians or other mental health practitioners in connection with treatment are also subject to the limitation.

Generally, Medicare Contractors must apply the limitation only to treatment services. However, diagnostic psychological and neuropsychological testing services performed to evaluate a patient's progress during treatment are considered part of treatment and are subject to the limitation.

D. Services Not Subject to the Limitation

1. Diagnosis of Alzheimer's Disease or Related Disorder - When the primary diagnosis reported for a particular service is Alzheimer's Disease or an Alzheimer's related disorder, Medicare Contractors must look to the nature of the service that has been rendered in determining whether it is subject to the limitation. Alzheimer's disease is coded 331.0 in the "International Classification of Diseases, 9th Revision", which is outside the code range 290-319 that represents mental, psychoneurotic and personality disorders. Additionally, Alzheimer's related disorders are identified by contractors under ICD-9 codes that are within the 290-319 code range (290.XX or others as contractors determine appropriate) or outside the 290-319 code range as determined appropriate by contractors. When the primary treatment rendered to a patient with a diagnosis of Alzheimer's disease or a related disorder is psychotherapy, it is subject to the limitation. However, typically, treatment provided to a patient with a diagnosis of Alzheimer's Disease or a related disorder represents medical management of the patient's condition (such as described under CPT code 90862 or any successor code) and is not subject to the limitation. CPT code 90862 describes pharmacologic management, including prescription, use, and review of medication with no more than minimal medical psychotherapy.

2. Brief Office Visits for Monitoring or Changing Drug Prescriptions - Brief office visits for the sole purpose of monitoring or changing drug prescriptions used in the treatment of mental, psychoneurotic and personality disorders are not subject to the limitation. These visits are reported using HCPCS code M0064 or any successor code (brief office visit for the sole purpose of monitoring or changing drug prescriptions used in the treatment of mental, psychoneurotic, and personality disorders). Claims where the diagnosis reported is a mental, psychoneurotic, or personality disorder (other than a diagnosis specified in subsection A) are subject to the limitation except for the procedure identified by HCPCS code M0064 or any successor code.

3. Diagnostic Services –Medicare Contractors do not apply the limitation to psychiatric diagnostic evaluations and diagnostic psychological and neuropsychological tests performed to establish or confirm the patient's diagnosis. Diagnostic services include psychiatric diagnostic evaluations billed under CPT codes 90801 or 90802 (or any successor codes) and, psychological and neuropsychological tests billed under CPT code range 96101-96118 (or any successor code range).

An initial visit to a practitioner for professional services often combines diagnostic evaluation and the start of therapy. Such a visit is neither solely diagnostic nor solely therapeutic. Therefore, contractors must deem the initial visit to be diagnostic so that the limitation does not apply. Separating diagnostic and therapeutic components of a visit is not administratively feasible, unless the practitioner already has separately identified them on the bill. Determining the entire visit to be therapeutic is not justifiable since some diagnostic work must be done before even a tentative diagnosis can be made and certainly before therapy can be instituted. Moreover, the patient should not be disadvantaged because therapeutic as well as diagnostic services were provided in the initial visit. In the rare cases where a practitioner's diagnostic services take more than one visit, Medicare

contractors must not apply the limitation to the additional visits. However, it is expected such cases are few. Therefore, when a practitioner bills for more than one visit for professional diagnostic services, Medicare contractors may find it necessary to request documentation to justify the reason for more than one diagnostic visit.

4. Partial Hospitalization Services Not Directly Provided by a Physician or a Practitioner - The limitation does not apply to partial hospitalization services that are not directly provided by a physician, clinical psychologist, nurse practitioner, clinical nurse specialist or a physician assistant. Partial hospitalization services are billed by hospital outpatient departments and community mental health centers (CMHCs) to Medicare Contractors. However, services furnished by physicians, clinical psychologists, nurse practitioners, clinical nurse specialists, and physician assistants to partial hospitalization patients are billed separately from the partial hospitalization program of services. Accordingly, these professional's mental health services to partial hospitalization patients are paid under the physician fee schedule by Medicare Contractors and may be subject to the limitation. (See chapter 4, section 260.1C).

E. Computation of Limitation

Medicare Contractors determine the Medicare approved payment amount for services subject to the limitation. They:

- Multiply the approved amount by the limitation percentage amount;
- Subtract any unsatisfied deductible; and,
- Multiply the remainder by 0.8 to obtain the amount of Medicare payment.

The beneficiary is responsible for the difference between the amount paid by Medicare and the full Medicare approved amount.

The following examples illustrate the application of the limitation in various circumstances as it is gradually reduced under section 102 of the Medicare Improvements for Patients and Providers Act (MIPPA). Please note that although the calendar year 2009 Part B deductible of $135 is used under these examples, the actual deductible amount for calendar year 2010 and future years is unknown and will be subject to change.

Example #1: In 2010, a clinical psychologist submits a claim for $200 for outpatient treatment of a patient's mental disorder. The Medicare-approved amount is $180. Since clinical psychologists must accept assignment, the patient is not liable for the $20 in

excess charges. The patient previously satisfied the $135 annual Part B deductible. The limitation reduces the amount of incurred expenses to 68 ¾ percent of the approved amount. Medicare pays 80 percent of the remaining incurred expenses. The Medicare payment and patient liability are computed as follows:

1. Actual charges $200.00
2. Medicare-approved amount $180.00
3. Medicare incurred expenses (0.6875 x line 2) $123.75
4. Unmet deductible $0.00
5. Remainder after subtracting deductible (line 3 minus line 4).......$123.75
6. Medicare payment (0.80 x line 5) $99.00
7. Patient liability (line 2 minus line 6)..$81.00

Example #2: In 2012, a clinical social worker submits a claim for $135 for outpatient treatment of a patient's mental disorder. The Medicare-approved amount is $120. Since clinical social workers must accept assignment, the patient is not liable for the $15 in excess charges. The limitation reduces the amount of incurred expenses to 75 percent of the approved amount. The patient previously satisfied $70 of the $135 annual Part B deductible, leaving $65 unmet. The Medicare payment and patient liability are computed as follows:

1. Actual charges $135.00
2. Medicare-approved amount $120.00
3. Medicare incurred expenses (0.75 x line 2) $90.00
4. Unmet deductible $65.00
5. Remainder after subtracting deductible (line 3 minus line 4)........$25.00
6. Medicare payment (0.80 x line 5) $20.00
7. Patient liability (line 2 minus line 6).......................................$100.00

Example #3: In calendar year 2013, a physician who does not accept assignment submits a claim for $780 for services in connection with the treatment of a mental disorder that did not require inpatient hospitalization. The Medicare-approved amount is $750. Because the physician does not accept assignment, the patient is liable for the $30 in excess charges. The patient has not satisfied any of the $135 Part B annual deductible. The Medicare payment and patient liability are computed as follows:

1. Actual charges $780.00
2. Medicare-approved amount $750.00
3. Medicare incurred expenses (0.8125 x line 2) $609.38
4. Unmet deductible $135.00
5. Remainder after subtracting deductible (line 3 minus line 4) $474.38
6. Medicare payment (0.80 x line 5) $379.50
7. Patient liability (line 1 minus line 6) $400.50

Example #4: A patient's Part B expenses during calendar year 2014 are for a physician's services in connection with the treatment of a mental disorder that initially required

inpatient hospitalization, with subsequent physician services furnished on an outpatient basis. The patient has not satisfied any of the $135 Part B deductible. The physician accepts assignment and submits a claim for $780. The Medicare-approved amount is $750. Since the limitation will be completely phased out as of January 1, 2014, the entire $750 Medicare-approved amount is recognized as the total incurred expenses because such expenses are no longer reduced. Also, there is no longer any distinction between mental health services the patient receives as an inpatient or outpatient. The Medicare payment and patient liability are computed as follows:

1. Actual charges $780.00
2. Medicare-approved amount $750.00
3. Medicare incurred expenses (1.00 x line 2) $750.00
4. Unmet deductible $135.00
5. Remainder after subtracting deductible (line 3 minus line 4) $615.00
6. Medicare payment (0.80 x line 5) $492.00
   Beneficiary liability (line 2 minus line 6) $258.00

Glossary

72-hour rule. Policy requiring billing and payment for certain outpatient services provided on the date of an IPPS admission, or during the three calendar days prior to the date of admission, to be included with the bill and payment for the inpatient admission. Non-IPPS hospitals have a one-day payment window. Also known as the payment window or the three-day rule, this Medicare policy has been adopted by other payers.

aberrant. Deviation or departure from the normal or usual course, condition, or pattern.

abstractor. Person who selects and extracts specific data from the medical record and enters the information into computer files.

abuse. In medical reimbursement, an incident that is inconsistent with accepted medical, business, or fiscal practices and directly or indirectly results in unnecessary costs to the Medicare program, improper reimbursement, or reimbursement for services that do not meet professionally recognized standards of care or which are medically unnecessary. Examples of abuse include excessive charges, improper billing practices, billing Medicare as primary instead of other third-party payers that are primary, and increasing charges for Medicare beneficiaries but not to other patients.

academic underachievement disorder. Failure to achieve in most school tasks despite adequate intellectual capacity, supportive environment, and apparent effort.

accredited record technician. Former AHIMA certification describing medical records practitioners; now known as a registered health information technician (RHIT).

acrophobia. Abnormal, intense fear of heights.

activities of daily living. Self-care activities often used to determine a patient's level of function such as bathing, dressing, using a toilet, transferring in and out of bed or a chair, continence, eating, and walking.

acute alcohol intoxication. Psychic and physical state resulting from alcohol ingestion characterized by slurred speech, unsteady gait, poor coordination, flushed face, nystagmus, sluggish reflexes, strong smell of alcohol, loud speech, emotional instability (e.g., jollity followed by gloominess), excessive socializing, talkativeness, and poorly inhibited sexual and aggressive behavior.

adaptation reaction. Abnormal or maladaptive reaction with emotional or behavioral characteristics as a result of a life event or stressor that is usually temporary.

add-on code. CPT code representing a procedure performed in addition to the primary procedure and designated with a + in the CPT book. Add-on codes are never reported for stand-alone services but are reported secondarily in addition to the primary procedure.

adjudication. Processing and review of a submitted claim resulting in payment, partial payment, or denial. In relationship to judicial hearings, it is the process of hearing and settling a case through an objective, judicial procedure.

adjusted average per capita cost. Estimated average cost of Medicare benefits for an individual, based upon criteria including age, sex, institutional status, Medicaid, disability, and end-stage renal failure.

adjustment reaction or disorder. Abnormal or maladaptive reaction with emotional or behavioral characteristics as a result of a life event or stressor that is usually temporary.

adjustment reaction or disorder with brief depression. Short-term depressive symptoms following a life event or stressor.

adjustment reaction or disorder with depression. State of depression associated with an abnormal or maladaptive reaction with emotional or behavioral characteristics as a result of a life event or stressor that is usually temporary.

adjustment reaction or disorder with emotional disturbance. Abnormal or maladaptive reaction with emotional disturbance as a result of a life event or stressor that is usually temporary.

adjustment reaction or disorder with mixed conduct and emotional disturbance. Abnormal or maladaptive reaction with emotional or behavioral characteristics as a result of a life event or stressor that is usually temporary.

adjustment reaction or disorder with prolonged depression. Depressive symptoms following a life event or stressor that extends over an extended period of time.

admission date. Date the patient was admitted to the health care facility for inpatient care, outpatient service, or for the start of care.

affective psychosis. Severe disturbance of mood or emotion that adversely affects the thinking process and may be accompanied by delusions or hallucinations.

affective psychosis, bipolar manic. Manic-depressive psychosis, circular type, in which the manic form is currently present.

affective psychosis, bipolar mixed. Manic-depressive psychosis, circular type, in which both manic and depressive symptoms are present at the same time.

affective psychosis, depressed type. Manic-depressive psychosis in which there is a widespread depressed mood of gloom and wretchedness with some degree of anxiety, reduced activity, or restlessness and agitation. There is a marked tendency to recurrence; in a few cases this may be at regular intervals.

affective psychosis, depressed type atypical. Affective depressive disorder that cannot be classified as a manic-depressive psychosis, depressed type or chronic depressive personality disorder, or as an adjustment disorder.

affective psychosis, manic type. State of elation or excitement out of keeping with the individual's circumstances and varying from enhanced liveliness (hypomania) to violent, almost uncontrollable, excitement. Aggression and anger, flight of ideas, distractibility, impaired judgment, and grandiose ideas are common.

affective psychosis, mixed type. Manic-depressive psychosis syndrome corresponding to both the manic and depressed types that cannot be classified more specifically.

age eligibility for Part B. Individuals must be 65 years of age or older, a resident and citizen of the United States or an alien lawfully admitted for permanent residence who has resided in the United States continually for the five years preceding his/her application for enrollment for Part B benefits, and eligible for Medicare Part A benefits.

aggressive personality. Personality disorder characterized by instability of mood with uncontrollable outbursts of anger, hate, violence, or affection demonstrated by words or actions.

agoraphobia. Profound anxiety or fear of leaving familiar settings like home, or being in unfamiliar locations or with strangers or crowds; almost always preceded by a phase during which there are recurrent panic attacks.

ailurophobia. Abnormal, intense fear of cats.

Al-Anon, Alateen. Alcoholic support groups.

alcohol abstinence syndrome. Cessation of prolonged heavy drinking of alcohol that results in tremor of hands, tongue, and eyelids that can also include nausea and vomiting, dry mouth, headache, heavy perspiration, fitful sleep, acute anxiety attacks, mood depression, feelings of guilt and remorse, and irritability.

alcohol amnestic syndrome. Prominent and lasting reduction of memory span, including striking loss of recent memory, disordered time appreciation, and confabulation, occurring in alcoholics as the sequel to an acute alcoholic psychosis or, more rarely, in the course of chronic alcoholism. It is usually accompanied by peripheral neuritis and may be associated with Wernicke's encephalopathy.

alcohol delirium. Organic alcoholic psychotic state, acute or subacute, manifested by clouded consciousness, disorientation, fear, illusions, delusions, hallucinations of any kind, notably visual and tactile, restlessness, tremor, and sometimes fever.

alcohol dependence syndrome. Chronic, progressive state of dependence upon alcohol that is both psychological and physical with periodic or continuous episodes impairing health and the ability to function emotionally, socially, and occupationally.

alcohol intoxication, pathological. Acute psychotic episodes induced by relatively small amounts of alcohol. These are regarded as individual idiosyncratic reactions to alcohol, not due to excessive consumption and without conspicuous neurological signs of intoxication.

alcohol withdrawal delirium (delirium tremens). Acute or subacute organic psychotic states in alcoholics, characterized by clouded consciousness, disorientation, fear, illusions, delusions, hallucinations of any kind, notably visual and tactile, restlessness, tremor, and sometimes fever.

alcohol withdrawal hallucinosis. Psychosis usually of less than six months' duration, with slight or no clouding of consciousness and much anxious restlessness in which auditory hallucinations, mostly of voices uttering insults and threats, predominate.

alcohol withdrawal syndrome. Cessation of prolonged heavy drinking of alcohol that results in tremor of hands, tongue, and eyelids that can also include nausea and vomiting, dry mouth, headache, heavy perspiration, fitful sleep, acute anxiety attacks, mood depression, feelings of guilt and remorse, and irritability.

alcoholic dementia. Nonhallucinatory dementias occurring in association with alcoholism, but not characterized by the features of

either alcohol withdrawal delirium (delirium tremens) or alcohol amnestic syndrome (Korsakoff's alcoholic psychosis).

alcoholic hallucinosis. Psychosis usually of less than six months' duration, with slight or no clouding of consciousness and much anxious restlessness in which auditory hallucinations, mostly of voices uttering insults and threats, predominate.

alcoholic jealousy. Chronic paranoid psychosis characterized by delusional jealousy and associated with alcoholism.

alcoholic paranoia. Chronic paranoid psychosis characterized by delusional jealousy and associated with alcoholism.

alcoholic polyneuritic psychosis. Disturbance of long- and short-term memory that is attributed to alcohol use or dependence and affects emotional, social, and occupational function.

alcoholic psychoses. Organic psychotic states due mainly to excessive consumption of alcohol that may be exacerbated by nutritional defects.

alcoholic syndrome, chronic. Numerous symptoms caused by constant, long-time ingestion of alcohol affecting the nervous and gastrointestinal systems.

alcoholism, acute. Psychic and physical state resulting from alcohol ingestion characterized by slurred speech, unsteady gait, poor coordination, flushed face, nystagmus, sluggish reflexes, strong smell of alcohol, loud speech, emotional instability (e.g., jollity followed by gloominess), excessive socializing, talkativeness, and poorly inhibited sexual and aggressive behavior.

alcoholism, chronic. Chronic, progressive state of dependence upon alcohol that is both psychological and physical with periodic or continuous episodes impairing health and the ability to function emotionally, socially, and occupationally.

alexia. Impairment of the ability to comprehend written words that may be acquired as a result of a cerebral lesion or a developmental disorder.

algophobia. Abnormal, intense fear of pain.

allowable charge. Fee schedule amount for a medical service as determined by the physician fee schedule methodology published annually by CMS.

altering patient records. Inappropriately changing or amending patient records, usually to obtain reimbursement or because of pending audits and legal review of records.

alternative delivery system. Any health care delivery system other than traditional fee-for-service.

amnesia, psychogenic. Sudden onset of dissociative hysteria in the absence of an organic mental disorder where there is a temporary disturbance in the ability to recall important personal information that has already been registered and stored in memory that is greater than ordinary forgetfulness.

amnestic syndrome. Amnestic dementia in which the patient has no short-term or long-term memories but is not delirious.

amoral personality. Personality disorder characterized by disregard for social obligations, lack of feeling for others, and impetuous violence or callous unconcern and self-rationalization of behavior.

anancastic (anankastic) neurosis. Feeling of subjective compulsion to carry out an action, dwell on an idea, recall an experience, or ruminate on an abstract topic or to perform a quasiritual that may result in anxiety or inner struggle as the individual tries to cope with the behavior.

anancastic (anankastic) personality. Feeling of subjective compulsion to perform an action or a thought process that causes anxiety if there is interruption or discontinuance of the action or thought by the self or others.

anorexia nervosa. Psychological eating disorder characterized by an intense fear of gaining weight, an unrealistic perception of body image that perpetuates the feeling of being fat or having too much fat, even though the body is emaciated, and an accompanying refusal to maintain normal body weight. This condition typically affects young women in adolescent years and also manifests with amenorrhea, depression, denial, and peculiar behaviors or obsessions over food.

Antikickback Act. National legislation that prohibits knowing or willful solicitation or receipt of remuneration in return for referring, recommending, or arranging for the purchase, lease, or ordering of items or services for which payment will be made from any federal or state health care program.

anxiety hysteria. Neurotic state with abnormally intense dread of certain objects or specific situations that would not normally affect the individual.

anxiety state. Apprehension, tension, or uneasiness that stems from the anticipation of danger, the source of which is largely unknown or unrecognized.

anxiety state, atypical. Anxiety disorder that does not fulfill the criteria of generalized or panic attack anxiety.

anxiety state, generalized. Disorder of at least six months' duration manifested by diffuse and persistent anxiety without the specific symptoms that characterize phobic disorders, panic disorder, or obsessive-compulsive disorder.

anxiety state, panic attack. Episodic and often chronic, recurrent disorder manifested by discrete periods of sudden onset, intense apprehension, fearfulness, or terror often associated with feelings of impending doom.

APA. American Psychiatric Association.

aphasia. Partial or total loss of the ability to comprehend language or communicate through speaking, the written word, or sign language. Aphasia may result from stroke, injury, Alzheimer's disease, or other disorder. Common types of aphasia include expressive, receptive, anomic, global, and conduction.

appropriateness of care. Proper setting of medical care that best meets the patient's care or diagnosis, as defined by a health care plan or other legal entity.

arrhythmias. Heart disorder of rhythm or rate, due to an electrical conduction system malfunction.

arteriosclerotic dementia. Dementia attributable, because of physical signs (confirmed by examination of the central nervous system), to degenerative arterial disease of the brain.

asocial personality. Personality disorder characterized by disregard for social obligations, lack of feeling for others, and impetuous violence or callous unconcern and self-rationalization of behavior.

assessment. Process of collecting and studying information and data, such as test values, signs, and symptoms.

assignment of benefits. Authorization from the patient allowing the third-party payer to pay the provider directly for medical services. Under Medicare, an assignment is an agreement by the hospital or physician to accept Medicare's payment as the full payment and not to bill the patient for any amounts over the allowance amount, except for deductible and/or coinsurance amounts or noncovered services.

astasia-abasia, hysterical. Form of conversion hysteria in which the individual is unable to stand or walk although the legs are otherwise under control.

asthenic personality. Personality disorder characterized by passive compliance with the wishes of elders and others and a weak, inadequate response to the demands of daily life. Those with the disorder may be intellectual or emotional with little capacity for enjoyment.

attention deficit disorder. Syndrome characterized by short attention span, distractibility, and overactivity without significant disturbance of conduct or delay in specific skills.

auditing and monitoring. Regular review of an organization's claim development and submission process from the point where service for a patient is initiated to the submission of a claim for payment. Monitoring involves a system of checks of and controls over, as well as a method of reporting, all areas of compliance, including regulations and audits.

authorization. Verbal or written agreement indicating that a third-party payer will pay for services rendered by the provider as set forth in the authorization.

autism. Developmental disorder connected with neurophysiological factors, manifesting in early childhood with definitively impaired communication and social interaction marked by the inability to reciprocate in play, recognize other's feelings or existence, mimic or imitate, or seek comfort. Unusual activities and interests may be present, restricting others, as well as severe behavioral problems.

autism, childhood. Syndrome beginning in the first 30 months of life affecting interaction with others, characterized by abnormal response to auditory and visual stimuli accompanied by difficulty understanding spoken language and limiting the ability to communicate or develop social skills.

autism, infantile. Syndrome beginning in the first 30 months affecting interaction with others, characterized by abnormal response to auditory and visual stimuli, accompanied by difficulty understanding spoken language and limiting the ability to communicate or develop social skills.

avoidant personality. Excessive social inhibitions and shyness, a tendency to withdraw from opportunities for developing close relationships, and a fearful expectation of being belittled and humiliated.

AWP. 1) Average wholesale price. Pharmaceutical price based on common data that is included in a pharmacy provider contract. 2) Any willing provider. Describing statutes requiring a provider network to accept any provider who meets the network's usual selection criteria.

barbiturate abuse. Cases in which an individual has taken barbiturates to the detriment of his/her health or social functioning in doses above or for periods beyond those normally regarded as therapeutic.

BBA. Balanced Budget Act of 1997. Legislation to cut federal spending and balance the federal budget.

beneficiary. Person entitled to receive Medicare or other payer benefits who maintains a health insurance policy claim number.

bestiality. Sexual relations between humans and animals.

biofeedback. Process by which a person learns to influence autonomic or involuntary nervous system responses and physiologic responses normally regulated voluntarily, but whose control has been affected by trauma or disease.

bipolar disorder. Manic-depressive psychosis that has appeared in both the depressive and manic form, either alternating or separated by an interval of normality. Atypical: Episode of affective psychosis with some, but not all, of the features of the one form of the disorder in individuals who have had a previous episode of the other form of the disorder.

body-rocking. Disorders in which voluntary repetitive stereotyped movements, which are not due to any psychiatric or neurological condition, constitute the main feature.

borderline personality. Disorder that is characterized by instability in behavior, mood, self-image, and interpersonal relationships that are intense, unstable, and may shift dramatically. The disorder is manifested by impulsive and unpredictable behavior or expressions of boredom, emptiness, or fear of being alone.

Bouffée délirante. Paranoid states apparently provoked by some emotional stress such as imprisonment, immigration, or strange and threatening environments; frequently manifested as an attack or threat.

Briquet's disorder. Chronic, but fluctuating, neurotic disorder that begins early in life and is characterized by recurrent and multiple somatic complaints for which medical attention is sought but that are not due to any apparent physical illness.

bulimia. Episodic pattern of overeating (binge eating) followed by purging or extreme exercise accompanied by an awareness of the abnormal eating pattern with a fear of not being able to stop eating.

capitation. Contractual agreement whereby the provider is paid a fixed amount for treating enrolled patients regardless of utilization.

carve-out. Medical benefits for a specific type of care considered covered by separate guidelines or not covered by the payer.

case management. Ongoing review of cases by professionals to assure the most appropriate utilization of services.

catagonic stupor. Psychomotor disturbances often alternating between extremes such as hyperkinesis or excitement and stupor or automatic obedience and negativism. May be accompanied by depression, hypomania, or submission to physical constraints.

Catalepsy schizophrenia. Psychomotor disturbances often alternating between extremes such as hyperkinesis or excitement and stupor or automatic obedience and negativism. May be accompanied by depression, hypomania, or submission to physical constraints.

catastrophic case management. Method of reviewing ongoing cases in which the patient sustains catastrophic or extremely costly medical problems.

catastrophic stress. Acute transient disorders of any severity and nature of emotions, consciousness, and psychomotor states (singly or in combination) that occur in individuals, without any apparent pre-existing mental disorder, in response to exceptional physical or mental stress, such as natural catastrophe or battle, and which usually subside within hours or days.

catatonia (schizophrenic). See Catalepsy schizophrenia.

Centers for Medicare and Medicaid Services. Federal agency that oversees the administration of the public health programs such as Medicare, Medicaid, and State Children's Insurance Program.

certification. Approval by a payer's case manager to continue care for a given number of days or visits.

character neurosis. Deeply ingrained maladaptive patterns of behavior generally recognizable by adolescence or earlier and continuing throughout most of adult life, although often becoming less obvious in middle or old age. The personality is abnormal either in the balance of its components, quality and expression, or in its total aspect.

charts. Compilation of documents maintained by the provider for each patient that includes treatment/progress notes, test orders and results, correspondence from other health care providers, and other documents pertinent to the patient's care.

civil monetary penalty. Fine imposed on providers or suppliers by the DOJ for prohibited conduct in federal health care benefit programs, Medicare, and Medicaid. The monetary penalty may be up to $10,000 or three times the amount claimed, whichever is greater.

claims review. Examination of a submitted demand for payment by a Medicare contractor, insurer, or other group to determine payment liability, eligibility, reasonableness, or necessity of care provided.

claustrophobia. Abnormal, intense fear of closed spaces.

clay eating. Compulsive eating of nonnutritive substances that are not food, such as dirt or gravel, flaking paint, or plaster. This is seen most often in children in the second year and usually remits in childhood, but is also seen in developmentally disabled persons, people with zinc or iron deficiencies, and pregnant women.

clean claim. Submitted bill for services rendered that does not need to be investigated by the payer, passes all internal billing edits and payer specific edits, and is paid without the need for further information.

Clinical Laboratory Improvement Amendments. Federal regulations imposed in 1988 to define laboratory certification and accreditation, proficiency testing, quality assurance, personnel standards, and program administration.

clinical social worker. Individual who possesses a master's or doctor's degree in social work and, after obtaining the degree, has performed at least two years of supervised clinical social work. A clinical social worker must be licensed by the state or, in the case of states without licensure, must completed at least two years or 3,000 hours of post-master's degree supervised clinical social work practice under the supervision of a master's level social worker.

clumsiness syndrome. Disorders in which the main feature is a serious impairment in the development of motor coordination that is not explicable in terms of general intellectual disabilities and is commonly associated with perceptual difficulties.

CMS manual system. Web-based manuals organized by functional area that contain all program instructions in the National Coverage Determinations Manual, the Medicare Benefit Policy Manual, Pub. 100, one-time notifications, and manual revision notices.

CMS manuals. Official government manuals prepared by CMS that detail procedures for processing and paying Medicare claims, preparing reimbursement forms, and billing procedures. These manuals were converted to web-based manuals (referred to as IOM, or Internet-only manuals) on October 1, 2003. At the time of the conversion, the manuals were streamlined, updated, and consolidated. Manuals may be accessed at http://www.cms.gov/manuals.

cognitive. Being aware by drawing from knowledge, such as judgment, reason, perception, and memory.

coinsurance. Percentage of the allowed charges paid by a beneficiary toward the cost of care.

combat fatigue. Brief, episodic, or recurrent disorders lasting less than six months after the onset of trauma.

community mental health center. Facility providing outpatient mental health day treatment, assessments, and education as appropriate to community members.

comorbid condition. Condition present on hospital admission that is not the primary reason for treating the patient, but one that affects the patient's care.

compensation neurosis. Type of neurosis in which features of secondary gain, such as a situation of financial advantage, are prominent.

complexity. Difficulty of clinical decision-making: low complexity follows well-known and established parameters and protocols; moderate complexity takes into account extra factors, such as comorbidities; high complexity relies on case-by-case analysis, without the assistance of established protocols.

compliance. Satisfying official coding and/or billing requirements.

compliance plan. Established methods to eliminate errors in coding, billing, and other issues through auditing and monitoring, training, or other corrective actions. Such a plan also provides an avenue for employees and others to report problems.

component code. In the National Correct Coding Initiative (NCCI), the column II code that cannot be charged to Medicare when the column I code is reported.

comprehensive codes. In the National Correct Coding Initiative (NCCI), the column I code that is reported to Medicare and precludes reporting column II codes.

compulsive conduct disorder. Great internal tension resulting from an impulse, drive, or temptation to perform some action that is harmful to the individual or to others that may provide short-term pleasure, gratification, or release and may be followed by regret, self-reproach, or guilt; can take the form of intermittent explosive disorder, isolated explosive disorder, kleptomania, pathological gambling, and pyromania.

compulsive neurosis. Feeling of subjective compulsion to carry out an action, dwell on an idea, recall an experience, or ruminate on an abstract topic or to perform a quasi-ritual that may result in anxiety or inner struggle as the individual tries to cope with the behavior.

compulsive personality. Feelings of personal insecurity, excessive doubt, and incompleteness leading to excessive conscientiousness, stubbornness, perfectionism, meticulous accuracy, and caution with persistent checking in an individual who may also have intrusive thoughts or impulses.

concentration camp syndrome. Brief, episodic, or recurrent disorders lasting six months or more following the trauma.

conduct disorders. Socially inappropriate, abnormal, aggressive, destructive behavior, or delinquency in individuals of any age not related to life stressors but possibly associated with emotional disturbances without other psychiatric conditions.

conduct disorders, impulse control disorder. Great internal tension resulting from an impulse, drive, or temptation to perform some action that is harmful to the individual or to others that may provide short-term pleasure, gratification, or release and may be followed by regret, self-reproach, or guilt; can take the form of intermittent explosive disorder, isolated explosive disorder, kleptomania, pathological gambling, and pyromania.

conduct disorders, mixed disturbance of conduct and emotions. Emotional disturbance demonstrated by anxiety, misery, or obsessive manifestations resulting in undersocialized or socially disturbed conduct.

conduct disorders, socialized conduct disorder. Acquired values or behavior of a peer group that the individual is loyal to and with whom he or she characteristically steals, is truant, stays out late at night, and is sexually promiscuous or engages in other socially delinquent practices.

conduct disorders, undersocialized conduct disturbance, aggressive type. Persistent pattern of disrespect for the feelings and well-being of others, aggressive antisocial behavior, and failure to develop close and stable relationships with others as manifested by physical aggression, cruel behavior, hostility, verbal and physical abuse, stealing, vandalism, lying, and defiance of authority.

conduct disorders, undersocialized conduct disturbance, unaggressive type. Lack of concern for the rights and feelings of others resulting from a failure to establish a normal degree of affection, empathy, or bond with others. May be manifested by self-protection with fear, timidity, whining, making demands, and throwing tantrums, or by exploitation and self-gain through lying and stealing without apparent guilt.

confusional state, acute. Short-lived organic, psychotic states, lasting hours or days and characterized by clouded consciousness, disorientation, fear, illusions, delusions, hallucinations (notably visual and tactile), restlessness, tremor, and sometimes fever.

confusional state, epileptic. Short-lived organic, psychotic states, triggered by an epileptic episode, lasting hours or days and characterized by clouded consciousness, disorientation, fear, illusions, delusions, hallucinations (notably visual and tactile), restlessness, tremor, and sometimes fever.

confusional state, subacute. Organic, psychotic states characterized by clouded consciousness, disorientation, fear, illusions, delusions, hallucinations of any kind (notably visual or tactile), restlessness, tremor, and sometimes fever. The symptoms, usually of a lesser degree than acute, last for several weeks or longer, during which time they may show marked fluctuations in intensity.

connective tissue. Body tissue made from fibroblasts, collagen, and elastic fibrils that connects, supports, and holds together other tissues and cells and includes cartilage, collagenous, fibrous, elastic, and osseous tissue.

Consolidated Omnibus Budget Reconciliation Act. Federal law that allows and requires past employees to be covered under company health insurance plans for a set premium, allowing individuals to remain insured when their current plan or position has been terminated.

consultation. Advice or opinion regarding diagnosis and treatment or determination to accept transfer of care of a patient rendered by a medical professional at the request of the primary care provider.

conversion hysteria. Restriction of the field of consciousness or disturbance of motor or sensory function resulting in symbolic or psychological advantage, primarily of a body part as manifested by paralysis, tremor, blindness, deafness, and seizures.

coordination disorder. Disorders in which the main feature is a serious impairment in the development of motor coordination that is not explicable in terms of general intellectual disabilities and is commonly associated with perceptual difficulties.

coordination of benefits. Agreement that prevents double payment for services when the member is covered by two or more sources. The agreement dictates which organization is primarily and secondarily responsible for payment.

copayment. Cost-sharing arrangement in which a covered person pays a specified portion of allowed charges. In relation to Medicare, the copayment designates the specific dollar amount that the patient must pay and coinsurance designates the percentage of allowed charges.

corporate integrity agreement. Agreement between the government and a provider who has entered into a settlement with the government due to a health care fraud and abuse investigation. Providers must agree to follow the corporate integrity agreement, which is essentially a government-mandated compliance program.

Correct Coding Council. Develops coding methodologies based on established coding conventions to control improper coding that leads to inappropriate and increased payment of Part B claims.

Correct Coding Initiative edits. CCI edits are of two main types. Comprehensive/component edits are applied to code combinations in which one of the codes is a component of the more **comprehensive code.** Only the comprehensive code is paid. Mutually exclusive edits are applied to code combinations in which one of the codes is considered impossible to perform or improbable to be performed with the other code. Current CCI edits have been incorporated in the Outpatient Code Editor except for anesthesiology edits.

counseling. Discussion with a patient and/or family concerning one or more of the following areas: diagnostic results, impressions, and/or recommended diagnostic studies; prognosis; risks and benefits of management (treatment) options; instructions for management (treatment) and/or follow-up; importance of compliance with chosen management (treatment) options; risk factor reduction; and patient and family education.

Coverage Issues Manual. Revised and renamed the *National Coverage Determinations Manual* in the CMS manual system, it contained national coverage decisions and specific medical items, services, treatment procedures, or technologies paid for under the Medicare program. This manual has been converted to the *Medicare National Coverage Determinations Manual* (NCD manual), Pub. 100-03.

covered services. Diagnostic or treatment services that are considered medically necessary and met coverage and program guidelines.

CPT codes. Codes maintained and copyrighted by the AMA and selected for use under HIPAA for outpatient facility and nondental professional transactions.

credentialing. 1) Reviewing the medical degrees, licensure, malpractice, and any disciplinary record of medical providers for panel and quality assurance purposes and to grant hospital privileges. 2) Coding certification.

culture shock. Stress reaction associated with an individual's assimilation into a new culture vastly different from one in which he or she was raised.

Current Procedural Terminology. Definitive procedural coding system developed by the American Medical Association that lists descriptive terms and identifying codes to provide a uniform language that describes medical, surgical, and diagnostic services for nationwide communication among physicians, patients, and third parties.

cyclic schizophrenia. Pronounced affective manic or depressive features intermingled with schizophrenic features that tends toward remission without permanent defect, but which is prone to recur.

cyclothymic personality. Mood disorder manifested by fast and repeated alterations between hypomanic and depressed moods. Treatment consists of psychotherapy and/or medication.

date of service. Day the encounter or procedure is performed or the day a supply is issued.

deductible. Predetermined dollar amount of covered billed charges that the patient must pay toward the cost of care.

delirium. Transient organic psychotic condition with a short course in which there is a rapidly developing onset of disorganization of higher mental processes manifested by some degree of impairment of information processing, impaired or abnormal attention, perception, memory, and thinking. Manifested by clouded consciousness, confusion, disorientation, delusions, illusions, and vivid hallucinations.

delirium tremens. Acute or subacute organic psychotic states in alcoholics, characterized by clouded consciousness, disorientation, fear, illusions, delusions, hallucinations (notably visual and tactile), restlessness, tremor, and sometimes fever.

delirium, acute. Short-lived organic, psychotic states, lasting hours or days and characterized by clouded consciousness, disorientation, fear, illusions, delusions, hallucinations (notably visual and tactile), restlessness, tremor, and sometimes fever.

delirium, subacute. Organic, psychotic state characterized by clouded consciousness, disorientation, fear, illusions, delusions, hallucinations (notably visual and tactile), restlessness, tremor, and sometimes fever. The symptoms, lesser than those in an acute phase, last for several weeks or longer. During this time they may show marked fluctuations in intensity.

delusional syndrome. Organic disorder including hallucinations, beliefs about being followed, being poisoned, etc., and not meeting criteria for schizophrenia.

dementia. Progressive decrease in intellectual functioning of sufficient severity to interfere with occupational or social performance and with the impairment of memory and abstract thinking, the ability to learn new skills, problem solving, and judgment. May involve personality change or impairment in impulse control.

dementia, alcoholic. Nonhallucinatory dementias occurring in association with alcoholism but not characterized by the features of either alcohol withdrawal delirium (delirium tremens) or alcohol amnestic syndrome (Korsakoff's alcoholic psychosis).

dementia, arteriosclerotic. Dementia attributable, because of physical signs (confirmed by examination of the central nervous system), to degenerative arterial disease of the brain.

dementia, multi-infarct. Dementia attributable, because of physical signs (confirmed by examination of the central nervous system), to degenerative arterial disease of the brain caused by multiple infarctions (an ischemic condition causing local tissue death).

dementia, presenile. Dementia occurring usually before the age of 65 in patients with the relatively rare forms of diffuse or lobar cerebral atrophy usually caused by an associated neurological condition.

dementia, repeated infarct. Dementia attributable, because of physical signs (confirmed by examination of the central nervous system), to degenerative arterial disease of the brain caused by repeated infarctions (an ischemic condition causing local tissue death).

dementia, senile. Dementia occurring usually after the age of 65 in which any cerebral pathology other than that of senile atrophic change can be reasonably excluded.

dementia, senile, delirium. Senile dementia with a superimposed reversible episode of acute confusional state.

dementia, senile, delusional type. Progressive type of senile dementia characterized by development in advanced old age, with delusions, varying from simple, poorly formed paranoid delusions to highly formed paranoid delusional states, and hallucinations.

dementia, senile, depressed type. Progressive type of senile dementia characterized by development in advanced old age, with depressive features, ranging from mild to severe forms of manic-depressive affective psychosis. May include disturbance of the sleep-waking cycle and preoccupation with dead people.

dementia, senile, paranoid type. Progressive type of senile dementia characterized by development in advanced old age, with delusions, varying from simple, poorly formed paranoid delusions to highly formed paranoid delusional states, and hallucinations.

dementia, senile, simple type. Dementia occurring usually after the age of 65 in which any cerebral pathology other than that of senile atrophic change can be reasonably excluded.

denial. Refusal by an insurance plan to pay for services, procedures, or supplies. A denial may be made due to coverage limitations, medical necessity issues, or failure to follow appropriate prior authorization or claim submission guidelines.

depersonalization syndrome. Patient feels detached from his or her body and experiences the feeling of being an automaton or in a dream-like state. Depersonalization must be a primary symptom and not part of schizophrenia or another disorder.

depression. Disproportionate depressive state with behavior disturbance that is usually the result of a distressing experience and may include preoccupation with the psychic trauma and anxiety.

depression anxiety. Disproportionate depression with behavior disturbance that is usually the result of a distressing experience and may include delusions or hallucinations, anxiety, and preoccupation with the psychic trauma that preceded the illness.

depression, endogenous. Manic-depressive psychosis in which there is a widespread depressed mood of gloom and wretchedness with some degree of anxiety, reduced activity, or restlessness and agitation. There is a marked tendency to recurrence; in a few cases this may be at regular intervals.

depression, monopolar. Manic-depressive psychosis in which there is a widespread depressed mood of gloom and wretchedness with some degree of anxiety, reduced activity, or restlessness and agitation. There is a marked tendency to recurrence; in a few cases this may be at regular intervals.

depression, neurotic. Disproportionate depression with behavior disturbance that is usually the result of a distressing experience and may include delusions or hallucinations, anxiety, and preoccupation with the psychic trauma that preceded the illness.

depression, psychotic. Manic-depressive psychosis in which there is a widespread depressed mood of gloom and wretchedness with some degree of anxiety, reduced activity, or restlessness and agitation. There is a marked tendency to recurrence; in a few cases this may be at regular intervals.

depression, psychotic reactive. Manic-depressive psychosis in which there is a widespread depressed mood of gloom and wretchedness with some degree of anxiety, reduced activity, or restlessness and agitation. There is a marked tendency to recurrence; in a few cases this may be at regular intervals.

depression, reactive. Disproportionate depression with behavior disturbance that is usually the result of a distressing experience and may include delusions or hallucinations, anxiety, and preoccupation with the psychic trauma that preceded the illness.

depressive personality or character. Affective personality disorder characterized by lifelong predominance of a chronic nonpsychotic disturbance involving either intermittent or sustained periods of depressed mood marked by worry, pessimism, low output of energy, and a sense of futility.

depressive reaction. State of depression associated with an abnormal or maladaptive reaction with emotional or behavioral characteristics as a result of a life event or stressor that is usually temporary.

derealization. Awareness of the disturbed perception of external objects or parts of one's own body as changed in their quality, unreal, remote, or automatized.

developmental delay disorders, arithmetical disorder. Serious impairment in the development of arithmetical skills without obvious intellectual disabilities and with adequate schooling.

developmental delay disorders, articulation disorder. Delay in the development of normal word-sound production resulting in defects of articulation frequently identified by omissions or substitutions of consonants.

developmental delay disorders, coordination disorder. Serious impairment in the development of motor coordination that is not explicable in terms of general intellectual disabilities and is commonly associated with perceptual difficulties.

developmental delay disorders, mixed development disorder. Delay in the development of a specific skill such as reading, arithmetic, speech, or coordination, frequently associated with lesser delays in other skills.

developmental delay disorders, motor retardation. Serious impairment in the development of motor coordination that is not explicable in terms of general intellectual disabilities and is commonly associated with perceptual difficulties.

developmental delay disorders, reading disorder or retardation. Serious impairment in the development of reading or spelling skills. May include speech, language, right-left identification, and motor problems or psychosocial factors without general intellectual disabilities or with adequate schooling.

developmental delay disorders, specific. Non-neurologic disorder demonstrated by specific delay in development not explained by general intellectual disabilities or inadequate schooling that may be related to biological maturation.

developmental delay disorders, speech or language disorder. Serious impairment or delay in the development of speech or language (syntax or semantic) with frequent articular defect of consonant sound that is not explicable in terms of general intellectual disabilities.

diagnosis. Determination or confirmation of a condition, disease, or syndrome and its implications.

Diagnostic and Statistical Manual of Mental Disorders, Fourth Edition, Text Revision (DSM-IV-TR). Manual used by mental health care providers to assist in determining the diagnosis and treatment of mental health disorders including, but not limited to, substance abuse, depression, and schizophrenia.

dipsomania. Chronic, progressive state of dependence upon alcohol that is both psychological and physical with periodic or continuous episodes impairing health and the ability to function emotionally, socially, and occupationally.

disorganized schizophrenia. Solitary, disorganized schizophrenic state with prominent affective changes, delusions, hallucinations, and fleeting, fragmented, irresponsible, or unpredictable behavior that is manifested by purposeless giggling or self-satisfied, self-absorbed smiling, or by a lofty manner, grimaces, mannerisms, pranks, hypochondriacal complaints, and reiterated phrases.

dissociative hysteria. Restriction of the field of consciousness or disturbance of motor or sensory function resulting in symbolic or psychological advantage, primarily selective amnesia. May be manifested by change of personality or wandering.

downcoding. Reporting a lower-level code for a service so that an additional code may be used rather than using one higher-level and more comprehensive code.

drug abuse. Individual, for whom no other diagnosis is possible, has come under medical care because of the maladaptive effect of a drug on which he is not dependent (see Drug dependence) and that he has taken on his own initiative to the detriment of his health or social functioning.

drug dependence. Psychic and physical dependence, resulting from taking a drug, characterized by behavioral and other responses that always include a compulsion to take a drug on a continuous or periodic basis to experience its psychic effects, and sometimes to avoid the discomfort of its absence.

drug intoxication, pathological. Individual idiosyncratic reactions to comparatively small quantities of a drug, which take the form of acute, brief psychotic states of any type.

drug psychoses. Organic mental syndromes that are due to consumption of drugs (notably amphetamines, barbiturates, and opiate and LSD groups) and solvents.

drug withdrawal syndrome. States associated with drug withdrawal ranging from severe, as specified for alcohol withdrawal delirium (delirium tremens), to less severe states characterized by one or more symptoms such as convulsions, tremor, anxiety, restlessness, gastrointestinal and muscular complaints, and mild disorientation and memory disturbance.

drug-induced hallucinosis. Hallucinatory states with auditory hallucinations, anxiety, or restlessness of more than a few days but not more than a few months' duration, associated with large or prolonged intake of drugs, notably of the amphetamine and LSD groups.

drug-induced organic delusional syndrome. Paranoid states of more than a few days but not more than a few months' duration, associated with large or prolonged intake of drugs, notably of the amphetamine and LSD groups.

drunkenness, acute. Current psychic and physical state resulting from alcohol ingestion, characterized by slurred speech.

drunkenness, pathologic. Physical state resulting from alcohol ingestion, affecting the psychological state, causing slurred speech.

drunkenness, simple. State of inebriation due to alcohol consumption without conspicuous neurological signs of intoxication.

drunkenness, sleep. Inability to fully arouse from the sleep state, characterized by failure to attain full consciousness after arousal due to alcohol consumption.

duplicate coverage inquiry. Request made to insurance companies or medical providers to determine whether there is other medical coverage under another plan.

dyscalculia. Serious impairment in the development of arithmetical skills without obvious intellectual deficit and with adequate schooling.

dyslalia. Delay in the development of normal word-sound production resulting in defects of articulation frequently identified by omissions or substitutions of consonants.

dyslexia. Serious impairment of reading skills such as word blindness and strephosymbolia (letter or word reversal) that is not explicable in terms of general intellectual disabilities or of inadequate schooling.

dysmenorrhea. Painful menstruation that may be primary, or essential, due to prostaglandin production and the onset of menstruation; secondary due to uterine, tubal, or ovarian abnormality or disease; spasmodic arising uterine contractions; or obstructive due to some mechanical blockage or interference with the menstrual flow.

dysmenorrhea, psychogenic. Painful menstruation due to disturbance of psychic control.

dyspareunia. Pain experienced during or after intercourse, commonly occurring in the clitoris, vagina, or labia.

dyspraxia syndrome. Organic disorder affecting patient's ability to perform coordinated acts and not due to psychotic diagnosis.

dyssocial personality. Personality disorder characterized by disregard for social obligations, lack of feeling for others, and impetuous violence or callous unconcern and self-rationalization for behavior.

dysuria, psychogenic. Difficulty in passing urine due to psychic factors.

eating disorder. Conspicuous disturbance in eating behavior such as anorexia, bulimia, pica, and psychogenic rumination.

eccentric personality. Personality disorder characterized by oddities of behavior that do not conform to the clinical syndromes of personality disorders described elsewhere.

elective admission. Admission made at the discretion of the patient and facility based on available resources.

elective mutism. Pervasive and persistent refusal to speak in situations not attributable to a mental disorder, such as withdrawal in a specific stressful situation, shyness, or social withdrawal disorders.

electromechanical equipment. Mechanical devices or systems that are electrically activated, as by a solenoid. May also include the use of computerized equipment for testing or training.

emancipation disorder. Adjustment reaction in adolescents or young adults following recent assumption of independence from parental control or supervision. Manifested by difficulty in making independent decisions, increased dependence on parental advice, and adoption of values deliberately oppositional to parents.

emergency. Serious medical condition or symptom (including severe pain) resulting from injury, sickness, or mental illness that arises suddenly and requires immediate care and treatment, generally received within 24 hours of onset, to avoid jeopardy to the life, limb, or health of a covered person.

emergency admission. Admission in which the patient requires immediate medical or psychiatric attention because of life-threatening, severe, and potentially disabling conditions.

emotional disturbances specific to childhood and adolescence. Less well-differentiated, long-term emotional disorders characteristic of the childhood period not caused by stressors; can take the form of academic underachievement disorder, elective mutism, identity disorder, introverted disorder of childhood, misery and unhappiness disorder, oppositional disorder, overanxious disorder, and shyness disorder of childhood.

employee assistance program (EAP). Services designed to help employees, their family members, and employers find solutions for workplace and personal problems that affect morale, productivity, or financial issues, such as workplace stress, family/marital concerns, legal or financial problems, elder care, child care, substance abuse, emotional/stress issues, and other daily living concerns.

encopresis. Fecal incontinence from inability to control bowel movements.

encounter. Direct personal contact between a patient and a physician, or other person who is authorized by state licensure law and, if applicable, by hospital staff bylaws, to order or furnish hospital services for diagnosis or treatment of the patient.

endogenous depression. Manic-depressive psychosis in which there is a widespread depressed mood of gloom and wretchedness with some degree of anxiety, reduced activity, or restlessness and agitation. There is a marked tendency to recurrence; in a few cases this may be at regular intervals.

enuresis. Urinary incontinence, without specification as to type.

epileptic confusional or twilight state. Short-lived organic, psychotic states, caused by an epileptic episode, lasting hours or days, characterized by clouded consciousness, disorientation, fear, illusions, delusions, hallucinations of any kind, notably visual and tactile, restlessness, tremor, and sometimes fever.

evaluation. Dynamic process in which the physical, occupational, sports, or other therapist makes clinical judgments based on data gathered during the examination.

excitation catatonic. Psychomotor disturbances often alternating between extremes such as hyperkinesis or excitement and stupor or automatic obedience and negativism. May be accompanied by depression, hypomania, or submission to physical constraints.

excitation psychogenic. Psychological factors usually provoked by emotional stress, causing affective psychosis, with symptoms similar to manic-depressive psychosis, manic type.

excitation reactive. Affective psychosis, usually a response to emotional stress with symptoms similar to manic-depressive psychosis, manic type.

exhaustion delirium. Acute transient disorders of any severity and nature of emotions, consciousness, and psychomotor states (singly or in combination) that occur in individuals, without any apparent pre-existing mental disorder, in response to exceptional physical or mental stress, such as natural catastrophe or battle. The symptoms usually subside within hours or days.

exhibitionism. Sexual deviation in which the main sexual pleasure and gratification is derived from exposure of the genitals to a person of the opposite sex.

explosive personality disorder. Instability of mood with uncontrollable outbursts of anger, hate, violence, or affection demonstrated by words or actions.

face to face. Interaction between two parties, usually provider and patient, that occurs in the physical presence of each other.

factitious illness. Hysterical neurosis in which there are physical or psychological symptoms that are not real, genuine, or natural, which are produced by the individual and are under his or her voluntary control.

factitious illness, physical symptom type. Presentation of physical symptoms that may be total fabrication, self-inflicted, an exaggeration or exacerbation of a pre-existing physical condition, or any combination or variation of these.

factitious illness, psychological symptom type. Voluntary production of symptoms suggestive of a mental disorder with behavior that may mimic psychosis or the individual's idea of psychosis.

fanatic personality. Excessive self-reference and sensitiveness to setbacks or to what are taken to be humiliations and rebuffs, a tendency to distort experience by misconstruing the neutral or friendly actions of others as hostile or contemptuous, and a combative and tenacious sense of personal rights that may be manifested as jealousy or excessive self-importance, excessive sensitivity, or aggression.

fatigue neurosis. Neurotic disorder characterized by fatigue, irritability, headache, depression, insomnia, difficulty in concentration, and lack of capacity for enjoyment (anhedonia).

fee for service. Payment for services, usually physician services, on a service-by-service basis rather than an alternative payment system like capitation. Fee-for-service arrangements may be discounted or undiscounted rates.

fee schedule. List of codes and related services with pre-established billing amounts by a provider, or payment amounts by a payer that could be percentages of billed charges, flat rates, or maximum allowable amounts established by third-party payers. Medicare fee schedules apply to clinical laboratory, radiology, and durable medical equipment services.

feeble-minded. Individuals with an IQ of 50-70 who can develop social and communication skills, have minimal retardation in sensorimotor areas, and often are not distinguished from normal children until a later age and can learn academic skills up to approximately the sixth-grade level. As adults they can usually achieve social and vocational skills adequate for minimum self-support but may need guidance and assistance when under social or economic stress. This is also known as a high grade defect.

fetishism. Sexual deviation in which nonliving objects are utilized as a preferred or exclusive method of stimulating erotic arousal.

finger-flicking. One of a number of voluntary repetitive stereotypical movements that are not due to any psychiatric or neurological condition, manifested by head banging, head nodding and nystagmus, rocking, twirling, finger-flicking mannerisms, and eye poking. Finger-flicking is common in cases of intellectual disability with sensory impairment or with environmental monotony.

fiscal intermediary. Federally designated contractor that processes Medicare claims for Part A benefits and some Part B claims.

focused medical review. Process of targeting and directing medical review efforts on Medicare claims where the greatest risk of inappropriate program payment exists. The goal is to reduce the number of noncovered claims or unnecessary services. CMS analyzes national data such as internal billing, utilization, and payment data and provides its findings to the FI. Local medical review policies are developed identifying aberrances, abuse, and overutilized services. Providers are responsible for knowing national Medicare coverage and billing guidelines and local medical review policies, and for determining whether the services provided to Medicare beneficiaries are covered by Medicare.

Folie a deux. Mainly delusional psychosis, usually chronic and often without florid features, that appears to have developed as a result of a close, if not dependent, relationship with another person who already has an established similar psychosis.

fourth and fifth digits. Digits used in the ICD-9-CM coding system to provide more specific information about the diagnosis or procedure being coded. Certain ICD-9-CM codes require a fourth and fifth digit in order to be complete.

fraud. Intentional deception, misrepresentation, or a statement that is known to be false that could result in an unauthorized benefit to the patient, provider, or other persons.

fraud alert. CMS and the OIG periodically issue fraud alert statements that identify activities felt to pose legal and enforcement risks and urge incorporation of this information into existing compliance plans where appropriate.

frigidity. Psychosexual dysfunction in which there is partial or complete failure to attain or maintain the lubrication-swelling response of sexual excitement until completion of the sexual act.

frontal lobe syndrome. Changes in behavior following damage to the frontal areas of the brain. including reduction in self-control, foresight, creativity, spontaneity, emotional vivaciousness, and empathy.

fugue, psychogenic. Form of dissociative hysteria characterized by an episode of wandering with inability to recall one's prior identIty. Both onset and recovery are rapid. Following recovery, there is no recollection of the events that took place during the fugue state.

function. Special, normal, or proper action of any part or organ, including activities identified by an individual as essential to supporting physical and psychological well-being, as well as to creating a personal sense of meaningful living.

functional activities. Activities that are goal directed and task specific.

gambling, pathological. Disorder of impulse control characterized by a chronic and progressive preoccupation with gambling and urge to gamble, with subsequent gambling behavior that compromises, disrupts, or damages personal, family, and vocational pursuits.

Ganser's syndrome. Psychotic-like condition, but without symptoms and signs of a traditional psychosis. Occurring in prisoners who feign insanity or who suffer head injury.

gatekeeper. Primary care physician in a health care system in which a member's care must be provided by a primary care physician unless the physician refers the member to a specialist or approves the care provided by a specialist.

geographic practice cost indexes (GPCI). Cost indexes used to adjust for differences among geographic areas. Under the resource-based relative value scale, there are three GPCIs for each locality, one for work, practice expense, and malpractice.

Gilles de la Tourette syndrome. Familial neuropsychiatric disorder of variable expression that is characterized by multiple recurrent involuntary tics involving body movements (e.g., eye blinks, grimaces, or knee bends) and vocalizations (e.g., grunts, snorts, or utterance of inappropriate words). This syndrome often has one or more associated behavioral or psychiatric conditions (e.g., attention deficit disorder or obsessive-compulsive behavior) and is more common in males than females. It usually has an onset in childhood and often stabilizes or ameliorates in adulthood.

grief reaction. Short-term depressive symptoms following a life event or stressor.

gross stress reaction. Acute transient disorders of any severity and nature of emotions, consciousness, and psychomotor states (singly or in combination) that occur in individuals, without any apparent pre-existing mental disorder, in response to exceptional physical or mental stress such as natural catastrophe or battle. The symptoms usually subside within hours or days.

group delinquency. Acquisition of values or behavior of a peer group to which an individual is loyal and with whom the person characteristically steals, is truant, stays out late at night, is sexually promiscuous, or engages in other socially delinquent practices.

habit spasm. Tic disorder limited to three or less that starts in childhood and persists into adult life and rarely has a verbal component.

hangover. State of inebriation due to alcohol consumption without conspicuous neurological signs of intoxication.

HCPCS. Healthcare Common Procedure Coding System.

HCPCS Level I. Healthcare Common Procedure Coding System Level I. Numeric coding system used by physicians, facility outpatient departments, and ambulatory surgery centers (ASC) to code ambulatory, laboratory, radiology, and other diagnostic services for Medicare billing. This coding system contains only the American Medical Association's Physicians' Current Procedural Terminology (CPT) codes. The AMA updates codes annually.

HCPCS Level II. Healthcare Common Procedure Coding System Level II. National coding system, developed by CMS, that contains alphanumeric codes for physician and nonphysician services not included in the CPT coding system. HCPCS Level II covers such things as ambulance services, durable medical equipment, and orthotic and prosthetic devices.

HCPCS modifiers. Two-character code (AA-ZZ) that identifies circumstances that alter or enhance the description of a service or supply. They are recognized by carriers nationally and are updated annually by CMS.

health care provider. Entity that administers diagnostic and therapeutic services.

Health Insurance Portability and Accountability Act of 1996 (HIPAA). Federal law that allows persons to qualify immediately for comparable health insurance coverage when they change employment relationships. Title II, subtitle F, of HIPAA gives the Department of Health and Human Services the authority to mandate the use of standards for the electronic exchange of health care data; to specify what medical and administrative code sets should be used within those standards; to require the use of national identification systems for health care patients, providers, payers (or plans), and employers (or sponsors); and to specify the types of measures required to protect the security and privacy of personally identifiable health care information.

health maintenance organization (HMO). Medical health insurance coverage that pays claims based on provider cost, per diem, or charge basis. Hospitals contract with an HMO to provide care at a contractually reduced price. HMO members pay a set monthly amount for coverage and are treated without additional cost, except for a copayment or deductible amount. Like all managed care organizations, HMOs use a variety of mechanisms to control costs, including utilization management, discounted provider fee schedules, and financial incentives. HMOs use primary care physicians as gatekeepers and emphasize preventive care.

hebephrenia. Solitary, disorganized schizophrenic state with prominent affective changes, delusions, hallucinations, and fleeting, fragmented, irresponsible, or unpredictable behavior manifested by purposeless giggling or self-satisfied, self-absorbed smiling, or by a lofty manner, grimaces, mannerisms, pranks, hypochondriacal complaints, and reiterated phrases.

Heller's syndrome. Dementia in which a child becomes mute with irritability, tantrums, and other behavioral disorders.

high-grade defect. Individuals with an IQ of 50-70 who can develop social and communication skills, have minimal retardation in sensorimotor areas, and often are not distinguished from normal children until a later age and can learn academic skills up to approximately the sixth-grade level. As adults they can usually achieve social and vocational skills adequate for minimum self-support but may need guidance and assistance when under social or economic stress.

homosexuality. Exclusive or predominant sexual attraction for persons of the same sex with or without physical relationships.

hospital addiction syndrome. Psychosomatic behavior with physical symptoms exhibited by some patients with histrionic personality disorder.

hospital hoboes. Chronic form of factitious illness in which the individual demonstrates a plausible presentation of voluntarily produced physical symptomatology of such a degree that he or she is able to obtain and sustain multiple hospitalizations or courses of treatment.

hospitalism. Mild or transient adjustment reaction characterized by withdrawal seen in hospitalized patients. May be manifested by elective mutism in young children.

hyperkinetic syndrome of childhood, attention deficit disorder. Hyperkinetic syndrome with short attention span, distractibility, and overactivity without significant disturbance of conduct or delay in specific skills.

hyperkinetic syndrome of childhood, hyperkinesis with developmental delay. Hyperkinetic syndrome associated with speech delay, clumsiness, reading difficulties, or other delays of specific skills.

hyperkinetic syndrome of childhood, hyperkinetic conduct disorder. Hyperkinetic syndrome associated with marked conduct disturbance but not developmental delay.

hyperkinetic syndrome of childhood, hypersomnia. Hyperkinetic syndrome associated with difficulty in initiating arousal from sleep or maintaining wakefulness.

hyperkinetic syndrome of childhood, persistent. Chronic difficulty in initiating arousal from sleep or maintaining wakefulness associated with major or minor depressive mental disorders.

hyperkinetic syndrome of childhood, transient. Episodes of difficulty in arousing from sleep or maintaining wakefulness associated with acute or intermittent emotional reactions or conflicts.

hyperkinetic syndromes of childhood. Disorders of short attention span and distractibility with impulsiveness, mood fluctuations, and aggression. In early childhood, characterized by disinhibited, poorly organized, and poorly regulated extreme overactivity; in adolescence, characterized by underactivity.

hypersomnia. Disorder identified by the need for excessive sleep.

hypochondriasis. Excessive concern with one's health in general or the integrity and functioning of some part of one's body or, less frequently, one's mind. Usually associated with anxiety and depression.

hypomania. Manic-depressive psychosis, circular type, in which the manic form is currently present.

hypomanic personality. Affective personality disorder characterized by lifelong predominance of a chronic, nonpsychotic disturbance involving either intermittent or sustained periods of abnormally elevated mood (unshakable optimism and an enhanced zest for life and activity).

hyposomnia. Disorder of initiating or maintaining sleep.

hysteria. Restrictions of the field of consciousness or disturbances of motor or sensory function that result in psychological advantage or have symbolic value. This is more commonly known as conversion disorder or dissociative disorder.

hysteria anxiety. Neurotic states with abnormally intense dread of certain objects or specific situations that would not normally affect the patient.

hysteria psychosis. Psychotic condition that is largely or entirely attributable to a recent life experience.

hysteria psychosis, acute. Affective psychosis with symptoms similar to manic-depressive psychosis, manic type, but apparently provoked by emotional stress.

hysterical personality. Personality disorder characterized by shallow, labile affectivity, dependence on others, craving for appreciation and attention, suggestibility, and theatricality. There may be sexual immaturity and, under stress, hysterical symptoms (neurosis) may develop.

ICD-10-CM. International Classification of Diseases, 10th Revision, Clinical Modification. Clinical modification of the alphanumeric classification of diseases used by the World Health Organization, already in use in much of the world, and used for mortality reporting in the United States. The implementation date for ICD-10-CM diagnostic coding system to replace ICD-9-CM in the United States is October 1, 2015.

identity disorder. Emotional disorder caused by distress over the inability to reconcile aspects of the self into a relatively coherent and acceptable sense of self, not secondary to another mental disorder. May be manifested by intense subjective distress regarding uncertainty about various issues relating to identity, including long-term goals, career choice, friendship patterns, values, and loyalties.

idiosyncratic alcohol intoxication. Acute psychotic episodes induced by relatively small amounts of alcohol. These are regarded as individual idiosyncratic reactions to alcohol, not due to excessive consumption and without conspicuous neurological signs of intoxication.

impairment. Loss or abnormality of anatomical, physiological, mental, or psychological structure or function. Secondary impairment originates from other, preexisting impairments.

impotence. Psychosexual or organic dysfunction in which there is partial or complete failure to attain or maintain erection until completion of the sexual act.

impulse control disorder. Great internal tension resulting from an impulse, drive, or temptation to perform some action that is harmful to the individual or to others. The action may provide short-term pleasure, gratification, or release but may be followed by regret, self-reproach, or guilt; can take the form of intermittent explosive disorder, isolated explosive disorder, kleptomania, pathological gambling, and pyromania.

inadequate personality. Personality disorder characterized by passive compliance with the wishes of elders and others and a weak, inadequate response to the demands of daily life. The individual may be intellectual or emotional with little capacity for enjoyment.

independent medical evaluation. Examination carried out by an impartial health care provider, generally board certified, to resolve a dispute related to the nature and extent of an illness or injury.

induced paranoid disorder. Mainly delusional psychosis, usually chronic and often without florid features, that appears to have developed as a result of a close, if not dependent, relationship with another person who already has an established similar psychosis.

inebriety. State of inebriation due to alcohol consumption without conspicuous neurological signs of intoxication.

infantile autism. Syndrome beginning in the first 30 months affecting interaction with others, characterized by abnormal response to auditory and visual stimuli accompanied by difficulty understanding spoken language and limiting the ability to communicate or develop social skills.

insight-oriented psychotherapy. Development of insight or affective understanding and the use of behavior modification techniques, supportive interactions, cognitive discussion of reality, or any combination of the above to provide therapeutic change.

insomnia. Inability to sleep.

intellectual disability. Condition of impaired cognitive functioning that is characterized by below average intelligence, whether congenital or acquired, and includes deficits in two or more adaptive behaviors or capabilities of conceptual skills (communication, time, money, academic), social skills (interpersonal, community), and practical skills (daily living, self-care, work).

intellectual disability, mild. Individuals with an IQ of 50-55 to 70 who can develop social and communication skills, have minimal delay in sensorimotor areas, and often are not identified until a later age and can learn academic skills up to approximately the sixth-grade level. As adults they can usually achieve social and vocational skills adequate for minimal self-support but may need guidance and assistance when under social or economic stress.

intellectual disability, moderate. Individuals with an IQ of 35-40 to 50-55 who have communication limitations and fair motor development. They have poor social awareness and are unlikely to progress beyond the second-grade level in academic subjects. As adults, they may achieve self-maintenance by performing unskilled or semi-skilled work under sheltered conditions with supervision and guidance when under mild social or economic stress.

intellectual disability, profound. Individuals with an IQ of less than 20-25 who have minimal capacity for sensorimotor functioning and need nursing care during the preschool period. They may develop some further motor skills and they may respond to minimal or limited training in self-help. During the adult years, some motor and speech development may occur, and they may achieve very limited self-care and require nursing care.

intellectual disability, severe. Individuals with an IQ of 20-25 to 35-40. They have poor motor development, minimal speech, and are generally unable to profit from training and self-help during the preschool period. They can talk or learn to communicate, can be trained in elementary health habits, and may profit from systematic habit training. During the adult years they may contribute partially to self-maintenance under complete supervision.

interactive psychotherapy. Use of physical aids and nonverbal communication to overcome barriers to therapeutic interaction between a clinician and a patient who has not yet developed or has lost either the expressive language communication skills to explain his/her symptoms and response to treatment, or the receptive communication skills to understand the clinician if he or she were to use ordinary adult language for communication.

intermittent explosive disorder. Recurrent, uncontrollable episodes of sudden and significant loss of control of aggressive impulses that cannot be accounted for by any other mental disorder and that are disproportionate to any psychosocial stressors and result in assault or property destruction followed by genuine regret or self-reproach.

introverted disorder of childhood. Emotional disturbance in children chiefly manifested by a lack of interest in social relationships and indifference to social praise or criticism.

introverted personality. Profound defect in the ability to form social relationships and to respond to the usual forms of social reinforcements, often referred to as loners who do not appear distressed by their social distance and are not interested in greater social involvement.

involutional melancholia. Manic-depressive psychosis in which there is a widespread depressed mood of gloom and wretchedness with some degree of anxiety, reduced activity, or restlessness and agitation. There is a marked tendency to recurrence; in a few cases this may be at regular intervals.

involutional paranoid state. Paranoid psychosis in which there are conspicuous hallucinations, often in several modalities. May be associated with mild affective symptoms and well-preserved personality.

isolated explosive disorder. Disorder of impulse control in which there is a single discrete episode characterized by failure to resist an impulse that leads to a single, violent, externally directed act that has a catastrophic impact on others and for which the available information does not justify the diagnosis of another mental disorder.

isolated phobia. Fear of a discrete object or situation, such as animals, heights, or small spaces, that is neither fear of leaving the familiar setting of the home (agoraphobia) or of being observed by others in certain situations (social phobia).

jet lag syndrome. Imbalance of a normal sleep pattern rhythm resulting from airplane travel through a number of time zones. Leads to fatigue, irritability, and other constitutional disturbances.

Joint Commission on Accreditation of Healthcare Organizations. Organization that accredits health care organizations. In the future, the JCAHO may play a role in certifying these organizations' compliance with the HIPAA A/S requirements. Previously known as the Joint Commission for the Accreditation of Hospitals.

Kanner's syndrome. Developmental disorder connected with neurophysiological factors, manifesting in early childhood with definitively impaired communication and social interaction marked by the inability to reciprocate in play, recognize other's feelings or existence, mimic or imitate, or seek comfort. Unusual activities and interests may be present, restricting others, as well as severe behavioral problems.

Korsakoff's psychosis alcoholic. Syndrome of prominent and lasting reduction of memory span, including striking loss of recent memory, disordered time appreciation, and confabulation, occurring in alcoholics as the sequel to an acute alcoholic psychosis or, more rarely, in the course of chronic alcoholism. It is usually accompanied by peripheral neuritis and may be associated with Wernicke's encephalopathy.

Korsakoff's psychosis nonalcoholic. Syndrome of prominent and lasting reduction of memory span, including striking loss of recent memory, disordered time appreciation, and confabulation frequently caused by substance abuse and malnutrition. An amnestic syndrome may be present in early states of presenile and senile dementia, arteriosclerotic dementia, and in encephalitis and other inflammatory and degenerative diseases and certain temporal lobe tumors.

latent schizophrenia. Eccentric or inconsequent behavior and anomalies of affect that give the impression of schizophrenia though no definite and characteristic schizophrenic anomalies, present or past, have been manifested.

LCSW. Licensed clinical social worker.

leave of absence days. Days during which a patient is discharged from the hospital temporarily. A patient may be placed on a leave of absence when readmission is expected for follow-up care or surgery and the patient does not require a hospital level of care during the interim period. Examples include situations in which surgery could not be scheduled immediately, a specific surgical team was not available, or further treatment is indicated following diagnostic tests but cannot begin immediately. Only one bill is prepared for a leave of absence, and one DRG payment is made.

lesbianism. Exclusive or predominant sexual attraction between women with or without physical relationship.

level of specificity. Diagnosis coding specificity (i.e., a three-digit disease code is assigned only when there are no four-digit codes within that category, a four-digit code is assigned only when there is no fifth-digit subclassification within that category, or a fifth digit is assigned for any category for which a fifth-digit subclassification is provided).

limitation of liability. Signed waiver a provider must obtain from the patient before performing a service that appears on a list of services Medicare classifies as medically unnecessary. The waiver notifies the patient in advance that the service may be denied coverage and that the patient is responsible for payment.

linking codes. To establish medical necessity, CPT and HCPCS Level II codes must be supported by the ICD-9-CM diagnosis and injury codes submitted on the claim form and supported by the documentation.

lobotomy syndrome. Changes in behavior following damage to the frontal areas of the brain resulting in general diminution of self-control, concentration, memory, intellect, foresight, creativity, and spontaneity, which may be manifested as increased irritability, selfishness, restlessness, slowness, dullness, loss of drive, and lack of concern for others. A considerable degree of recovery is possible and may continue over the course of several years.

local medical review policy. Carrier-specific policy applied in the absence of a national coverage policy to make local Medicare coverage decisions, including the development of a draft policy based on a review of medical literature, an understanding of local practice, and the solicitation of comments from the medical community and Carrier Advisory Committee.

LSD reaction. Acute intoxication from lysergic acid diethylamide abuse, manifested by hallucinatory states lasting a few days or less.

major depressive disorder. Manic-depressive psychosis in which there is a widespread depressed mood of gloom and wretchedness with some degree of anxiety, reduced activity, or restlessness and agitation. There is a marked tendency to recurrence; in a few cases this may be at regular intervals.

malingering. Feigning of illness, as the result of intentional deceit or as the result of mental illness.

mania. Manic-depressive psychosis characterized by states of elation or excitement out of keeping with the individual's circumstances and varying from enhanced liveliness (hypomania) to violent, almost uncontrollable, excitement. Aggression and anger, flight of ideas, distractibility, impaired judgment, and grandiose ideas are common.

manic disorder atypical. Manic-depressive psychosis characterized by states of elation or excitement out of keeping with the individual's circumstances and varying from enhanced liveliness (hypomania) to violent, almost uncontrollable, excitement. Aggression and anger, flight of ideas, distractibility, impaired judgment, and grandiose ideas are common.

manic-depressive psychosis. One of the affective psychotic states, including circular, manic, mixed, or atypical.

manic-depressive psychosis, depressed type. Manic-depressive psychosis in which there is a widespread depressed mood of gloom and wretchedness with some degree of anxiety, reduced activity, or restlessness and agitation. There is a marked tendency to recurrence; in a few cases this may be at regular intervals.

manic-depressive psychosis, manic type. Manic-depressive psychosis characterized by states of elation or excitement out of keeping with the individual's circumstances and varying from enhanced liveliness (hypomania) to violent, almost uncontrollable, excitement. Aggression and anger, flight of ideas, distractibility, impaired judgment, and grandiose ideas are common.

manic-depressive psychosis, mixed type. Manic-depressive psychosis syndrome corresponding to both the manic and depressed types that cannot be classified more specifically.

masochistic personality. Personality disorder in which the individual appears to arrange life situations so as to be defeated and humiliated.

Medicaid. Joint federal and state program that covers medical expenses for people with low incomes and limited resources who meet the criteria. The benefits for recipients vary from state to state.

medical necessity. Medically appropriate and necessary to meet basic health needs; consistent with the diagnosis or condition and national medical practice guidelines regarding type, frequency, and duration of treatment; rendered in a cost-effective manner.

medical review. Review by a Medicare administrative contractor, carrier, and/or quality improvement organization (QIO) of services and items provided by physicians, other health care practitioners, and providers of health care services under Medicare. The review determines if the items and services are reasonable and necessary and meet Medicare coverage requirements, whether the quality meets professionally recognized standards of health care, and whether the services are medically appropriate in an inpatient, outpatient, or other setting as supported by documentation.

Medicare. Federally funded program authorized as part of the Social Security Act that provides for health care services for people age 65 or older, people with disabilities, and people with end-stage renal disease (ESRD).

Medicare Carriers Manual. Manual the Centers for Medicare and Medicaid Services provides to Medicare carriers containing instructions for processing and paying Medicare claims, preparing reimbursement forms, billing procedures, and adhering to Medicare regulations. This has been replaced by the Medicare manual system.

Medicare fee schedule. Fee schedule based upon physician work, expense, and malpractice designed to slow the rise in cost for services and standardize payment to physicians regardless of specialty or location of service with geographic adjustments.

Medigap. Individual health insurance offered by a private entity to those persons entitled to Medicare benefits and is specifically designed to supplement Medicare benefits. It fills in some of the gaps in Medicare coverage by providing payment for some of the charges, deductibles, coinsurance amounts, or other limitations imposed by Medicare.

melancholia. Severe disturbance of mood or emotion that adversely affects the thinking process and that may be accompanied by delusions or hallucinations.

melancholia involutional. Manic-depressive psychosis in which there is a widespread depressed mood of gloom and wretchedness with some degree of anxiety, reduced activity, or restlessness and agitation. There is a marked tendency to recurrence; in a few cases this may be at regular intervals.

mental retardation, mild. Individuals with an IQ of 50 to 70 who can develop social and communication skills, have minimal retardation in sensorimotor areas, and often are not distinguished from normal children until a later age and can learn academic skills up to approximately the sixth-grade level. As adults they can usually achieve social and vocational skills adequate for minimal self-support but may need guidance and assistance when under social or economic stress.

mental retardation, moderate. Individuals with an IQ of 35 to 49 who can talk or learn to communicate and have fair motor development. They have poor social awareness and are unlikely to progress beyond the second-grade level in academic subjects. As adults, they may achieve self-maintenance by performing unskilled or semi-skilled work under sheltered conditions with supervision and guidance when under mild social or economic stress.

mental retardation, profound. Individuals with an IQ of less than 20 who have minimal capacity for sensorimotor functioning and need nursing care during the preschool period. They may develop some further motor skills, and they may respond to minimal or limited training in self-help. During the adult years some motor and speech development may occur, and they may achieve very limited self-care and need nursing care.

mental retardation, severe. Individuals with an IQ of 20 to 34. They have poor motor development, minimal speech, and are generally unable to profit from training and self-help during the preschool period. They can talk or learn to communicate, can be trained in elementary health habits, and may profit from systematic habit training. During the adult years they may contribute partially to self-maintenance under complete supervision.

merycism. Regurgitation of food, without nausea, retching, or disgust followed by ejection or chewing with reswallowing. Frequently seen with failure to thrive or weight loss developing after a period of normal functioning. This condition may afflict any age group, but it is particularly found in the mentally retarded population.

minimal brain dysfunction. Disorders of short attention span and distractibility with impulsiveness, mood fluctuations, and aggression. In early childhood, characterized by uninhibited, poorly organized, and poorly regulated extreme overactivity; in adolescence, characterized by underactivity.

misery and unhappiness disorder. Emotional disorder characteristic of childhood in which the main symptoms involve misery and unhappiness and may include eating and sleep disturbances.

mood swings. Mild disorders of mood (depression and anxiety or elation and excitement, alternating or occurring episodically) seen in affective psychosis.

motor tic disorders. Disorders of no known organic origin with quick, involuntary, apparently purposeless, and frequently repeated movements of the face or other body part that are not due to any neurological condition. May be manifested singly or simultaneously, alternately, or consecutively.

motor-verbal tic disorder. Rare disorder occurring in individuals of any level of intelligence in which facial tics and tic-like throat noises become more marked and more generalized. Later, whole words or short sentences (often with obscene content) are cried out spasmodically and involuntarily.

multi-infarct dementia or psychosis. Dementia attributable, because of physical signs (confirmed by examination of the central nervous system), to degenerative arterial disease of the brain.

multiple operations syndrome. Chronic form of factitious illness in which the individual demonstrates a plausible presentation of voluntarily produced physical symptomatology of such a degree that he or she is able to obtain and sustain multiple hospitalizations or courses of treatment.

multiple personality. Domination of the individual at any one time by one of two or more distinct, fully integrated, and complex personalities with memories, behavior patterns, and social friendships, that determine the nature of the individual's acts when uppermost in consciousness.

Munchausen syndrome. Emotional condition in which patient exhibits physical, but psychosomatic, symptoms.

mysophobia. Abnormal, intense fear of dirt or germs.

narcissistic personality. Marked by an inflated sense of self-worth and indifference to the welfare of others. Achievement deficits and failure at meeting social responsibilities are justified and sustained by a boastful arrogance, expansive fantasies, facile rationalization, and frank prevarication.

National Center for Health Statistics. Division of the Centers for Disease Control and Prevention that compiles statistical information used to guide actions and policies to improve the public health of U.S. citizens. The NCHS maintains the ICD-10-CM coding system.

national coverage policy. Statement of Medicare coverage decisions that applies to all practitioners in states and regions. These policies indicate whether and under what circumstances procedures, services, and supplies are covered.

nebulizer. Latin for mist, a device that converts liquid into a fine spray and is commonly used to deliver medicine to the upper respiratory, bronchial, and lung areas.

nervous debility. Neurotic disorder characterized by fatigue, irritability, headache, depression, insomnia, difficulty in concentration, and lack of capacity for enjoyment (anhedonia).

neurasthenia. Mental disorder brought about by stress or anxiety. Manifestations are varied and may include weakness, exhaustion, chest pain, gastrointestinal complaints, palpitations, tachycardia, abnormal sensation of the hands and feet, hyperventilation, vertigo, syncope, or abnormal perspiration.

neurosis. Mental disorder without any demonstrable organic basis in which the individual may have considerable insight and has unimpaired reality testing, in that he or she usually does not confuse his morbid subjective experiences and fantasies with external reality and usually remains within socially acceptable limits. Manifestations include excessive anxiety, hysterical symptoms, phobias, obsessional and compulsive symptoms, and depression.

neurotic delinquency. Emotional disturbance demonstrated by anxiety, misery, or obsessive manifestations resulting in undersocialized or socially disturbed conduct.

neurotic disorders. Mental disorders without any demonstrable organic basis in which the individual may have considerable insight and has unimpaired reality testing, in that he or she usually does not confuse his morbid subjective experiences and fantasies with external reality and usually remains within socially acceptable limits. Manifestations include excessive anxiety, hysterical symptoms, phobias, obsessional and compulsive symptoms, and depression.

neurotic disorders, anxiety states. Anxiety with physical and mental manifestations, not attributable to real danger and occurring diffusely, in attacks or as a persisting state.

neurotic disorders, compensation neurosis. Certain unconscious neurotic reactions focusing on secondary gain, such as a situational or financial advantage.

neurotic disorders, depersonalization. Awareness of the disturbed perception of external objects or parts of one's own body as unreal, remote, automatized, or changed in their quality.

neurotic disorders, hysteria. Restriction of the field of consciousness or disturbances of motor or sensory function that result in psychological advantage or symbolic value. There are three subtypes of neurotic mental disorders, including conversion type, dissociative type, and factitious illness. Conversion type: Psychogenic disturbance of function in some part of the body, e.g., paralysis, tremor, blindness, deafness, seizures. Dissociative type: Elective amnesia, changes of personality (multiple personality), or sometimes a wandering state (fugue). Factitious illness: Physical or psychological symptoms that are not real, genuine, or natural that are produced by the individual and are under his voluntary control.

neurotic disorders, hysteria conversion type. Restriction of the field of consciousness or disturbance of motor or sensory function resulting in symbolic or psychological advantage, primarily of a body part as manifested by paralysis, tremor, blindness, deafness, and seizures.

neurotic disorders, hysteria dissociative type. Restriction of the field of consciousness or disturbance of motor or sensory function resulting in symbolic or psychological advantage, primarily of a body part as manifested by selective amnesia, changes of personality, or a wandering state (fugue).

neurotic disorders, hysteria factitious illness. Restriction of the field of consciousness or disturbance of motor or sensory function resulting in symbolic or psychological advantage, primarily of a body part as manifested by physical or psychological symptoms that are not real, genuine, or natural, that are produced by the individual and are under his voluntary control.

neurotic disorders, neurasthenia. Neurotic disorder characterized by fatigue, irritability, headache, depression, insomnia, difficulty in concentration, and lack of capacity for enjoyment (anhedonia).

neurotic disorders, obsessive-compulsive. Feeling of subjective compulsion to carry out an action, dwell on an idea, recall an experience, ruminate on an abstract topic, or perform a quasi-ritual that may result in anxiety or inner struggle as the individual tries to cope with the behavior.

neurotic disorders, with depression. Disproportionate depression with behavior disturbance that is usually the result of a distressing experience and may include delusions or hallucinations, anxiety, and preoccupation with the psychic trauma that preceded the illness.

neurotic disorders, with phobia. Neurotic states with abnormally intense dread of certain objects or specific situations that would not normally affect the patient.

neurotic disorders, with somatization. Chronic, but fluctuating, neurotic disorder that begins early in life and is characterized by recurrent and multiple somatic complaints for which medical attention is sought but that are not apparently due to any physical illness.

new patient. Patient who is receiving face-to-face care from a provider/qualified health care professional or another physician/qualified health care professional of the exact same specialty and subspecialty who belongs to the same group practice for the first time in three years. For OPPS hospitals, a patient who has not been registered as an inpatient or outpatient, including off-campus provider based clinic or emergency department, within the past three years.

night terrors. Pathology of arousal from stage 4 sleep in which the individual experiences excessive terror and extreme panic (screaming, verbalizations), symptoms of autonomic activity, confusion, and poor recall of event.

nightmare. Intense, terrifying dream that most commonly occurs during REM sleep at the end of the night or in the early morning hours. Underlying causes may be physiological, such as a high fever, or psychological, such as stress or trauma.

nymphomania. Female individual with abnormal and excessive need or desire for sexual intercourse.

objectives. Measurable behavioral statements of expected behavior or outcome.

observation. Perception of events.

observation patient. Patient who needs to be monitored and assessed for inpatient admission or referral to another site for care

obsessional personality. Feelings of personal insecurity, excessive doubt, and incompleteness leading to excessive conscientiousness, stubbornness, perfectionism, meticulous accuracy, and caution with persistent checking in an individual who may also have intrusive thoughts or impulses.

obsessional phobia. Subjective compulsion to carry out an action, dwell on an idea, recall an experience, ruminate on an abstract topic, or perform a quasi-ritual that may result in anxiety or inner struggle as the individual tries to cope with the behavior.

occupational neurosis. Functional disorder of a group of muscles used chiefly in one's occupation, marked by the occurrence of spasm, paresis, or lack of coordination on attempt to repeat certain habitual movements (e.g., writer's cramp).

off-site. Place other than the provider's usual place of practice.

Office of Inspector General. Agency within the Department of Health and Human Services that is ultimately responsible for investigating instances of fraud and abuse in the Medicare and Medicaid and other government health care programs.

on-site. Regular place of practice of the provider; his or her primary clinic or department location.

oneirophrenia. Schizophrenic disorder with ideas of reference and emotional turmoil where external things, people, and events may become charged with personal significance for the patient; characterized by a dream-like state with slight clouding of consciousness and perplexity although.

oppositional disorder of childhood or adolescence. Pervasive opposition to all in authority as demonstrated by continuous argumentativeness and an unwillingness to respond to reasonable persuasion in an individual without conduct disorder, adjustment disorder, or a psychosis of childhood.

organic affective syndrome. Patient may exhibit a number of changes in personality such as amotivation, depression, outbursts and poor social judgment.

organic personality syndrome. Persistent personality disturbance of nonpsychotic origin featuring affective instability, bursts of aggression, apathy and indifference, impaired social judgment, and suspiciousness or paranoid ideation.

organic psychosyndrome focal. Nonpsychotic organic mental disorder resembling postconcussion syndrome associated with localized diseases of the brain or surrounding tissues.

organic psychotic conditions. Impairment of orientation, memory, comprehension, calculation, learning capacity, and judgment that may include shallowness or liability of affect, or a more persistent disturbance of mood, lowering of ethical standards, exaggeration or emergence of personality traits, and diminished capacity for independent decision making.

organic psychotic conditions, mixed paranoid and affective. Organic psychosis in which depressive and paranoid symptoms are the main features.

organic psychotic conditions, transient. Generally reversible states characterized by clouded consciousness, confusion, disorientation, illusions, and often vivid hallucinations usually due to some intra- or extracerebral toxic, infectious, metabolic, or other systemic disturbance.

organic psychotic conditions, transient, acute delirium. Short-lived states, lasting hours or days, of transient organic psychotic conditions.

organic psychotic conditions, transient, subacute delirium. States of transient organic psychotic conditions in which the symptoms, usually less florid than in the acute form, last for several weeks or longer with marked fluctuations in intensity.

organic reaction. Generally reversible states characterized by clouded consciousness, confusion, disorientation, illusions, and often vivid hallucinations usually due to some intra- or extracerebral toxic, infectious, metabolic, or other systemic disturbance.

out of area. Medical care received out of the geographic area that may or may not be covered depending on the plan.

out of plan. In health care contracting, services of a provider who is not a member of the preferred provider network.

outcome measures. Standards assessing the quality of patient care by measuring the change in a patient's performance following health services.

outcomes. Condition, behavior, or attributes of a patient at the end of therapy or of a disease process, including the degree of wellness and the need for continuing care, medication, support, counseling, or education.

outlier. Case classified to a specific MS-DRG but with exceptionally high costs compared with other cases classified to the same MS-DRG. The fiscal intermediary or MAC makes a payment in addition to the original MS-DRG amount for these situations. A cost outlier is paid an amount in excess of the cut-off threshold for a given MS-DRG. The day outlier no longer applies.

overanxious disorder. Ill-defined emotional disorder of childhood involving anxiety and fearfulness.

panic disorder. Episodic and often chronic, recurrent disorder manifested by discrete periods of sudden onset, intense apprehension, fearfulness, or terror often associated with feelings of impending doom.

panphobia. Abnormal, intense fear of everything.

paranoia. Rare chronic psychosis in which logically constructed systematized delusions of grandeur, persecution, or somatic abnormality have developed gradually without concomitant hallucinations or the schizophrenic type of disordered thinking.

paranoia, alcoholic. Chronic paranoid psychosis associated with alcoholism.

paranoia, querulans. Paranoid state that may present as schizophrenic or affective state symptoms is different from other paranoid states and psychogenic paranoid psychosis.

paranoia, senile. Paranoid psychosis in which there are conspicuous hallucinations, often in several modalities. May be associated with mild affective symptoms and well-preserved personality.

paranoid personality. Excessive self-reference and sensitiveness to setbacks or to what are taken to be humiliations and rebuffs, a tendency to distort experience by misconstruing the neutral or friendly actions of others as hostile or contemptuous, and a combative and tenacious sense of personal rights that may be manifested as jealousy or excessive self-importance, excessive sensitivity, or aggression.

paranoid reaction. Paranoid states apparently provoked by some emotional stress such as imprisonment, immigration, or strange and threatening environments. Frequently manifested as an attack or threat.

paranoid schizophrenia. Pronounced affective manic or depressive features intermingled with schizophrenic features that tend toward remission without permanent defect but that are prone to recur.

paranoid state, involutional. Paranoid psychosis in which there are conspicuous hallucinations, often in several modalities. May be associated with mild affective symptoms and well-preserved personality.

paranoid state, senile. Paranoid psychosis in which there are conspicuous hallucinations, often in several modalities. May be associated with mild affective symptoms and well-preserved personality.

paranoid state, simple. Psychosis, acute or chronic, with fixed, elaborate, and systemized delusions, especially of being influenced, persecuted, or treated in some special way, that is not attributable to schizophrenia or affective psychosis.

paranoid traits. Excessive self-reference and sensitiveness to setbacks or to what are taken to be humiliations and rebuffs, a tendency to distort experience by misconstruing the neutral or friendly actions of others as hostile or contemptuous, and a combative and tenacious sense of personal rights that may be manifested as jealousy or excessive self-importance, excessive sensitivity, or aggression.

paraphilia. Abnormal sexual inclinations or behavior directed primarily either toward people not of the opposite sex, or toward sexual acts not associated with coitus normally, or toward coitus performed under abnormal circumstances; can take the form of exhibitionism, fetishism, homosexuality, nymphomania, pedophilia, satyriasis, sexual masochism, sexual sadism, transvestism, voyeurism, and zoophilia.

paraphrenia. Paranoid psychosis in which there are conspicuous hallucinations, often in several modalities. May be associated with mild affective symptoms and well-preserved personality.

participating provider. Provider who has contracted with the health plan to deliver medical services to covered persons.

passive personality. Passive compliance with the wishes of elders and others and a weak inadequate response to the demands of daily life. The person may be intellectual or emotional with little capacity for enjoyment.

passive-aggressive personality. Aggressive behavior manifested in passive ways, such as obstructionism, pouting, procrastination, intentional inefficiency, or stubbornness often arising from resentment at failing to find gratification in a relationship with an individual or institution upon which the individual is over dependent.

pathological personality. Deeply ingrained maladaptive patterns of behavior generally recognizable by adolescence or earlier and continuing throughout most of adult life, although often becoming less obvious in middle or old age. The personality is abnormal either in the balance of its components, quality, and expression, or in its total aspect.

patient problem. Disease, condition, illness, injury, symptom, sign, finding, complaint, or other reason for an encounter, with or without a diagnosis being established at the time of the encounter.

pedophilia. Sexual deviations in which an adult engages in sexual activity with a child of the same or opposite sex.

peer review. Evaluation of the quality of the total health care provided by medical staff with equivalent training, such as a physician-to-physician or nurse-to-nurse evaluation.

peregrinating patient. Someone who fakes or grossly exaggerates a physical or psychiatric illness, apparently under voluntary control, to avoid work, military service, or prosecution, or to obtain financial gain or drugs. The behavior is recognizable and understandable in light of the individual's circumstances.

personality disorder, affective type. Chronic, intermittent personality disorder without clear onset that is characterized by lifelong predominance of a pronounced mood.

personality disorder, anancastic type. Feelings of personal insecurity, excessive doubt, and incompleteness leading to excessive conscientiousness, stubbornness, perfectionism, meticulous accuracy, and caution with persistent checking in an individual who may also have intrusive thoughts or impulses.

personality disorder, antisocial type. Disregard for social obligations, lack of feeling for others, and impetuous violence or callous unconcern and self-rationalization of behavior.

personality disorder, asthenic type. Passive compliance with the wishes of elders and others and a weak inadequate response to the demands of daily life. The individual may be intellectual or emotional with little capacity for enjoyment.

personality disorder, avoidant type. Excessive social inhibitions and shyness, a tendency to withdraw from opportunities for developing close relationships, and a fearful expectation that the individual will be belittled and humiliated.

personality disorder, borderline type. Instability in behavior, mood, self-image, and interpersonal relationships that are intense, unstable, and may shift dramatically. Manifested by impulsive and unpredictable behavior or expressions of boredom, emptiness, or fear of being alone.

personality disorder, chronic depressive type. Affective personality disorder characterized by lifelong predominance of a chronic, nonpsychotic disturbance involving either intermittent or sustained periods of depressed mood manifested by worry, pessimism, low output of energy, and a sense of futility.

personality disorder, chronic hypomanic type. Affective personality disorder characterized by lifelong predominance of a chronic, nonpsychotic disturbance involving either intermittent or sustained periods of abnormally elevated mood (unshakable optimism and an enhanced zest for life and activity).

personality disorder, compulsive type. Feelings of personal insecurity, excessive doubt, and incompleteness leading to excessive conscientiousness, stubbornness, perfectionism, meticulous accuracy, and caution with persistent checking in an individual who may also have intrusive thoughts or impulses.

personality disorder, cyclothymic type. Chronic nonpsychotic disturbance involving depressed and elevated mood, lasting at least two years, separated by periods of normal mood.

personality disorder, dependent type. Passive compliance with the wishes of elders and others and a weak, inadequate response to the demands of daily life. The individual may be intellectual or emotional with little capacity for enjoyment.

personality disorder, eccentric type. Oddities of behavior that do not conform to the clinical syndromes of personality disorders described elsewhere.

personality disorder, explosive type. Instability of mood with uncontrollable outbursts of anger, hate, violence, or affection demonstrated by words or actions.

personality disorder, histrionic type. Shallow, labile affectivity, dependence on others, craving for appreciation and attention, suggestibility, and theatricality. There may be sexual immaturity and, under stress, hysterical symptoms (neurosis) may develop.

personality disorder, hysterical type. Shallow, labile affectivity, dependence on others, craving for appreciation and attention, suggestibility, and theatricality. There may be sexual immaturity and, under stress, hysterical symptoms (neurosis) may develop.

personality disorder, inadequate type. Personality disorder characterized by passive compliance with the wishes of elders and others and a weak, inadequate response to the demands of daily life and may be intellectual or emotional with little capacity for enjoyment.

personality disorder, introverted type. Profound defect in the ability to form social relationships and to respond to the usual forms of social reinforcements often referred to as loners who do not appear distressed by their social distance and are not interested in greater social involvement.

personality disorder, masochistic type. Personality disorder in which the individual appears to arrange life situations so as to be defeated and humiliated.

personality disorder, narcissistic type. Interpersonal difficulties caused by an inflated sense of self-worth and indifference to the welfare of others wherein achievement deficits and social lack of responsibility are justified and sustained by a boastful arrogance, expansive fantasies, facile rationalization, and frank prevarication.

personality disorder, paranoid type. Excessive self-reference and sensitiveness to setbacks or to what are taken to be humiliations and rebuffs, a tendency to distort experience by misconstruing the neutral or friendly actions of others as hostile or contemptuous, and a combative and tenacious sense of personal rights that may be manifested as jealousy or excessive self-importance, excessive sensitivity, or aggression.

personality disorder, passive type. Passive compliance with the wishes of elders and others and a weak inadequate response to the demands of daily life and may be intellectual or emotional with little capacity for enjoyment.

personality disorder, passive-aggressive type. Aggressive behavior manifested in passive ways, such as obstructionism, pouting, procrastination, intentional inefficiency, or stubbornness often arising from resentment at failing to find gratification in a relationship with an individual or institution upon which the individual is over dependent.

personality disorder, schizoid type. Withdrawal from social and other contacts with autistic preference for detachment, fantasy, and introspective reserve that may include slightly eccentric behavior or avoidance of competitive situations.

personality disorder, schizotypal type. Schizoid personality disorder manifested by various oddities of thinking, perception, communication, and behavior that may be manifested as magical thinking, ideas of reference, or paranoid ideation, recurrent illusions, and derealization (depersonalization), or social isolation.

personality disorders. Deeply ingrained maladaptive patterns of behavior generally recognizable by adolescence or earlier and continuing throughout most of adult life, although often becoming less obvious in middle or old age. The personality is abnormal either in the balance of its components, quality, and expression, or in its total aspect.

phobia. Broad-range anxiety with abnormally intense dread of certain objects or specific situations that would not normally have that effect.

phobia, isolated. Broad-range anxiety with abnormally intense dread of certain objects or specific situations that would not normally have that effect.

phobia, obsessional. Subjective compulsion to carry out an action, dwell on an idea, recall an experience, ruminate on an abstract topic, or perform a quasi-ritual that may result in anxiety or inner struggle as the individual tries to cope with the behavior.

phobia, simple. Fear of a discrete object or situation, such as animals, heights, or small spaces, that is neither fear of leaving the familiar setting of the home (agoraphobia) nor of being observed by others in certain situations (social phobia).

phobia, social. Fear of social situations such as public speaking, blushing, eating in public, writing in front of others, using public lavatories, or being in situations under the possible scrutiny by others with fear of acting in a fashion that will be considered shameful.

pica. Compulsive eating of nonnutritive substances that are not food, such as dirt or gravel, flaking paint, or plaster. This is seen most often in children in the second year and usually remits in childhood, but it is also seen in developmentally disabled persons, people with zinc or iron deficiencies, and pregnant women.

plan of treatment. Written documentation of the type of therapy services (e.g., physical, occupational, speech-language pathology, cardiac rehabilitation) to be provided to a patient and of the amount, frequency, and duration (in days, weeks, months) of the services to be provided. An active treatment plan must identify the diagnosis, the anticipated goals of the treatment, the date the plan was established, and the type of modality or procedure to be used.

point of service plan. Health benefit plan allowing the covered person to choose to receive a service from a participating or nonparticipating provider, with different benefit levels associated with the use of participating providers.

postconcussion syndrome. States occurring after generalized contusion of the brain that may resemble frontal lobe syndrome or neurotic disorders, and may include headache, giddiness, fatigue,

insomnia, mood fluctuation, and a subjective feeling of impaired intellectual function with extreme reaction to normal stressors.

postcontusion syndrome or encephalopathy. States occurring after generalized contusion of the brain that may resemble frontal lobe syndrome or neurotic disorders, and may include headache, giddiness, fatigue, insomnia, mood fluctuation, and a subjective feeling of impaired intellectual function with extreme reaction to normal stressors.

postencephalitic syndrome. Nonpsychotic organic mental disorder resembling the postconcussion syndrome associated with central nervous system infections.

postleucotomy syndrome. Changes in behavior following damage to the frontal areas of the brain resulting in general diminution of self-control, concentration, memory, intellect, foresight, creativity, and spontaneity, which may be manifested as increased irritability, selfishness, restlessness, slowness, dullness, loss of drive, and lack of concern for others.

posttraumatic brain syndrome, nonpsychotic. States occurring after generalized contusion of the brain that may resemble frontal lobe syndrome or neurotic disorders that may include headache, giddiness, fatigue, insomnia, mood fluctuation, and a subjective feeling of impaired intellectual function with extreme reaction to normal stressors.

posttraumatic organic psychosis. Generally reversible states characterized by clouded consciousness, confusion, disorientation, illusions, and often vivid hallucinations usually due to some intra- or extracerebral toxic, infectious, metabolic, or other systemic disturbance.

posttraumatic stress disorder. Development of characteristic symptoms (re-experiencing the traumatic event, numbing of responsiveness to or involvement with the external world, and a variety of other autonomic, dysphoric, or cognitive symptoms) after experiencing a psychologically traumatic event or events outside the normal range of human experience (e.g., rape or assault, military combat, natural catastrophes such as flood or earthquake, or other disasters, such as an airplane crash, fires, or bombings).

posttraumatic stress disorder, acute. Brief, episodic, or recurrent disorders lasting less than six months after the onset of trauma.

posttraumatic stress disorder, prolonged. Brief, episodic, or recurrent disorders lasting six months or more following the trauma.

PPO. Preferred provider organization. Program that establishes contracts with providers of medical care. Usually the benefit contract provides significantly better benefits and lower member cost for services received from preferred providers, encouraging covered persons to use these providers, who may be reimbursed on a discounted basis.

precertification. Confirmation that a payer covers a given procedure for a given patient, including admission or continued stay.

preexisting condition. Symptom that causes a person to seek diagnosis, care, or treatment for which medical advice or treatment was recommended or received by a physician within a certain time period before the effective date of medical insurance coverage. The preexisting condition waiting period is the time the beneficiary must wait after buying health insurance before coverage begins for a condition that existed before coverage was obtained.

preferred provider organization. Program that establishes contracts with providers of medical care. Usually the benefit contract provides significantly better benefits and lower member cost for services received from preferred providers, encouraging covered persons to use these providers, who may be reimbursed on a discounted basis.

premature ejaculation. Ejaculation that occurs before the individual wishes it, because of recurrent and persistent absence of reasonable voluntary control of ejaculation and orgasm during sexual activity.

presbyophrenia. Psychotic, chronic, mild states of memory disturbance and intellectual deterioration accompanied by increased irritability, querulousness, lassitude, and complaints of physical weakness associated with old age and brain damage classifiable as organic, senile, or presenile dementia, delirium, delusions, hallucinosis, and depression.

presenile dementia. Dementia occurring usually before the age of 65 in patients with the relatively rare forms of diffuse or lobar cerebral atrophy usually caused by an associated neurological condition.

principal diagnosis. Condition established after study to be chiefly responsible for occasioning the admission of the patient to the hospital for care.

principal procedure. Procedure performed for definitive treatment rather than for diagnostic or exploratory purposes, or that was necessary to treat a complication. Usually related to the principal diagnosis.

psychalgia. Pains of mental origin, such as headache or backache, for which a more precise medical or psychiatric diagnosis cannot be made.

psychasthenia. Somatoform disorder, the term used by the French psychiatrist Pierre Janet, to describe all psychoneuroses not classified as hysteria.

psychic factors associated with physical diseases. Mild mental disturbances or psychic factors of any type thought to have played a major part in the etiology of physical conditions that usually involve tissue damage but that may include asthma, dermatitis, eczema, duodenal ulcer, ulcerative colitis, and urticaria. Describes conditions not classifiable elsewhere.

psychic shock. Sudden disturbance of mental equilibrium produced by strong emotional response to physical or mental stress.

psycho-organic syndrome. Generally reversible states characterized by clouded consciousness, confusion, disorientation, illusions, and often vivid hallucinations usually due to some intra- or extracerebral toxic, infectious, metabolic, or other systemic disturbance and are generally reversible.

psychoneurosis. Mental disorders without any demonstrable organic basis in which the individual may have considerable insight and has unimpaired reality testing, in that he or she usually does not confuse his morbid subjective experiences and fantasies with external reality and usually remains within socially acceptable limits. Manifestations include excessive anxiety, hysterical symptoms, phobias, obsessional and compulsive symptoms, and depression.

psychopathic constitutional state. Deeply ingrained maladaptive patterns of behavior generally recognizable by adolescence or earlier and continuing throughout most of adult life, although often becoming less obvious in middle or old age. The personality is abnormal either in the balance of its components, quality, and expression, or in its total aspect.

psychopathic personality. Deeply ingrained maladaptive patterns of behavior generally recognizable by adolescence or earlier and continuing throughout most of adult life, although often becoming less obvious in middle or old age. The personality is abnormal either in the balance of its components, quality, and expression, or in its total aspect.

psychophysiological disorders. Various physical symptoms or types of physiological malfunctions of mental origin, usually manifested in the autonomic nervous system.

psychosexual dysfunctions. Recurrent and persistent dysfunction encountered during sexual activity that may be lifelong or acquired, generalized or situational, and total or partial.

psychosexual dysfunctions, functional dyspareunia. Recurrent and persistent genital pain associated with coitus.

psychosexual dysfunctions, functional vaginismus. Recurrent and persistent involuntary spasm of the musculature of the outer one-third of the vagina that interferes with sexual activity.

psychosexual dysfunctions, gender identity disorder. Preferring to be of the other sex and strongly preferring the clothes, toys, activities, and companionship of the other sex. May include cross-dressing in children or adults.

psychosexual dysfunctions, inhibited female orgasm. Recurrent and persistent inhibition of the female orgasm as manifested by a delay or absence of orgasm following a normal sexual excitement phase during sexual activity.

psychosexual dysfunctions, inhibited male orgasm. Recurrent and persistent inhibition of the male orgasm as manifested by a delay or absence of either the emission or ejaculation phases or, more usually, both, following an adequate phase of sexual excitement.

psychosexual dysfunctions, inhibited sexual desire. Persistent inhibition of desire for engaging in a particular form of sexual activity.

psychosexual dysfunctions, inhibited sexual excitement. Recurrent and persistent inhibition of sexual excitement during sexual activity, manifested either by partial or complete failure to attain or maintain erection until completion of the sexual act (impotence), or partial or complete failure to attain or maintain the lubrication-swelling response of sexual excitement until completion of the sexual act (frigidity).

psychosexual dysfunctions, premature ejaculation. Ejaculation that occurs before the individual wishes it, because of recurrent and persistent absence of reasonable voluntary control of ejaculation and orgasm during sexual activity.

psychosexual dysfunctions, psychosexual gender identity disorders. Behavior occurring in preadolescents of immature psychosexuality, or in adults, in which there is incongruity between the individual's anatomic sex and gender identity.

psychosexual dysfunctions, transsexualism. Fixed belief that the overt anatomical sex is wrong, resulting in behavior that is directed toward either changing the sexual organs by operation or completely concealing the anatomical sex by adopting both the dress and behavior of the opposite sex.

psychosis. Impairment of mental function that has progressed to a degree that interferes grossly with insight, ability to meet some ordinary demands of life, or to maintain adequate contact with reality.

psychosis, acute. Affective psychosis with symptoms similar to manic-depressive psychosis, manic type, but apparently provoked by emotional stress.

psychosis, affective. Severe disturbance of mood or emotion that adversely affects the thinking process. May be accompanied by delusions or hallucinations.

psychosis, alcoholic. Organic psychotic states due mainly to excessive consumption of alcohol that may be exacerbated by nutritional defects.

psychosis, atypical childhood. Atypical infantile psychosis manifested by stereotyped repetitive movements, hyperkinesis, self-injury, retarded speech development, echolalia, or impaired social relationships that is particularly common in those with mental retardation and is not as severe as infantile autism.

psychosis, borderline, of childhood. Atypical infantile psychosis manifested by stereotyped repetitive movements, hyperkinesis, self-injury, retarded speech development, echolalia, or impaired social relationships that is particularly common in those with mental retardation but not as severe as infantile autism.

psychosis, child. Group of disorders in children, characterized by distortions in the timing, rate, and sequence of many psychological functions involving language development and social relations in which the severe qualitative abnormalities are not normal for any stage of development.

psychosis, depressive. Manic-depressive psychosis in which there is a widespread depressed mood of gloom and wretchedness with some degree of anxiety, reduced activity, or restlessness and agitation. There is a marked tendency to recurrence; in a few cases this may be at regular intervals.

psychosis, depressive type. Depressive psychosis with severe behavioral disturbance, apparently provoked by saddening stress such as a bereavement or a severe disappointment or frustration. The delusions are more often understandable in the context of the life experiences.

psychosis, disintegrative. Congenital or acquired condition in which normal or near-normal development for the first few years is followed by the rapid loss of social skills and of speech, together with a severe disorder of emotions, behavior, overactivity, repetitive motion, and relationship problems.

psychosis, epileptic. Organic psychotic condition associated with epilepsy.

psychosis, excitative type. Affective psychosis with symptoms similar to manic-depressive psychosis, manic type, but apparently provoked by emotional stress.

psychosis, hypomanic. States of elation or excitement out of keeping with the individual's circumstances and varying from enhanced liveliness (hypomania) to violent, almost uncontrollable, excitement. Aggression and anger, flight of ideas, distractibility, impaired judgment, and grandiose ideas are common.

psychosis, hysterical. Psychotic condition that is largely or entirely attributable to a recent life experience.

psychosis, induced. Mainly delusional psychosis, usually chronic and often without florid features, that appears to have developed as a result of a close, if not dependent, relationship with another person who already has an established similar psychosis.

psychosis, infantile. Syndrome beginning in the first 30 months of life affecting interaction with others, characterized by abnormal response to auditory and visual stimuli accompanied by difficulty understanding spoken language and limiting the ability to communicate or develop social skills.

psychosis, infective. Generally reversible states characterized by clouded consciousness, confusion, disorientation, illusions, and often vivid hallucinations usually due to some intra- or extracerebral toxic, infectious, metabolic, or other systemic disturbance.

psychosis, Korsakoff's, alcoholic. Syndrome of prominent and lasting reduction of memory span, including striking loss of recent memory, disordered time appreciation, and confabulation, occurring in alcoholics as the sequel to an acute alcoholic psychosis or, more rarely, in the course of chronic alcoholism. It is usually accompanied by peripheral neuritis and may be associated with Wernicke's encephalopathy.

psychosis, Korsakoff's, nonalcoholic. Syndrome of prominent and lasting reduction of memory span, including striking loss of recent memory, disordered time appreciation, and confabulation frequently caused by substance abuse and malnutrition. An amnestic syndrome may be present in early states of presenile and senile dementia, arteriosclerotic dementia, and in encephalitis and other inflammatory and degenerative diseases and certain temporal lobe tumors.

psychosis, manic-depressive. Severe disturbance of mood or emotion that adversely affects the thinking process and that may be accompanied by delusions or hallucinations.

psychosis, multi-infarct. Dementia attributable, because of physical signs (confirmed by examination of the central nervous system), to degenerative arterial disease of the brain.

psychosis, paranoid chronic. Rare chronic psychosis in which logically constructed systematized delusions of grandeur, persecution, or somatic abnormality have developed gradually without concomitant hallucinations or the schizophrenic type of disordered thinking.

psychosis, paranoid protracted reactive. Paranoid psychosis of any type that is triggered by some event and that is more protracted than a paranoid reaction.

psychosis, paranoid psychogenic, acute. Paranoid states apparently provoked by some emotional stress such as imprisonment, immigration, or strange and threatening environments. Frequently manifested as an attack or threat.

psychosis, postpartum. Any psychosis occurring within a fixed period (approximately 90 days) after childbirth.

psychosis, psychogenic, depressive. Depressive psychosis with severe behavioral disturbance, apparently provoked by saddening stress such as a bereavement or a severe disappointment or frustration. The delusions are more often understandable in the context of life experiences.

psychosis, puerperal. Psychosis occurring within a fixed period (approximately 90 days) after childbirth.

psychosis, reactive, brief. Florid psychosis of at least a few hours' duration but lasting no more than two weeks, with sudden onset immediately following a severe environmental stress and eventually terminating in complete recovery to the pre-psychotic state.

psychosis, reactive, confusion. Mental disorders with clouded consciousness, mild to moderate disorientation, and diminished accessibility often accompanied by excessive activity and apparently provoked by emotional stress.

psychosis, reactive, depressive. Depressive psychosis with severe behavioral disturbance, apparently provoked by saddening stress such as a bereavement or a severe disappointment or frustration. The delusions are more often understandable in the context of life experiences.

psychosis, schizo-affective. Pronounced affective manic or depressive features are intermingled with schizophrenic features that tend toward remission without permanent defect but that are prone to recur.

psychosis, schizophreniform. Fundamental disturbance of personality and characteristic distortion of thinking, often a sense of being controlled by alien forces, delusions, disturbed perception, abnormal affect out of keeping with the real situation, and auditory or visual hallucinations with fear that intimate thoughts, feelings, and acts are known by others although clear consciousness and intellectual capacity are usually maintained.

psychosis, schizophreniform, affective type. Pronounced affective manic or depressive features intermingled with schizophrenic features that tend toward remission without permanent defect but that are prone to recur.

psychosis, schizophreniform, confusional type. Schizophrenic disorder with ideas of reference and emotional turmoil where external things, people, and events may become charged with personal significance for the patient. Characterized by a dream-like state with slight clouding of consciousness and perplexity. External things, people, and events may become charged with personal significance for the patient.

psychosis, senile. Progressive type of senile dementia characterized by development in advanced old age, with delusions, varying from simple, poorly formed paranoid delusions to highly formed paranoid delusional states, and hallucinations.

psychosomatic disorders. Variety of physical symptoms or types of physiological malfunctions of mental origin, usually manifested in the autonomic nervous system.

psychotherapy. Treatment for mental illness and behavioral disturbances in which the clinician establishes a professional contract with the patient and, through definitive therapeutic communication, attempts to alleviate the emotional disturbances, reverse or change maladaptive patterns of behavior, and encourage personality growth and development.

pyromania. Recurrent failure to resist impulses to set fires without regard for the consequences, or with deliberate destructive intent and an intense fascination with the setting of fires, seeing fires burn, and a satisfaction with the resultant destruction.

qui tam actions. Legal action against an individual or entity believed to be involved in fraud against the government. Under the False Claims Act, any individual who has such knowledge can file a lawsuit in his or her own name and in the name of the United States government. An

employee usually brings these types of lawsuits for actions he or she believes constitute fraud or abuse on the part of the employer.

referral. Approval from the primary care physician to see a specialist or receive certain services. May be required for coverage purposes before a patient receives care from anyone except the primary physician.

registered health information administrator (RHIA). Accreditation for medical record administrators, previously known as a registered records administrator (RRA), through AHIMA.

registered health information technician (RHIT). Accreditation for medical records practitioners, previously known as accredited records technician (ART), through AHIMA.

relationship problems of childhood. Emotional disorders characteristic of childhood that involve a state of affairs existing between two parties' problems and issues.

release of information. Authorization from the patient that allows the hospital to release to the insurer or other payer the medical and billing information for determining coverage eligibility, medical necessity, the final diagnosis, and any procedures performed or as needed to process a claim for reimbursement.

repeated infarct dementia. Dementia attributable, because of physical signs (confirmed by examination of the central nervous system), to degenerative arterial disease of the brain.

Restzustand (schizophrenia). Continued disturbance of personality with flat affect, odd beliefs or perceptions, and speech poverty without delusions, without hallucinations, and without disorganized speech or behavior and a history of schizophrenia. Emotional response is blunted, but this thought disorder does not prevent the accomplishment of routine work.

rumination obsessional. Constant preoccupation with certain thoughts, with the inability to dismiss them from the mind; also known as neurotic disorder, obsessive-compulsive.

rumination psychogenic. Regurgitation of food, without nausea, retching, or disgust followed by ejection or chewing with reswallowing. Frequently seen with failure to thrive or weight loss developing after a period of normal functioning. This condition may afflict any age group, but it is particularly found in the mentally retarded population,

RVS. Relative value study. Guide that shows the relationship between the time, resources, competency, experience, severity, and other factors necessary to perform procedures that is multiplied by a dollar conversion factor to determine a monetary value for the procedure.

RVU. Relative value unit. Value assigned a procedure based on difficulty and time consumed. Used for computing reimbursement under a relative value study.

safe harbor. Protected business arrangement that might otherwise constitute a violation of the antikickback statute, such as those deemed to promote competition, improve quality of care, or confer a cost savings.

sanction. Imposition of penalties or exclusion of a provider for fraud or infractions such as an inappropriate use of services, providing procedures that may harm the patient, or applying inferior techniques.

Sander's disease. Rare, chronic psychosis in which logically constructed systematized delusions of grandeur or persecution, or somatic abnormality have developed gradually without concomitant hallucinations or the schizophrenic type of disordered thinking.

Satyriasis. Pathologic or exaggerated sexual desire or excitement in males.

schizoid personality disorder. Withdrawal from social and other contacts with autistic preference for detachment, fantasy, and introspective reserve that may include slightly eccentric behavior or avoidance of competitive situations.

schizophrenia. Fundamental disturbance of personality and characteristic distortion of thinking, often a sense of being controlled by alien forces, delusions, disturbed perception, abnormal affect out of keeping with the real situation, and auditory or visual hallucinations with fear that intimate thoughts, feelings, and acts are known by others although clear consciousness and intellectual capacity are usually maintained.

schizophrenia, acute episode. Schizophrenic disorder with ideas of reference and emotional turmoil where external things, people, and events may become charged with personal significance for the patient. Characterized by a dreamlike state with slight clouding of consciousness and perplexity. External things, people, and events may become charged with personal significance for the patient.

schizophrenia, atypical. Schizophrenia of florid nature that cannot be classified as simple, catatonic, hebephrenic, paranoid, or any other type.

schizophrenia, borderline. Eccentric or inconsequent behavior and anomalies of affect that give the impression of schizophrenia though no definite and characteristic schizophrenic anomalies, present or past, have been manifested.

schizophrenia, catatonic type. Psychomotor disturbances often alternating between extremes such as hyperkinesis or excitement and stupor or automatic obedience and negativism. May be accompanied by depression, hypomania, or submission to physical constraints.

schizophrenia, cenesthopathic. Schizophrenia of florid nature that cannot be classified as simple, catatonic, hebephrenic, paranoid, or any other type.

schizophrenia, childhood type. Group of disorders in children, characterized by distortions in the timing, rate, and sequence of many psychological functions involving language development and social relations in which the severe qualitative abnormalities are not normal for any stage of development.

schizophrenia, chronic undifferentiated. Continued disturbance of personality with flat affect, odd beliefs or perceptions, and speech poverty without delusions, without hallucinations, and without disorganized speech or behavior and a history of schizophrenia. Emotional response is blunted, but this thought disorder does not prevent the accomplishment of routine work.

schizophrenia, cyclic. Pronounced affective manic or depressive features intermingled with schizophrenic features that tend toward remission without permanent defect but that are prone to recur.

schizophrenia, disorganized type. Solitary, disorganized schizophrenic state with prominent affective changes, delusions, hallucinations, and fleeting, fragmented, irresponsible or unpredictable behavior that is manifested by purposeless giggling or self-satisfied, self-absorbed smiling, or by a lofty manner, grimaces,

mannerisms, pranks, hypochondriacal complaints, and reiterated phrases. Also known as hebephrenic schizophrenia.

schizophrenia, hebephrenic type. Solitary, disorganized schizophrenic state with prominent affective changes, delusions, hallucinations, and fleeting, fragmented, irresponsible or unpredictable behavior that is manifested by purposeless giggling or self-satisfied, self-absorbed smiling, or by a lofty manner, grimaces, mannerisms, pranks, hypochondriacal complaints, and reiterated phrases. Also known as disorganized schizophrenia.

schizophrenia, latent. Eccentric or inconsequent behavior and anomalies of affect that give the impression of schizophrenia though no definite and characteristic schizophrenic anomalies, present or past, have been manifested.

schizophrenia, paranoid type. Schizophrenia with relatively stable delusions, which may be accompanied by hallucinations and erratic behavior, disturbed conduct, gross thought disorder, flat affect, and fragmentary delusions of persecution, jealousy, anatomic change, exalted birth, or messianic mission.

schizophrenia, paranoid type, prepsychotic. Eccentric or inconsequent behavior and anomalies of affect that give the impression of schizophrenia though no definite and characteristic schizophrenic anomalies, present or past, have been manifested.

schizophrenia, paranoid type, prodromal. Eccentric or inconsequent behavior and anomalies of affect that give the impression of schizophrenia though no definite and characteristic schizophrenic anomalies, present or past, have been manifested.

schizophrenia, paranoid type, pseudoneurotic. Eccentric or inconsequent behavior and anomalies of affect that give the impression of schizophrenia though no definite and characteristic schizophrenic anomalies, present or past, have been manifested.

schizophrenia, paranoid type, pseudopsychopathic. Eccentric or inconsequent behavior and anomalies of affect that give the impression of schizophrenia though no definite and characteristic schizophrenic anomalies, present or past, have been manifested.

schizophrenia, paranoid type, residual. Continued disturbance of personality with flat affect, odd beliefs or perceptions, and speech poverty without delusions, without hallucinations, and without disorganized speech or behavior and a history of schizophrenia. Emotional response is blunted, but this thought disorder does not prevent the accomplishment of routine work.

schizophrenia, paranoid type, schizoaffective type. Pronounced affective manic or depressive features that are intermingled with schizophrenic features and that tend toward remission without permanent defect but that are prone to recur.

schizophrenia, paranoid type, simple type. Insidious development of oddities of conduct, inability to meet the demands of society, and decline in total performance with increasing social impoverishment, self-absorption, idleness, and aimless.

schizophrenia, paranoid type, simplex. Insidious development of oddities of conduct, inability to meet the demands of society, and decline in total performance with increasing social impoverishment, self-absorption, idleness, and aimless. Also known as simple paranoid schizophrenia type.

schizophrenia, prepsychotic. Eccentric or inconsequent behavior and anomalies of affect that give the impression of schizophrenia though no definite and characteristic schizophrenic anomalies, present or past, have been manifested.

schizophrenia, prodromal. Seldom recognized term to describe a condition of eccentric or inconsequent behavior and anomalies of affect that give the impression of schizophrenia though no definite and characteristic schizophrenic anomalies, present or past, have been manifested.

schizophrenia, pseudoneurotic. Eccentric or inconsequent behavior and anomalies of affect that give the impression of schizophrenia though no definite and characteristic schizophrenic anomalies, present or past, have been manifested.

schizophrenia, residual. Continued disturbance of personality with flat affect, odd beliefs or perceptions, and speech poverty without delusions, without hallucinations, and without disorganized speech or behavior and a history of schizophrenia. Emotional response is blunted, but this thought disorder does not prevent the accomplishment of routine work.

schizophrenia, undifferentiated acute. Schizophrenia of florid nature that cannot be classified as simple, catatonic, hebephrenic, paranoid, or any other types.

schizophrenic syndrome of childhood. Group of disorders in children, characterized by distortions in the timing, rate, and sequence of many psychological functions involving language development and social relations in which the severe qualitative abnormalities are not normal for any stage of development.

schizophreniform attack. Schizophrenic disorder with ideas of reference and emotional turmoil in which external things, people, and events may become charged with personal significance for the patient. Characterized by a dreamlike state with slight clouding of consciousness and perplexity. External things, people, and events may become charged with personal significance for the patient.

schizophreniform disorder. Schizophrenic disorder with ideas of reference and emotional turmoil in which external things, people, and events may become charged with personal significance for the patient. Characterized by a dreamlike state with slight clouding of consciousness and perplexity. External things, people, and events may become charged with personal significance for the patient.

schizophreniform psychosis. Fundamental disturbance of personality, and characteristic distortion of thinking, often a sense of being controlled by alien forces, delusions, disturbed perception, abnormal affect out of keeping with the real situation, and auditory or visual hallucinations with fear that intimate thoughts, feelings, and acts are known by others although clear consciousness and intellectual capacity are usually maintained.

schizophreniform psychosis, affective type. Pronounced affective manic or depressive features that are intermingled with schizophrenic features and that tend toward remission without permanent defect but that are prone to recur.

schizophreniform psychosis, confusional type. Schizophrenic disorder with ideas of reference and emotional turmoil in which external things, people, and events may become charged with personal significance for the patient. Characterized by a dreamlike state with slight clouding of consciousness and perplexity. External things, people, and events may become charged with personal significance for the patient.

schizotypal personality. Schizoid personality disorder manifested by various oddities of thinking, perception, communication, and behavior that may be manifested as magical thinking, ideas of reference, or paranoid ideation, recurrent illusions and derealization (depersonalization), or social isolation.

sensitiver Beziehungswahn. Paranoid state that may present as schizophrenic or affective state symptoms. Different from other paranoid states and psychogenic paranoid psychosis.

sensitivity reaction of childhood or adolescence. Persistent and excessive shrinking from familiarity or contact with all strangers of sufficient severity as to interfere with peer functioning, yet there are warm and satisfying relationships with family members.

separation anxiety disorder. Exaggerated distress, usually of a child, at separation from parents, home, or other familial surroundings with anxiety to the point of panic.

sequencing codes. Codes reported according to ranking guidelines defining severity, time, and skill required to treat the diagnosed condition and cost of the service for procedures.

sexual deviations. Abnormal sexual inclinations or behavior directed primarily toward people not of the opposite sex, sexual acts not associated with coitus normally, or coitus performed under abnormal circumstances; can take the form of exhibitionism, fetishism, homosexuality, nymphomania, pedophilia, satyriasis, sexual masochism, sexual sadism, transvestism, voyeurism, and zoophilia.

sexual masochism. Sexual deviation in which sexual arousal and pleasure are produced in an individual by his own physical or psychological suffering and insistent and persistent fantasies where sexual excitement is produced as a result of suffering.

sexual sadism. Sexual deviation in which actual or fantasized infliction of pain on someone else causes sexual excitement.

shared paranoid disorder. Mainly delusional psychosis, usually chronic and often without florid features, that appears to have developed as a result of a close, if not dependent, relationship with another person who already has an established similar psychosis.

shifting sleep-work schedule. Sleep disorder in which the phase-shift disruption of the 24-hour sleep-wake cycle occurs due to rapid changes in the individual's work schedule.

short sleeper. Individuals who typically need only four to six hours of sleep within the 24-hour cycle.

shyness disorder of childhood. Persistent and excessive shrinking from familiarity or contact with all strangers of sufficient severity as to interfere with peer functioning, yet there are warm and satisfying relationships with family members.

sibling jealousy or rivalry. Emotional disorder related to competition between siblings for the love of a parent or for other recognition or gain.

signature. Physician's signature acknowledges that he/she has performed or supervised the service or procedure and that the transcription has been read and corrections made before signing. Signed or initialed laboratory and x-ray results show auditors that the physician has reviewed the information.

simple phobia. Fear of a discrete object or situation, such as animals, heights, or small spaces, that is neither fear of leaving the familiar setting of the home (agoraphobia) or of being observed by others in certain situations (social phobia).

situational disturbance, acute. Acute transient disorders of any severity and nature of emotions, consciousness, and psychomotor states (singly or in combination) that occur in individuals, without any apparent pre-existing mental disorder, in response to exceptional physical or mental stress, such as natural catastrophe or battle. Usually subside within hours or days.

SOAP. Subjective, objective, assessment, plan. When documenting patients' visits, the SOAP approach has been used historically as it standardizes physician documentation and easily adapts to history, exam, and medical decision-making. The steps are defined as follows: 1) Subjective: The information the patient tells the physician. 2) Objective: The physician's observed, objective overview, including the patient's vital signs and the findings of the physical exam and any diagnostic tests. 3) Assessment: A list the physician prepares in response to the patient's condition, including the problem, diagnoses, and reasons leading the physician to the diagnoses. 4) Plan: The physician's workup or treatment planned for each problem in the assessment.

social phobia. Fear of social situations such as public speaking, blushing, eating in public, writing in front of others, or using public lavatories or being in situations of possible scrutiny by others, with fear of acting in a fashion that will be considered shameful.

social withdrawal of childhood. Emotional disturbance in children chiefly manifested by a lack of interest in social relationships and indifference to social praise or criticism.

socialized conduct disorder. Acquired values or behavior of a peer group that the individual is loyal to and with whom the individual characteristically steals, is truant, stays out late at night, and is sexually promiscuous or engages in other socially delinquent practices.

somatization disorder. Chronic, but fluctuating, neurotic disorder that begins early in life and is characterized by recurrent and multiple somatic complaints for which medical attention is sought but that are not apparently due to any physical illness.

somatoform disorder atypical. Excessive concern with one's health in general or the integrity and functioning of some part of one's body or, less frequently, one's mind. Usually associated with anxiety and depression.

spasmus nutans. Specific type of nystagmus of infancy that usually occurs between the ages of 4 months to 1 year of age. It involves symptoms of fine, rapid jerking of the eyes back and forth (horizontally or vertically), head nodding, and head tilting.

specific academic or work inhibition. Adjustment reaction with a specific academic or work inhibition in an individual whose intellectual capacity, skills, and previous academic or work performance have been at least adequate, and in which the inhibition occurs despite apparent effort and is not due to any other mental disorder.

stammering. Disorders in the rhythm of speech in which the individual knows precisely what he or she wishes to say but at the time is unable to say it because of an involuntary, repetitive prolongation or cessation of a sound.

starch eating disorder. Compulsive eating of nonnutritive substances that are not food, such as dirt or gravel, flaking paint, or plaster. This is seen most often in children in the second year and usually remits in childhood, but it is also seen in developmentally disabled persons, people with zinc or iron deficiencies, and pregnant women.

status postcommotio cerebri. States occurring after generalized contusion of the brain that may resemble frontal lobe syndrome or neurotic disorders. May include headache, giddiness, fatigue, insomnia, mood fluctuation, and a subjective feeling of impaired intellectual function with extreme reaction to normal stressors.

stereotyples. Voluntary repetitive stereotypical movements, which are not due to any psychiatric or neurological condition, manifested by head banging, head nodding and nystagmus, rocking, twirling, finger-flicking mannerisms, and eye poking. Common in cases of intellectual disabilities with sensory impairment or with environmental monotony.

stress reaction, acute. Acute transient disorders of any severity and nature of emotions, consciousness, and psychomotor states (singly or in combination) that occur in individuals, without any apparent pre-existing mental disorder, in response to exceptional physical or mental stress, such as natural catastrophe or battle, and that usually subside within hours or days.

stress reaction, chronic. Abnormal or maladaptive reaction with emotional or behavioral characteristics as a result of a life event or stressor that is usually temporary.

stupor, psychogenic. Psychotic condition that is largely or entirely attributable to a recent life experience.

stuttering. Frequent repetition of words or parts of words that disrupts the smooth flow of speech.

subjective insomnia complaint. Complaint of insomnia made by the individual, which has not been investigated or proven.

supplier. Person or entity that furnishes or provides health care supplies, such as durable medical equipment or medical-surgical supplies.

systematized delusions. Rare, chronic psychosis in which logically constructed systematized delusions of grandeur, persecution, or somatic abnormality have developed gradually without concomitant hallucinations or the schizophrenic type of disordered thinking.

tension headache. Headache of mental origin, such as tension or anxiety, for which a more precise medical or psychiatric diagnosis cannot be made.

therapeutic goal. Patient's expected level of performance, including the amount of independence, supervision, or assistance that will be needed and the equipment or environmental adaptation required, at the completion of the therapeutic course.

tic. Spasmodic contraction or movement, usually of the muscles of the face or extremities.

tic, chronic motor tic disorder. Tic disorder (rapid, jerky movements over which the person it affects seems to have no control. It usually starts in childhood and persists into adult life and rarely has a verbal component.

tic, Gilles de la Tourette's disorder (motor-verbal tic disorder). Rare disorder occurring in individuals of any level of intelligence in which facial tics and tic-like throat noises become more marked and more generalized, and as the disorder progresses, whole words or short sentences (often with obscene content) are cried out spasmodically and involuntarily.

tic, transient tic disorder of childhood. Facial or other tics beginning in childhood but limited to one year in duration.

tobacco use disorder. Cases in which tobacco is used to the detriment of a person's health or social functioning or in which there is tobacco dependence.

TQM. Total quality management. Concept that quality is an organic part of a plan's service and a provider's care and can be quantified and constantly improved.

tranquilizer abuse. Cases in which an individual has taken drugs classified as tranquilizers to the detriment of his health or social functioning, in doses above or for periods beyond those normally regarded as therapeutic.

transient organic psychotic condition. Generally reversible states characterized by clouded consciousness, confusion, disorientation, illusions, and often vivid hallucinations usually due to some intra- or extracerebral toxic, infectious, metabolic, or other systemic disturbance.

transsexualism. Fixed belief that the overt anatomical sex is wrong, resulting in behavior directed toward changing the sexual organs surgically or completely concealing the anatomical sex by adopting both the dress and behavior of the opposite sex.

transvestism. Sexual deviation with recurrent and persistent dressing in clothes of the opposite sex. In the early stage, transvestism is for the purpose of sexual arousal.

treatment planning. Projected series and sequences of procedures necessary to restore the health of the patient, based on a problem or specific diagnosis and a complete evaluation of the patient.

twilight state, confusional. Short-lived organic, psychotic states, lasting hours or days, characterized by clouded consciousness, disorientation, fear, illusions, delusions, hallucinations of any kind, notably visual and tactile, restlessness, tremor, and sometimes fever.

twilight state, psychogenic. Mental disorders with clouded consciousness, mild to moderate disorientation, and diminished accessibility, often accompanied by excessive activity and apparently provoked by emotional stress.

unbundling. Separately packaging costs or services that might otherwise be billed together including billing separately for health care services that should be combined according to the industry standards or commonly accepted coding practices.

underbilled services. Uncoded or undercoded services that are often the result of medical records that lack the detail necessary to code at full reimbursement levels.

undersocialized conduct disorder. Lack of concern for the rights and feelings of others resulting from a failure to establish a normal degree of affection, empathy, or bond with others and may be manifested by self-protection with fear, timidity, whining, demanding behavior, and tantrums, or by exploitation and self-gain with lying and stealing without apparent guilt.

undocumented services. Billed service for which the supporting documentation has not been recorded or is unavailable to substantiate the service.

unsocialized aggressive disorder. Lack of concern for the rights and feelings of others resulting from a failure to establish a normal degree of affection, empathy, or bond with others. May be manifested by self-protection with fear, timidity, whining, demanding behavior, and tantrums, or by exploitation and self-gain with lying and stealing without apparent guilt.

unusual circumstances. Unusual or aberrant conditions affecting a patient encounter that should be documented.

unusual service. Procedure or service that is unusual or unique, or an aberrant finding, result, response, procedure, method, or behavior that affects the patient's treatment.

urgent admission. Admission in which the patient requires immediate attention for treatment of a physical or psychiatric problem.

usual, customary, and reasonable. Fees charged for medical services that are considered normal, common, and in line with the prevailing fees in a given geographical area.

utilization review. Formal assessment of the medical necessity, efficiency, and/or appropriateness of health care services and treatment plans on a prospective, concurrent, or retrospective basis.

vaginismus. Spontaneous contractions of the muscles surrounding the vagina, causing it to constrict or close. Symptoms include vaginal pain with attempted vaginal exam or intercourse; penetration is sometimes difficult or impossible. Vaginismus may be classified as primary, in which intercourse has never been possible due to the muscular contractions, or secondary, in which intercourse was possible at one time but penetration is no longer possible due to the contractions.

Vorbeireden. Symptom of providing the approximate answer or talking past the point, or at cross purposes as seen in the Ganser syndrome. A form of factitious illness that is also associated with malingering or brain injuries.

voyeurism. Repetitively seeking out situations in which the individual looks at unsuspecting people who are either naked, in the act of disrobing, or engaging in sexual activity that may stimulate sexual excitement of the observer, frequently with orgasm.

Wernicke-Korsakoff syndrome. Amnestic dementia where the patient cannot remember short-term or long-term memories but is not delirious.

withdrawal reaction of childhood or adolescence. Emotional disturbance in children chiefly manifested by a lack of interest in social relationships and indifference to social praise or criticism.

word deafness. Developmental delay in the comprehension of speech sounds.

workers' compensation. State-governed system designated to administer and regulate the provision and cost of medical treatment and wage losses arising from a worker's job-related injury or disease, regardless of who is at fault. In exchange, the employer is protected from being sued.

xenophobia. Abnormal, intense fear of strangers.

Zoophilia. Sexual or anal intercourse with animals.